YOU
AND YOUR CAR

YOU
AND YOUR CAR

Professional hints and tricks of the trade to enable you to get the most out of your motoring

Editor Jack Hay, Consultant Editor of *Car Mechanics*

With an introduction by **James Hunt**

PELHAM BOOKS
London

First published in Great Britain by
Pelham Books Ltd
27 Wrights Lane
London W8
1984

Paperback edition first published 1986
© 1984 The Paul Press Ltd
Introduction © 1984 by James Hunt

British Library Cataloguing in Publication Data

You and Your Car: professional hints and tricks of the trade to enable you to get the
most out of your motoring.

1. Automobiles–Maintenance and repair
I.Hay, Jack
629.28'722 TL 152

ISBN 0 7207 1707 8

You and Your Car was conceived, designed and
produced by The Paul Press Ltd, 22 Bruton Street,
London W1X 7DA

Consultant Editor Jack Hay
Contributing Editors Ted Connolly, Ian Pembarthy, David Scott

Art Director Stephen McCurdy
Editor Jeremy Harwood
Art Assistants Tony Paine, Aaron Hatcher

Illustrators Julian Baker/The Maltings Partnership,
Graham Duckett, Alan Thurston
Photographer Don Wood

Project Director Stephen McCurdy
Editorial Director Jeremy Harwood
Publishing Director Nigel Perryman

Typeset by Wordsmiths, Street, Somerset
Origination by Aero Offset Reproductions Limited, Eastleigh
Printed in Singapore

Contents

6
Introduction

8
Owning a car
Raising finance ■ Buying a new car ■ Buying a used car ■ Insurance
Warranties ■ Security devices ■ Cleaning and waxing ■ Restoring the shine
Rust-proofing

30
The anatomy of the car
Understanding and checking the engine, ignition, cooling, electrical, fuel,
hydraulic and suspension systems

62
Problem diagnosis
Dealing with a breakdown ■ Fault-finding guides to the engine,
lighting/electrics, noises and tyres

106
Problem solving
All the basic repairs and checks that you can make to keep your car on the
road, or get home in safety

144
Driving
Town, country and motorway driving ■ Safety in the car ■ Safety on the road
Towing

160
The keys to survival
How to choose a garage ■ What to tell a garage ■ Checking the work ■ Tools
and equipment ■ Using tools effectively ■ The survival tool kit

174
Improving your investment
Eliminating and repairing rust damage ■ Filling dents ■ Painting out
scratches ■ Spray painting ■ Choosing accessories to improve your car and
how to fit them

204
Index

Introduction

by James Hunt

Cars have now been a part of my life for some 22 years. At first, like many of my contemporaries, I thought of them as little more than a means of transportation – or as mobile centres of night-time entertainment – but then, as my thoughts turned more and more to racing, they began to fill my life.

I have never considered myself to be truly mechanically minded, but I quickly had to teach myself everything there was to know about cars – not just racing cars, even though I was a driver-mechanic, but road cars as well. Many were the times I almost failed to reach the circuit!

In those days, there was no textbook guide for innocents like me. We had to survive as best we could, even if this meant carrying out the most appallingly brutal operations on what were perfectly healthy, if over-used, pieces of machinery. When I was 17, I even trusted second-hand car dealers!

We survived, though, and, as time went on, I suppose we became more responsible. In 1975, for instance, Lord Hesketh, at the wheel of his Porsche, bet me that roadside bollards in Germany were made of polystyrene foam, not of concrete. He lost his bet, but, by that time, I was wise enough to make sure that we were having fun in someone else's car. More seriously, though, I found that the more I raced, the less inclined I was to drive quickly on public roads.

Since I retired, I have tried to put back a little of what I took from motor racing. I had thought about trying to join a road safety council, or a similar type of organization, but, on reflection, I thought it better to leave it to the experts. I was delighted, therefore, when I first saw a copy of *You and Your Car*. It seemed to me to capture many of the things that I have wanted to say about driving and road safety, while providing everything the average driver would need to know about car repairs and maintenance. Indeed, I only had to read a few pages to realize that there was much more to say about cars than I had ever imagined. I am glad that Jack Hay and his team were the ones who had to deal with all the hard work, but I wish they had done the job 15 years ago. If they had, I would have been saved a lot of heartache and unnecssary expense!

Some parts of the book rang bells based on bitter experience. Others were news to me. Though some of the tips and hints the book contains may seem 'obvious' at first sight, I can assure you from past experience that this is far from the case when you are confronted by a crisis. With the aid of *You and Your Car*, I am sure that you will be primed to react to most of the situations a motorist can face.

I didn't know, for instance, that you can help finance the cost of a new car by taking out a mortgage. That would have helped me a lot in the days when I was trying to raise £300 to buy a Mini. I wouldn't have had a house, mind, but I would have had the Mini! I was also intrigued by the tips on used and new car buying. If you are buying a new car, for instance, it is your right to insist that the car is perfect on delivery, but I know too many people who have been pushed into buying a car that wasn't exactly what they wanted. If the car is second-hand, remember to check it in daylight – the better to see dents – and run a magnet over the bodywork to find even the most carefully disguised filled-in holes.

I must confess to having borrowed the odd drop of petrol from other cars when I was racing in Europe in the early 1970s, so I was pleased to see that Jack has not forgotten to include a large section on car security. Window etching, in which you indelibly mark the car's windows with its registration number, seems to me to be a particularly good idea, and I also liked the advice about parking as far away as possible from your evening destination. An acquaintance of mine recently lost some valuable medals by omitting to do just that. I rarely wear ties, so have not had the dubious pleasure of having one caught in the fan belt, but on several occasions I have had to 'remove' a pair of tights from a passenger – strictly to replace a broken fan belt, of course, as neatly described in *You and Your Car!*

But it was the section on dealing with breakdowns that captured my attention the most, particularly as I seem to be prone to middle-of-the-night dramas. There are so many things here that make sense: when stranded on a motorway, leave the car from the near-side, rather than the off-side doors; if changing a wheel, keep the wheel nuts safe in the hub cap; if removing the radiator cap when the engine is warm, muffle the cap with a rag; if the battery is flat, remember it can still turn the engine over if you leave it for 20 minutes; and if the engine overheats, turn the heater up to its maximum first and, if this fails, remove the thermostat; cardboard

from a cereal packet can be used as a makeshift gasket; and broken bulbs can be removed by twisting them with a piece of cork. Best of all, though, is the answer to having the wrong-sized spanner for a bolt – jam a screwdriver between the rim of the spanner and the bolt and you have suddenly solved your problem.

Finally, I thoroughly endorse the sections devoted to driving and driving safety. Once a young driver has passed his or her test, it is taken for granted that he or she should know how to react in strange situations – on motorways, in rain, in fog. This means that the luckless driver is left to fend for himself or herself in the hard school of experience. Now, through *You and Your Car*, the process is made

simple. In fog, you will know that it is better to use the windscreen wipers and washers and to drive with the side windows open; in the wet, you will be able to deal with aquaplaning; and, in order to save fuel, you will know that you should drive in as high a gear as possible, never brake harshly and try to avoid traffic jams. Most of all, the section on Defensive Driving nicely captures what I believe is *the* golden rule of the road. If an accident is going to be 90% the fault of another motorist, it is up to you to provide the 10% of evasive action. Remember that it takes two to make an accident.

Take heed of all this advice and you will save much more than just the price of this superb book. You will also be a better and safer driver.

Owning a car

Whether you are buying a new or a second-hand car – especially if you are a first-time buyer – there are many things you must consider. How much can you afford? How will you raise the money? What are the running costs likely to be? And, in addition to such practical considerations, you will also be faced with the emotive choice of make, model, design and colour.

For instance, there are many ways in which you can raise the money to pay for your purchase. Yet this is not the end of the story by any means. Running costs, too, are a vital consideration. These can be broken down into various categories – insurance premiums, fuel consumption, cost of servicing and parts and so on. As a general rule, for example, the larger the engine size, the more your insurance premium will be and the heavier your fuel bills too.

These are only a few of the things you must take into consideration when weighing up the pros and cons of car ownership. Owning a car is a relationship – and, like all relationships, it has its ups and downs. In this book, you will find all the basic guidance and advice you will need to make car ownership a pleasure.

Insurance ratings

The cost of insurance is something that affects every motorist. All cars – whether new or second-hand – are insurance rated, the rating usually taking into account the cost of spare parts, repairs and engine size. The lowest rating group is one; this applies to the smallest type of family car, with an equally small engine. The average family saloon, fitted with a 1600cc engine, would normally have an insurance rating of around three or four, while a larger saloon, with an engine size of over two litres, would have a rating of five or six. A high-performance fuel-injection sports car would rate seven, eight, or even nine.

Pre-planning your purchase

Whether buying new or second-hand, choosing a car can be most exciting and you can easily get carried away by your feelings. Especially for the first-time buyer, it is well worthwhile sitting down and drawing up a list of the things you require the car to do and what will be its main uses. Then check that the car you like fulfills all these needs – or at least most of them.

A young single person, for instance, is on the whole unlikely to need a large estate car, while a busy housewife, who uses a car mainly for short trips to the local shops, would find it easier and more economical *not* to drive a large four-door saloon. This is a counsel of perfection, however, as most family cars are a compromise between the three-fold demands of shopping, holidays and commuting. For this reason, hatchbacks are now particularly popular as family designs, as they have the flexibility of becoming a small estate car, should the need arise. The modern sports car, too, is now longer an open-top tourer, but a small, fast saloon, fitted with a fuel-injected engine, rally-style seats and wide, low-profile tyres. If you want to feel the wind through your hair, most manufacturers offer a cabriolet version of their most popular model. It all depends on what you need and, in the end, the choice is up to you.

Buying new

If you are lucky enough to be able to afford a new car, the basic decision is make and model. Do you opt, instance, for a top model in a less expensive range, or for a basic model in a more expensive range? Other decisions you will have to take include the choice of colour, upholstery and accessories. Let your wallet or purse dictate your choice, not your heart.

When purchasing a new car, it is reasonable to assume that you can obtain a discount, especially if you are not trading in your old car as part of the purchase. Be prepared to walk away from that gleaming showroom model and to ignore the dulcet tones of the salesman if you are not offered a fair deal. Shop around and be determined in your search for a good discount.

You should also bear in mind that manufacturers discount heavily on models that are about to be replaced by new ones. You will still get the same warranty and service conditions on an older new car as you would on the very latest model. Remember, too, that the 'no interest' schemes some manufacturers offer can be a much better bargain than a discount in some cases.

When purchasing a new car, make sure that its condition lives up to the dealer's promises and that any defects you may discover are made good under the terms of the manufacturer's warranty. It is important that you check this thoroughly, while it is a good idea to see if you can pay a further premium to extend it.

Most manufacturers offer this option and it can prove good value for money. The period just after the normal warranty expires is the time when things can start going wrong with the car, with expensive garage bills becoming a regular event.

Buying second-hand
Buying a second-hand car is more complex than buying a new one as the condition of the vehicle must be the major consideration. The price asked – or even the price paid – is not necessarily a good guide to this. An 18-month-old car, for instance, can become a mechanical nightmare if many major parts suddenly become faulty; a car costing £500, with a new MoT certificate, can run reliably with little attention for a couple of years.

Making the right choice requires expert guidance. In this section, you will find plenty of useful information on what to look for when buying a car, particularly if it is second-hand. Certainly, any genuine seller should not object to you getting a third party to cast an expert eye over a potential purchase.

If, however, you can only afford to spend a small amount on a second-hand car, you should expect a fair degree of wear and tear. You should take into account how much that this is likely to cost you over the next year or so. Seeking expert advice in such circumstances is well worth the little extra it will cost – also, a defect found before you make the purchase could increase your bargaining power and get the cost of the car reduced from the original figure. In such a case, the cost of a professional inspection could

well pay for itself almost instantly.

If you are a novice, where can you get help? If you are buying really cheaply, it may not be worthwhile calling in a professional, though a knowledgeable friend could prove helpful, especially to check the car over for rust on the chassis and any likely major repairs. Do not take an MoT certificate as your sole guide to a car's condition.

Motoring organizations, such as the AA and the RAC, will inspect a second-hand car for you, while specialist companies also offer this service. All will supply a written report on your potential buy, showing what faults exist and whether they are in keeping with the car's mileage. They will also define for you what they consider to be excessive wear and tear. The decision whether to purchase is then yours.

Warranties
If you buy a second-hand car from a dealer, he is obliged by law to provide a basic warranty, but you should treat this simply as a safeguard against impending disaster. What you really need is a written guarantee, which you should check carefully, seeing exactly what it covers and making sure that there are no exceptions buried in its small print. Check to see what is the maximum amount you can claim and whether the warranty covers parts only.

If you are unhappy with the cover the dealer's warranty provides, you can arrange your own warranty through one of the companies that specialize in this service. The cost of this extra

cover will relate to the condition and mileage of the car.

If you buy privately, however, it is extremely unlikely that you will be offered any form of warranty at all. Here, thorough inspection is absolutely essential, as you will not be legally protected if problems develop.

Routine care
Once you have decided on your purchase, one of your main aims should be to keep it clean. As well as keeping the car attractive, this will protect the bodywork from road grime and so cut down the risk of corrosion.

It is easier to keep a clean car clean, so regular washing and the occasional polish will ensure that it stays in peak condition. When you wash the car, you should always use a proper car shampoo, as household detergents will scratch and dull the paintwork. Check over the paintwork on a regular basis for signs of chipping as well. Such chips should be dealt with immediately, thus avoiding rust problems at a later date.

If your car has suffered at the hands of its previous owner – characteristic signs of this are dull paint and tarnished metal trim – you can perform miracles with a little elbow grease, if you have a few hours to spare.

Car protection
Keeping your car secure is all part of the responsibilities of car ownership. With well over 400,000 cars being stolen each year – and with many more being broken into – you should certainly consider fitting some form of alarm system, as well as being particularly careful where and how you leave your car.

Raising finance

If you are one of the many people who cannot afford to buy a car outright, you will have to take out some form of loan. If you are considering this, there are a number of options – each one of which needs careful consideration before making a final decision. Remember, too, that whatever type of loan agreement you eventually obtain, it is best to put up as much cash as possible to reduce the loan to the minimum – indeed, in many cases, the cash percentage will be specified as a condition of the loan.

You need to know how much the loan will cost you in total – including interest – over what period and whether you will be free to sell the car during the repayment period. It is pointless to buy a car over a four-year period, say, and find yourself committed to a contract that forbids you to sell it within that time if you know the car will start to depreciate in value in two years.

Whatever you do, ensure that you will have completed all the repayments before, or on, the date you will want to re-sell the car. Alternatively, you should look for finance that does not bind you in this respect. Then, after a year or two, you will be free to sell the car, settle the balance and start afresh.

Bank loans

Exactly what type of finance you choose depends on your personal circumstances and where you are buying the car. If you are doing this privately and need a short-term loan to bridge the gap until you sell your existing car, try your bank manager. Provided you have a good banking record, the bank will probably offer a short-term bridging loan. If the borrowing period is extremely short and you can convince your bank that your car will be easy to sell, this may be lent without interest.

If you need a fairly large sum of money – and are not expecting money from your own car's sale – you will have to borrow over several years. The bank will tell you the rate of interest – this varies with the period of the loan – but it is simplest to ascertain what the total repayment will be. Generally, it is better to pay back as much as you can afford in the shortest possible time. If you can do this, the interest – and therefore the total sum repaid – will be less.

When you talk to your bank, you will probably be offered various alternative loan schemes. Your aim – and your bank manager's, too – will be to keep the repayments down to a manageable amount, but, at the same time, this will obviously affect the interest you will be paying. If you only need a short-term loan, for instance, it is often best to agree on an overdraft; if you are paying the bank back over an extended period, you will probably be advised to use one of the special loan schemes most banks operate for this type of purchase.

Finance brokers

A personal loan from a finance broker is another alternative. Such brokers usually insist on some form of security, such as your house or a life-insurance policy, or ask you to provide a guarantor in case you fail to meet the payments. The interest calculations are often complicated and you may eventually find that you are paying more than you originally expected. Check this carefully. In addition to the repayments, many brokers insist that you pay a small insurance premium each month, so that they are insured against any failure to repay.

Understanding interest

There are two types of interest – simple and compound. With the former, the percentage is added on to the sum borrowed and you pay that much extra and no more. With compound interest, the sum is added on to the outstanding balance of the loan at the end of each week – in other words, you are paying interest on the interest.

The first thing to establish is the exact interest rate. Obviously, such rates vary from company to company and according to the general state of the economy. But, for your guidance, the calculations here show exactly how one major finance company's scheme works.

The company offered to lend money at 21.7% interest. The monthly repayments for a loan of £1,000 were £37.06 over a three-year period, which meant that the total sum the borrower would have to repay was £1,334.16. Borrowing £2,000 meant spacing the repayments over four years at a monthly rate of £60.65. The total sum repaid would be £2,911.12. Borrowing £5,000 over 7½ years involved monthly payments of £107.05, meaning a total repayment of £9,634.50. This would be an extremely expensive way of buying a new car, since the car's resale value will inevitably drop dramatically over such a long period.

Other sources

If you are a house-owner, you can raise money by extending your mortgage through arrangement with a building society. This generally means you will make small repayments, but that these will be spread over a long period of time. Monthly outgoings are thus kept to the minimum, but the total sum involved is large. One advantage of this method, however, is that, you will almost certainly be free to sell the car before making all the repayments.

If you belong to a motoring organization, too, you may well find that it offers loans on special terms to its members.

Dealer schemes

If you are buying a car from a dealer, raising the money is usually simpler. Dealers in both new and used cars work with finance companies and will readily quote you terms. Once again, establish the total amount you will have to pay before deciding. Remember that, to increase the sales of their cars, some manufacturers encourage their franchised dealers to offer interest-free loans, so shop around to get the best deal possible.

Credit sale or hire purchase?

When buying a car from a dealer, you will usually be offered two options – a credit sale or a hire purchase agreement.

With a credit sale, you will usually be asked to pay a deposit and the repayment period will be limited to a maximum number of years. However, the car is your property as soon as you enter

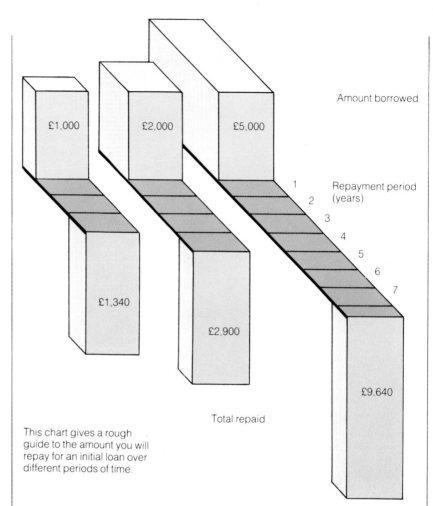

Amount borrowed

Repayment period (years)

Total repaid

This chart gives a rough guide to the amount you will repay for an initial loan over different periods of time.

into the contract and you can sell it at any time you wish.

Hire purchase, on the other hand, operates differently –you hire and purchase the car at the same time. The company which lends the money buys the car from the dealer and is then its legal owner. The vehicle is thus hired to you until the repayments have been completed, so you cannot re-sell the car until you have paid for it. However, you can agree a hire purchase without necessarily making a deposit, while the monthly repayments can be stretched over an extended period.

However you decide to borrow, remember the basic rule – to put down the largest deposit you can afford and repay the loan in the shortest possible time. Do not strain your general domestic budget with an excessive burden of repayments, however, and, when deciding how much you can afford to repay each month, remember to take into account general running costs, the possibility of unforeseen repairs and the car's inevitable depreciation in value.

Buying a new car

When you buy a new car, you are committing yourself to a major financial outlay. Unless you are using your purchase for business, or can afford a truly exotic model, it should never be regarded as a good investment. The inevitable running costs, inflation and the depreciation brought about by wear and tear mean that you will always lose money in the final result.

Which car you finally buy is often a compromise between what you would really like and what you can afford. By thinking carefully about your choice, however, you can ensure that your purchase will suit most of your needs, while cutting the inevitable financial depreciation to a minimum.

What should you spend?
Naturally, the first thing is to decide how much you can afford. With this in mind, look at the specifications of all the cars that fall within the price bracket you have selected. Do not necessarily be guided by brand loyalty, since a single manufacturer will not always be able to offer the same value across his range of cars – or even on the same model from year to year. If you need expert advice, check the motoring magazines and, if necessary, obtain back numbers containing the appropriate test articles.

In many cases, however, there is little to choose in quality between cars in the same price range. The final choice is then down to personal preference.

Narrowing the choice
Once you have made this initial assessment, start narrowing down the list of suitable cars by deciding what will be your car's main uses. If, for instance, you will doing a lot of town driving, look for a car that is manoeuverable and easy to park. The ideal car in this situation will probably be a small one, with a small, economical engine; any engine larger than 1300cc will probably prove uneconomical.

If, on the other hand, you plan much fast motorway driving, or if you live in a particularly hilly area, a larger-engined car is advisable. This will be able to maintain a higher cruising speed without mechanical strain, while using only fractionally more petrol than a over-worked smaller engine. If what you need is an all-purpose workhorse, compromise between the twin goals of economy and performance.

Study the fuel consumption figures that manufacturers produce for each of their models. These are usually based on what is termed the 'urban cycle' – in other words, town driving – at a constant 56mph (90kph) and a constant 70mph (112.6kph). Because these figures are achieved under ideal driving conditions, it is unlikely that you will be able to match them exactly. The best way to utilize them is to take them as a basis for comparison with other cars whose fuel consumption has been calculated under the same conditions.

Check for space
The amount of space available for passengers and luggage is just as important as performance and economy figures. Remember, too, that although the theoretical luggage space available in one car may well look bigger than that of another, the space in the first may not be completely useable because of the placing of the spare wheel, say, or because some of it is inaccessible. Above all, if the car is to be kept in a garage, check its overall dimensions to make sure it will fit.

If you carry heavy luggage or a full load of passengers regularly, the ultimate answer is an estate car, though such cars are generally more expensive than conventional saloons. A hatchback is a good compromise between the two.

The cost of driving
Insurance premiums vary considerably from one car to another. As well as taking into account your age, your driving record and your occupation, insurance companies and brokers always consider the performance of the car when calculating the premium you will have to pay. Generally speaking, the higher the car's performance, the larger the premium will be.

This is particularly important if you are considering what manufacturers term a 'tuned version' of a standard model. This will carry a higher premium, even though the engine size itself is the same as the standard model. Some insurance companies, too, charge higher premiums for foreign cars.

Budgeting for servicing
At the minimum, you should budget for a major service at least twice a year. To satisfy the manufacturer's warranty conditions, this must be carried out by an approved main dealer. Check the total price of such a service, including parts, in

	GOOD	FAIR	BAD
General performance			
General comfort			
Driving pleasure			
Fuel consumption			
Passenger space			
Luggage space			
Layout of controls			
Level of equipment			
Handling			
Visibility			
Heating/ventilation			
Town driving			
Open road driving			
Cost of servicing			
Prices of spare parts			
Insurance premiums			
Resale value			

This checklist is planned to include all the basic points you should remember when choosing a new car. Tick them off accordingly.

advance. It is also worth checking and comparing the prices of major components, such as clutches and exhausts, that may be required in a few years' time.

Some manufacturers claim that their cars need servicing only at 12,000-mile (19,354-km) intervals. Check exactly how much such a service will cost – it might be more than twice as much as a 6,000-mile (9,677-km) service for another make of car.

Calculating depreciation

Every car starts to lose its value as soon as it is driven out of the showroom. This decline is gradual for the following 12 to 18 months, but then the value begins to drop significantly. The best way to gauge depreciation is to look at the second-hand prices in used car buyers' guides.

The ultimate test

Never buy a car unless you have actually driven it. If the dealer will not offer you a test drive, buy elsewhere. Whatever sales claims a dealer or manufacturer makes, there is no point in buying a car if you personally find you do not enjoy driving it.

Sit in the driver's seat and fasten the seat belt. Make sure that you feel comfortable and that all the controls are easy to reach and to operate. Check that the all-round vision is good and there are no bad blind spots.

Check the back seat for ease of access and comfort. Push the front seats back as far as they will go and check the leg room behind them. Take your family along, too, and see how well everyone fits into the car. Check the luggage compartment for space, remembering that a high tailgate panel can sometimes make the loading of luggage difficult. Check the heating and ventilation as well.

On the actual test drive, see how the car copes with a broad variety of road and traffic conditions, making sure that you spend some time on fast roads and in heavy traffic. This will enable you to assess the levels of wind, tyre and mechanical noises, the car's cruising capabilities and how easy it is to manoeuvre. If possible, take two or more passengers along with you. This will help you to assess how the car performs and handles when fully laden.

Check that the ride is comfortable. If it is too stiff, the car may hold the road well, but will be tiring to drive on long journeys. On the other hand, too soft a ride may cause car sickness.

Making the purchase

Once you have singled out the car you want, always buy it from a main dealer with a manufacturer's franchise. Make absolutely certain that the price quoted by the dealer includes all of the equipment featured on the test model. Some of the items might have been optional extras. Ask for a firm on-the-road price – this should include road fund tax, VAT, delivery charges and number plates.

You will almost certainly be asked for a deposit and may well be requested to sign an order form, or some other type of formal contract. Check this last point carefully – making sure you read the small print – but, if possible, avoid signing anything. In some cases, cancelling an order – even for the best of reasons – could cost you your deposit.

Buying a used car/1

What to look for

Buying a second-hand car can lead to endless trouble and expense, unless you know what to look for. If, however, you make some basic checks beforehand, you will lessen the risk of making a bad buy. Above all, seek expert guidance, if you have any doubts. Motoring organizations will inspect a car for a standard fee, or you can have it checked by a qualified mechanic. If the owner objects, look elsewhere.

The first checks

The first basic rule is to always examine a car in daylight – and on a fine day, if possible. Check underneath the car first, poking all hollow box sections and the underside of the floor sharply with a stout screwdriver to check for signs of rust and corrosion.

If one isolated area has been covered with fresh underbody sealant, the metal is likely to have been repaired. If the repair has been done by a professional welder, it will probably be acceptable, but not if it has been patched up with body filler. Hold a small magnet against any suspect patches anywhere on the car. The magnet will not cling to body filler, or glass fibre. Inspect the exhaust along its entire length, looking for signs of rust, or splits in the silencer. Check the shock absorbers for signs of leaks.

Check the interior of the car. Lift the carpets. The paintwork underneath them should be clean and rust-free, while the carpets and floor should be dry.

Detailed body checks

Check the condition of the inner wings. Put your hand behind each wheel and feel for weak metal or holes. Look under the bonnet to check the front inner wings from the inside and look inside the boot to make a secondary check on the rear inner wings.

Carefully inspect all body panels for obvious signs of rust damage, such as bubbles, and check for repairs with the magnet test. Do not forget the edges of the bonnet and boot. Crouch at the front of the car and look along the sides – any areas that have been resprayed should show.

Make sure that all doors open and shut easily and fit squarely in their frames with an even amount of space all round them. Similarly check that the windows open and close freely and the door locks work from inside and outside.

Check the depth of tread on the tyres (see p.60), including the spare, and examine the inside and outside walls for splits, cracks or other signs of damage. Check the wheel rims for buckles or kerb damage. Check the car has a jack and wheel brace.

Checking the mileage

An acceptable average annual mileage is between 10,000 and 12,000 miles per year. If, bearing in mind the car's age, the reading is significantly lower, the odometer could have been altered.

If you suspect this, the rubbers on brake and clutch pedal can serve as clues. On a high-mileage car, the wear will be significant.

Under the bonnet

Remove the dipstick and examine the oil. This should be fairly clean – not a dirty black, which would indicate that the oil has not been changed regularly. Check the fluid level in the brake master cylinder reservoir – and the clutch reservoir level, if the system is hydraulic. If either is below the minimum, a leak exists – repairing this is a garage job – or the car has not been serviced properly. Check the coolant level in the radiator and look for oil leaks as well. See if there are rounded off nuts or damaged screws and surplus gasket compound around any of the key engine joints.

The road test

Never buy a second-hand car without insisting on a road test. Start by asking the owner to start the engine from cold. If blue smoke emerges from the exhaust to clear after a few seconds, the valve guides are probably worn. This is another garage job. Before driving off, apply the handbrake firmly and select third gear. Slowly let the clutch out. The engine should stall. If it continues to run, the clutch is slipping.

Once on the road, the steering should feel positive, but should not feed back jolts from the irregularities in the road surface. When you turn the wheel, you should get an immediate response. Play in the steering wheel means the steering, or suspension, is worn.

Find a quiet stretch of road and drive the car in a straight line, keeping away from the camber. Hold the steering wheel lightly and see if the car veers to one side. This can be caused by misaligned front wheels, or be the result of accident damage. Brake sharply. The car should pull up

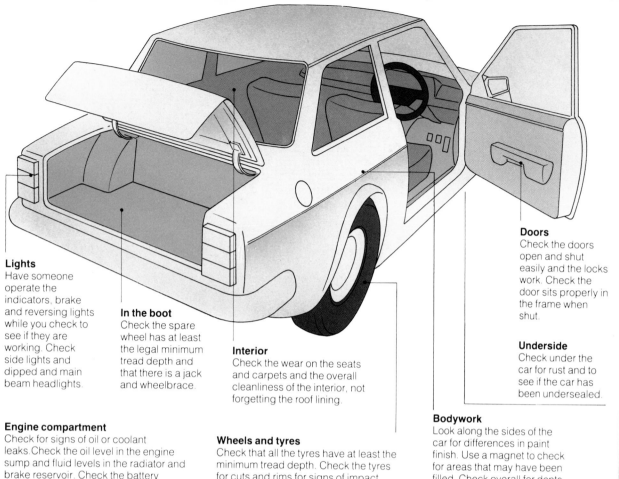

Lights
Have someone operate the indicators, brake and reversing lights while you check to see if they are working. Check side lights and dipped and main beam headlights.

In the boot
Check the spare wheel has at least the legal minimum tread depth and that there is a jack and wheelbrace.

Interior
Check the wear on the seats and carpets and the overall cleanliness of the interior, not forgetting the roof lining.

Doors
Check the doors open and shut easily and the locks work. Check the door sits properly in the frame when shut.

Underside
Check under the car for rust and to see if the car has been undersealed.

Engine compartment
Check for signs of oil or coolant leaks. Check the oil level in the engine sump and fluid levels in the radiator and brake reservoir. Check the battery terminals and electrolyte level.

Wheels and tyres
Check that all the tyres have at least the minimum tread depth. Check the tyres for cuts and rims for signs of impact damage.

Bodywork
Look along the sides of the car for differences in paint finish. Use a magnet to check for areas that may have been filled. Check overall for dents and scratches.

in a straight line. If it veers to one side, the brakes need garage attention.

The gears should change smoothly and the gearbox and differential should not whine. Check the gears for wear individually, selecting each one in turn and then blipping the throttle. If the gear lever slips back into neutral, the gearbox is worn. If there is excessive wear on the propshaft's universal joints – this applies to rear-wheel-drive cars – or the drive shafts are worn – on a front-wheel-drive car – you will also hear a loud clonking sound.

On front-wheel-drive cars, turn the car, using full lock. If constant velocity joints of the drive shaft are worn, you will hear a cracking sound.

Listening to the engine
You can check the condition of the engine's big-end bearings – albeit only roughly – by selecting top gear at about 25 mph (40kph) and then pushing the accelerator to the floor. A light tinkling sound indicates that the engine is 'pinking', which means the ignition timing is badly adjusted, or that the wrong grade of fuel is being used. If, however, you hear a heavy knocking sound, the big-end bearings are excessively worn. Curing this will be expensive.

A regular tapping sound that speeds up and down with the engine speed is probably due to maladjusted valve clearances. Though it is relatively simple to adjust these on an overhead-

valve (OHV) engine, it could mean a new camshaft on an overhead-cam (OHC) engine.

Make sure that the road test is long enough to check that the engine does not overheat and that the oil pressure remains at the correct level as the engine heats up. After driving for four or five miles, check the heater is working satisfactorily.

After the road test
After completing your test drive, let the engine tick-over for a minute or so and then ask the owner to rev it while you watch the exhaust. If clouds of blue smoke emerge, the piston rings and/or cylinder bores are worn and the engine needs a major overhaul. Black smoke indicates a poorly adjusted carburettor, a

Buying a used car/2

sticking choke, or a blocked air filter. Also watch out for droplets of water in the exhaust. They indicate a blown cylinder head gasket.

With the engine still running, raise the bonnet and listen for any knocking, rattling or rumbling sounds when the engine is ticking-over and when the owner revs the engine. Generally, the engine should run reasonably quietly. If in doubt, seek expert advice.

Listen for leaks in the exhaust as well, blocking the end of the exhaust pipe with a piece of rag. If there are no leaks, the engine should stall after a few seconds.

Turn off the engine and allow it to cool. While waiting for this, check the lights, including indicators and brake lights, the windscreen wipers and washers. Check that the steering wheel moves only fractionally – if at all – before the front wheels start to turn. Once the engine is cool, remove the radiator cap and start up again. As the engine warms, look inside the radiator filler neck while the owner increases the engine revs. Bubbles in the water signify a blown cylinder head gasket.

Checking the paperwork
Once you are satisfied with the car itself, check the paperwork. If the car is more than three years old, it must have an MoT certificate. Check the mileage on the certificate against the odometer reading to see how many miles the car has covered since its last test. Make sure that the details in the registration document tally.

Where to buy a second-hand car
If you are buying a second-hand car, you ideally should establish the car's complete service history and find out the exact use to which it has been put. Unfortunately, this is rarely possible. You will usually have to deal with a complete stranger, so you must check the car over thoroughly before deciding whether or not to buy it (see p.14). The tips here will help you to find the best places for a second-hand buy, so enabling you to end up with the car at the price you can afford as quickly as possible.

Assessing advertisements
Any advertisement you see – whether in a motoring magazine, a local newspaper, or on a postcard in a shop window – must satisfy certain basic legal requirements. It must be honest and give as accurate a description of the car as possible. However, there is still considerable room for manoeuvre for unscrupulous sellers, so you should treat any advertisement only as a rough guide.

Do not pay much attention to the stock phrases, such as 'ex-directors car' or 'one lady owner'. They may be true, but their use is no guarantee that the car has been properly cared for or maintained. Similarly, the phrase 'genuine reason for sale' means little or nothing. If the owner wants to sell the car because it is unreliable, then that is a 'genuine reason' to him or her.

Where to look
When you start to look for a second-hand car, the wide range of options open to you can seem bewildering. For instance, you could look at the post-card advertisements in local shop windows, but these are normally to be avoided, unless you want an inexpensive runabout, with a limited life. Far better to check the advertisements in local newspapers, as these offer a far wider range of models at varying prices. You can look at the 'free-sheets' now circulating in many areas as well.

There are also specialist car advertising magazines, often with a nation-wide circulation and the general motoring ones, which invariably carry a good selection of readers' second-hand cars. If you take this route, however, you may well have to travel a fair distance to examine the car you have chosen. To avoid a wasted journey, ask as many questions as possible over the telephone and also negotiate a rough price. It is better to find out at this early stage that the seller will not haggle, rather than embarking on a fruitless journey.

Buying by computer
Buying a car by computer is becoming increasingly popular. You contact the company by telephone and tell it what sort of car you want and what you want to spend. The company will tell you which cars of the type you want are on their computer inside your price range and in your local area. If your first choice is unavailable, the company will then tell you what other types of cars are on their computer in the same price range, or extend the information to cover a greater area. It is in the company's interest to be helpful since a commission is charged on sales – this is usually paid by the seller.

If the computer fails to find you a suitable car, you can ask for 'wanted' advertisements to be programmed into it. Then, when the right car comes along, the company will automatically put you in touch with the seller.

Buying at auction

One of the quickest ways of buying a second-hand car is at a car auction. Remember, though, that sellers usually take this route only when a speedy sale is the priority. Thus, though prices are likely to be attractive, care is needed because of the speed of the transaction.

The cars on sale will be displayed, so that they can be inspected, but you are not allowed to drive them. Make all of the checks you can (see p.14). Fix a maximum price in your mind and do not be tempted to go above it. Auctioneers are experienced enough to create an exciting atmosphere, in which people are often tempted to bid beyond their means. Often, if a car's reserve price is not reached, the auctioneer will tell the seller what the next best bid was and then the seller can negotiate privately with the bidder, if he or she wishes.

The actual terms of sale vary. Generally, once you have bought the car, you have a limited time – often, only a couple of hours – to find out if it has any major faults and then to return it. Use this time to road-test the car and take it back immediately if you find – or suspect – that anything is wrong.

It pays, too, to read the terms of sale carefully before completing any transaction. Auctioneers deal in both cash and guaranteed cheques. You can also put down a deposit. Also check you have insurance cover to drive the car away.

	PASS	FAIL
BODYWORK		
Underbody box sections		
Floor		
Door sills		
Other panels		
Fit of doors		
ENGINE		
Excessive noise		
Oil leaks		
Smoke in exhaust		
Water in exhaust		
TRANSMISSION		
Gearbox noise		
Jumping out of gear		
Differential whine		
Clutch slip		
Propshaft / driveshaft 'clonk'		
STEERING / SUSPENSION / BRAKES		
Shock absorbers		
Steering wander		
Excessive steering wheel play		
Uneven braking		
Hydraulic fluid loss		
Wheels / tyres		
GENERAL CHECKS		
Condition of interior		
Jack / wheelbrace		
Lights / instruments		

Tick the appropriate 'pass' or 'fail' box after you make each check. When all the checks are made, the chart will give a fair indication of the car's condition.

Dealing with a dealer

As with an auction, immediacy is the immediate advantage if you go to a second-hand car dealer, since his stock of cars will be on display. Additionally, any reputable dealer will almost certainly offer an attractive warranty (see p.18).

If you have any doubts, check whether the dealer is a member of the Motor Agents' Association – this is a fair test of credibility. Alternatively, ask if he will put you in touch with one or two of his recent customers and contact them to see what sort of service they received. It will also pay you to look at the dealer's workshops, or ask where repairs will be carried out in the event of any claim against his warranty.

The one big disadvantage of this route is price. The dealer is making a living out of selling cars and so must inevitably charge more than a private seller. For this reason, too, dealers are also more reluctant to drop their prices than individuals, who are probably more interested in making a sale than in maximizing their profit.

Insurance and warranties/1

Buying insurance

Many people agonize for hours over which type of car to buy, whether the vehicle concerned is to be second-hand or brand-new. Brochures are studied and performance and economy figures are compared – all to get the best value for money.

Very few people, however, take the same amount of trouble over their car insurance, often choosing the policy with the lowest premium on the assumption that 'all insurance policies are the same'.

Actually, this is far from the case. While the general terms are similar – especially for third party only, or third party, fire and theft policies – the small print varies considerably from policy to policy and company to company. If your car is stolen and not recovered, for instance, your policy remains in force while your claim is paid as far as most companies are concerned. This means that you lose some of your no claims bonus and there is no refund of the unused premium.

Choosing your cover

Should you take out fully comprehensive insurance, or simply rely on third party, fire and theft cover? Although price sometimes makes this decision for you – the former costs about twice as much as the latter – it is a good rule of thumb always to insure your car comprehensively, if you calculate that paying for major repairs after an accident could be beyond your means. It is obviously preferable to pay a higher insurance premium than to be unable to use your car because you simply cannot afford to have it repaired.

Of course, comprehensive insurance does far more than this. It pays compensation for other things as well – from the serious to the apparently minor, such as broken car windows or windscreens. Here, though, you should check your cover carefully to ensure that it provides *unlimited* insurance. Some policies pay only £50 or £100, but the windscreens of many modern cars can cost more than £150 to replace.

Choosing an insurer

If you want to deal directly with an insurance company as opposed to an insurance broker or consultant, then it makes sense to go to one with an office in your immediate area. While it may not matter how far away the office is when you arrange the insurance, it makes life easier if you can deal in person with your insurers if you are making a claim.

Before committing yourself to a particular insurance company, ask them the following questions, which are designed to expose points that most motorists fail to consider:

1. What happens to the policy if your car is a total write-off as a result of theft or an accident? Avoid companies that cancel the policy in these circumstances.
2. How much are the windows and windscreen insured for? A good comprehensive policy will give unlimited cover without extra charge.
3. Does the company have its own motor engineers, or does it use outside ones? Companies that have staff engineers tend to authorize repairs more quickly after an accident.
4. Does the local office handle claims? Some companies have centralized claims offices and this can delay inspection of your car after an accident. However, if the local office handles claims, or it has a 'tie-line' to the central bureau, this will minimize delay.
5. Can you pay the premium by instalments? Most major insurers offer this facility – usually over five months. The interest charge is minimal, making it a very economic way of paying the premium. Other companies accept credit cards, with some offering a choice between the two systems.
6. Does the registration number of your car appear on the certificate of insurance? If it does, this can be inconvenient, as you will have to tell your insurers *before* you change your car. Otherwise you will be uninsured. If the number does not appear, you usually have a few days grace – this can be extremely convenient if you buy another car at a weekend, or on a public holiday.
7. Does the company offer a 'bonus-protected' policy, or a 'guaranteed bonus' policy? Both of these allow you to make claims without losing your bonus – even if you were at fault. 'Bonus-protection' usually allows you to make two claims in a three- or five-year period without your bonus being affected; a 'guaranteed bonus' policy places no limit on the number of claims that you can make, though the insurers still retain the right to cancel the policy if they become dissatisfied with your claims record. Both types of policy are generally restricted to drivers aged at least 30 with maximum no claims bonus, although a few offer 'bonus-protection' to younger drivers.

8 Is the insurance company party to the 'knock-for-knock' agreement? Despite popular belief, it is generally to your advantage if your insurer uses this arrangement when settling claims.

If you deal direct with an insurance company, remember that it can offer only its own policies. For this reason, it is usually to your advantage to deal with an intermediary, such as a broker or insurance consultant, who has ready access to many insurance companies, including those, like Lloyds syndicates, that do not deal direct with the public.

Choosing an intermediary

Every insurance broker must meet the requirements of the Insurance Brokers Registration Act, which states that he or she must have adequate professional indemnity insurance, so that he is covered against any claim alleging negligence on his part. A claim of this nature could arise if a broker forgot to issue a cover note, so that a motorist was unwittingly uninsured at the time of an accident.

An insurance consultant, on the other hand, does not have to be 'registered'. If, however, he or she is a member of the Institute of Insurance Consultants, professional indemnity insurance is also required.

Whether you use a broker or consultant, you should ask the same questions that you would ask an insurance company, playing close attention to the answers to questions 4, 5 and 7. The answer to question 4 is important, because, if claims are being processed by an office some distance away, an

Small car, engine rating below 1000cc.	**1**
Small car, engine rating below 1300cc.	**2**
Medium-sized car, engine rating around 1600cc.	**3**
Large car, about 2 litres or sports version of smaller car	**4**
Large car with engine over 2 litres	**5**
Sports version with larger/uprated engine	**6**
Expensive car with large engine/imported model	**7**
Expensive, very fast car with large engine/imported model	**8**

This chart will give you a rough guide to the insurance group your car may fall into and therefore the cost of your insurance premium.

intermediary may be reluctant to check the progress of any claim by 'phone as often as he should. As far as question 5 is concerned, many brokers and consultants fail to advise their clients that credit facilities exist, as to do so would adversely affect their personal cash flow. If you are in doubt on this point, check with the company itself. And, as an intermediary's income comes through commission on the premiums, you may not be told about protected/guaranteed bonus policies. Obviously, if your premium goes up as a result of losing your no claims bonus, the broker or consultant will make more money out of you. Again, check with the insurance company if you are dissatisfied.

Remember, too, that an insurance *broker* has a legal obligation to reveal what his commission is if a client asks for the information. The normal commission range is between 10% and 12%. If you find that your broker's commission is higher, it may well be time to question whether your interests are being protected as they should.

If you decide to use an intermediary, there are a couple of extra questions that you should ask him, as well as those already mentioned:

1 Are any fees charged in connection with normal transactions, such as the issue of cover notes, or the renewal of your policy? Do not do business with anyone who charges fees – remember commission is being charged on your premium.

2 Are you being sent all the insurance company's documentation, when you are advised that premiums are due? Many intermediaries fail to do this, especially when it comes to the insurance company's renewal notice, which they will retain in order to make it more difficult for you to arrange insurance elsewhere. This notice is the only proof of a no claim's bonus entitlement that another insurance company will accept. Even more importantly, if you do not have the renewal notice in your possession, you are unlikely to be covered by the temporary cover note that is incorporated in it. You thus run the risk of driving without insurance should you be a few

Insurance and warranties/2

days late in paying the premium. Always insist on seeing *all* insurance company documents – it is the only way that you can be sure that you are not being charged hidden fees.

Claims

With care – and some luck – you will never have to make a claim on your policy. But if you do, you should be able to go to your intermediary for help and assistance – especially if you feel that the other party was at fault.

If you want someone to pursue your claim on your behalf, your broker or consultant may be willing to help, or you can consult a claims assessor. In either case, make sure that any payment for the service is agreed to be on a 'no recovery – no fee' basis. Otherwise you might end up throwing good money after bad.

Many people have had cause to regret their choice of insurer or intermediary when arranging car insurance. By using the guidelines here, together with personal recommendations from friends, you will reduce the risk to a minimum.

Warranties

When buying any goods, you are protected by law if what you buy is not up to a specified legal standard. The same applies to cars, though, because of their complexity, all such guarantees have certain limitations.

If you are buying a second-hand car, it should be one of your priorities to choose the best warranty scheme you can, always assuming that one is offered. A good scheme can be extremely worthwile if you drive a lot, or are dependent on a

garage to carry out repairs. However, such schemes vary considerably both in their cost and in the type of cover they provide, so you should weigh up their expense carefully against the service offered in return before making a final decision.

As the choice is so vast, selecting the scheme that best meets you needs can be as as complicated as picking a second-hand car itself. If you are buying a new car, however, matters are far simpler. All manufacturers universally offer a minimum of a 12-month or 12,000-mile (19,320-km) guarantee – you will find that some guarantees operate over a longer period or a higher mileage – the guarantee starting automatically from the moment of purchase.

Reading the small print

Even in these circumstances, it pays to read the small print. Generally, you will find that the warranty covers only the use of faulty materials, or bad workmanship. If a component breaks and the manufacturer believes that this is your fault, your claim may be disallowed. This problem can occur with clutches and brake linings in particular, while even a claim for a major engine component can be disputed, if it is obvious that you have driven the car thoughtlessly during the running-in period. You are also required to have the car serviced at the recommended intervals by an approved dealer.

Although an anti-corrosion guarantee may seem on first reading to protect you against virtually any form of rust damage, it is also likely to have strict conditions. It may state, for

example, that no claim can be made if the body starts rusting at the seams or if corrosion is caused by bad weather, so you will be covered only if you can show that the fault is caused by poor workmanship or the use of inferior materials.

Demonstrating this can be very difficult. You may also find you are required to have regular bodywork check-ups.

Pay first – claim later

Under the terms of some warranties, you may face a further problem. They may stipulate that you pay for any repairs out of your own pocket and claim later. This can be extremely inconvenient if a large-scale repair is involved, since you might find yourself waiting for some time for reimbursement.

The warranty may also state that repairs must be carried out by an approved dealer. If you break down, this may not always be possible.

What you should ask

If you are buying a new car, you should ask the dealer to give you written details of the warranty, so that you can go through them in detail before making the purchase. Raise any questionable points with the dealer (or warranty company) before agreeing to the terms.

Remember, too, that such warranties can be extended into the second and even third year of ownership – of course, at extra cost. If you decide to do this, check to see whether any of the original conditions alter. You could find, for instance, that the warranty no longer covers your clutch or brakes, or that the mileage you can drive is strictly limited. An anti-corrosion guarantee may also be affected.

Though you can get the fullest possible cover in these circumstances, you will have to pay proportionately more for it. The cost is also related to the type of car you own. The bigger and more expensive the car, the more money you will be asked to pay.

You may still be bound to have the car regularly serviced by an approved dealer. Do-it-yourself servicing and repairs could thus invalidate any claim, as could work carried out by an unauthorized garage. Some companies, however, allow both practices, provided that you can produce receipts for new parts on demand.

Second-hand cars

If you are buying second-hand, it is worth checking whether or not any existing warranty is transferable. If this is the case, the extra cost of the transfer may prove well worthwhile.

You will find that many second-hand car dealers are prepared to reduce their price, provided that you are prepared to forgo any form of guarantee. If not, you will be offered some form of warranty and charged the forecourt price. The most basic normally run for three months or 3,000 miles (4,830km), whichever is the sooner.

If a dealer offers you his own personal guarantee – not one backed by an independent company – this will quite frequently be limited to parts and not include the cost of labour. This can work out to be expensive. If, for example, a gearbox bearing fails, the replacement part itself may well cost just a few pounds, but the labour bill could run into hundreds.

Many dealers, however, offer warranties backed by companies that specifically supply second-hand car cover. What is on offer, however, differs widely, so, again, it is well worth reading the small print very carefully.

In general, a typical warranty will cover the cost of both spare parts and labour. However it will not cover anything that fails through normal wear and tear – the exhaust system or brake linings, for instance – but only components that fail because of a flaw in their manufacture. You may also find that the older the car is – or if it is a model noted for general unreliability – the stricter the warranty conditions and the proportionately higher the warranty's cost.

Whatever form of warranty is offered, it should be backed up with all the necessary documents. Read these carefully and, if necessary, contact the company to explain any details that you do not understand. It is also worth checking whether you can transfer the warranty to another owner if and when you decide to sell the car.

Arranging your own warranty

Even if you are not buying new or second-hand from a dealer, you can still obtain a warranty for your car independently. This means that you will have to approach one of the specialist warranty companies yourself.

As such companies usually transact their business through dealers, the quickest way to locate one is to ask at a few showrooms. If this fails, a local insurance broker may be able to help. When you make contact with the company, it is then up to you to explain exactly what you want covered, over what period and for what type of car. The cost of the warranty will depend on all three of these factors, plus the mileage you are likely to cover.

If your car is particularly expensive to maintain, or is fairly old, do not be surprised if the company declines to offer you warranty cover.

Rust-proofing

If you have your car professionally rust-proofed, you should obtain a totally independent warranty, quite apart from the general guarantee covering the vehicle as a whole. Such special warranties often lead to confusion – and argument – because their conditions are not fully understood. Generally, claims will only be upheld if the car has been rust-proofed at an approved centre and has been inspected for signs of rust damage on a regular basis. This could mean paying more money to have areas re-treated.

No warranty will protect you against rust that has already formed – it will cover only sound metal. In addition, it is only valid up to a specific date. If, for example, your car is three years and a day old and the guarantee covers cars for three years, you will have no come-back – even for the sake of a day.

With rust-proofing, as with all forms of warranty, it is essential to be fully aware of the conditions before entering into a binding agreement. It is far better to ask the awkward questions at an initial stage than to wait for months – or even years – to have a claim settled.

Car security

Virtually nothing can stop a determined professional thief stealing your car. But a good security device will probably deter him or her and almost certainly foil the amateur joy-rider.

Physical deterrents

You can make your choice from the dozens of security devices now available on the market. These vary considerably in price, according to their sophistication. The most basic are primarily designed to be visible deterrents, though they also make the car physically difficult to drive.

A steering lock is the best-known example of this type of device. One part of the lock hooks over the steering wheel and the other under the brake pedal. When locked in position, you can hardly turn the steering wheel, while the brake cannot be operated at all. Handbrake locks are also available. They fit over the handbrake lever to secure it in position, usually with a combination lock.

Although both these types of lock can be broken or forced open fairly easily, they still act as a deterrent to the majority of non-professional thieves. Wheel clamps are dearer, but even more off-putting.

A window etching kit is another visual deterrent. The etching fluid and stencils supplied in the kit enable you to etch the car registration number indelibly on each window. Though the etchings do not prevent the physical theft of the car, they are a substantial deterrent to the professional thief, since all the windows will have to be replaced before the car can be sold.

The easiest type of lock to use, and one of the cheapest, is the wheel lock (above). It hooks over the steering wheel and the brake pedal. More sophisticated, and more expensive, are alarms that are operated by a pendulum, or ultrasonics. D-I-Y kits are available (below), but you will need some electrical knowledge to fit them.

Electronic alarms

The cheapest types of electronic alarm are designed simply to immobilize the ignition. A control box is wired into the ignition circuit, breaking the flow of current when a concealed switch is thrown. Such a device will stop a thief driving the car away, but it will not prevent a forced entry.

The more complex – and expensive – security systems not only immobilize the ignition, but also sound the horn when a door, the boot, or the bonnet is disturbed. They run off the battery and are operated by micro-switches – similar to the switch that controls the interior courtesy light – that are wired to the horn and complete the circuit when activated by touch.

Such a system has two obvious advantages. You get the benefit of a device that gives a clearly audible warning if a forced entry is attempted, while it also makes the engine difficult to start. Some are armed by an internal switch, with a built-in delay to allow you to get in or out of the car before

setting off the alarm; others are armed externally, but this means that the body has to be drilled to take the switch and its wiring.

The most common way of arming an alarm is by the turn of a key, though a minority of the more expensive systems use other methods. Some rely on printed circuit key cards which, when removed from the control panel, break several vital circuits, so making the system extremely difficult for a thief to by-pass. Others are armed from outside the car, using a magnetic pad. The pad is held against the windscreen, where it activates a sensor mounted on the dashboard.

If you feel that the sound of the horn is inadequate, you can add a piercing siren to most of these systems, which is far louder. Some will even flash the headlights on and off.

Some alarms are operated by a concealed pendulum, which completes the circuit as it swings. Though this type of alarm was once popular, it had one major drawback. Such alarms were frequently set off accidentally, by stiff gusts of wind, say, or parking on a steep hill. However, the system has been greatly improved; the pendulum can now be adjusted to make it less sensitive and also can be set automatically to take inclines into account.

Ultrasonics and air pressure
The ultrasonic system is one of the most effective, but expensive, types of security device. It fills the car with ultrasonic sound waves, which set off an alarm if disturbed. Most ultrasonic systems also have a built-in ignition immobilizer.

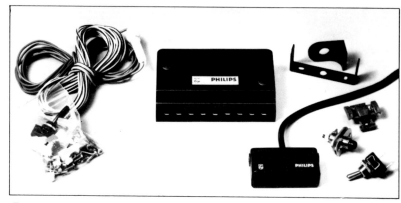

The most sophisticated type of alarm you can fit, is the ultrasonic type that is operated by changes in air pressure *(above)*. To safeguard expensive sports wheels, a set of wheel nuts with a lock that makes it impossible for them to be undone can be fitted *(below)*.

With soft-tops, the only effective way of securing the car is to fit a system based on air pressure. If the pressure drops or rises as a result of a thief opening a door or window, the system is activated. This type of system is also expensive.

Protecting accessories
With many of these systems, you can buy extra equipment to protect accessories, such as fog and driving lamps. These are wired into the circuit and the alarm sounds if they are disturbed.

You can also protect both car and accessories with a paging system. A small transmitter is fitted into your car and, if the vehicle or any accessory is disturbed, a personal paging alarm sounds in your pocket.

The obvious way to protect your wheels is to fit locking wheel nuts. These are either locked with a key or require a special spanner to loosen them.

The rules of security
Whether you decide to fit a security system or not, you should still follow the basic commonsense rules of security.

You should never leave valuables in a car. If this is unavoidable, either lock them in the boot or hide them under the seat. Many petty thieves are not interested in stealing cars – just in smashing the window to take what is inside.

Always lock the car – even if you are only leaving it for a few minutes.

Do not park in unlit or desolate areas at night. Darkness and peace and quiet are a thief's best friends. If possible, always park in a well-lit residential area, or, if this is difficult, at least park under a street lamp.

If you are spending the evening out – at a cinema or a theatre, for instance – park as far away as possible. Statistics show that cars parked close to places of entertainment are particularly at risk, since many thieves are on the look out for the opportunities provided by your prolonged absence – especially if they have seen you park.

Cleaning and waxing

By regularly cleaning and washing your car, you will not only keep the bodywork in its original pristine condition, but also provide the paintwork with additional protection. You will thus prolong its life and so help to maintain the car's resale value. You should clean your car thoroughly once a week – both inside and out – and polish it every three to four months, depending on the type of polish you use.

Basic cleaning

The simplest and best way to clean a car is still with a sponge and water. Though this may seem old-fashioned and laborious when compared to the speed of an automatic car-wash, there is little doubt that it generally produces a far more thorough result. As an alternative to a sponge, you can use a hose brush, which you connect to the water mains,

together with detergent tablets. Some brushes are fitted with their own control taps, so that you can regulate the water supply from the car.

Use warm water mixed with a good quality car shampoo. Many of these contain protective agents – these are especially useful when you are simply cleaning your car in between the regular polishing sessions. Your sponge should be clean and free from traces of dirt or grit that might scratch the paintwork.

Work from the top downwards – that is, from the roof, front screen and bonnet, rear screen and boot and then tackle the sides. Pay particular attention to hidden areas, such as those behind and underneath the bumpers. If you cannot reach them, make sure that they are flooded with suds. If your wheels are mucky, go over them with a stiff brush.

It may take up to three to four buckets full of water to clean the car thoroughly. Work patiently and make sure that the entire body is covered. If any dirt is left, it will scour the paintwork when you come to polish it. Rinse with buckets of clean water, or hose down the car.

Drying off

When you dry off the car, there is no substitute for a good quality chamois leather. Wet it under the tap until it is soft and gradually rub the car dry, working in the same order that you washed it and rinsing the leather frequently in clean water. Once you have finished, open all the doors and mop up any puddles – water may have crept in inside the slits and under the sills.

Polishing

Before you start polishing, wait about half an hour for the car to dry thoroughly, or, if the weather is fine, drive it for a few miles. If you polish the car while it is damp, the polish will smear.

Use a clean, soft cloth for the polishing. Mutton cloth is ideal. Do not use coarse cloth, or old articles of clothing with zips or buttons – either could scratch the paintwork. Polish the car in the same order that you washed and dried it. Work in small areas at a time.

Check the manufacturer's instructions carefully. Some polishes are designed to be left to dry on the car before they are cleaned off, but others should be wiped clear almost immediately. Always polish off with a clean cloth. Avoid polishing your car in bright sunlight, as the light could bleach and discolour the polish on the paintwork.

Your car should be washed once a week and waxed every three or four months to stop road dirt building up and dulling the paintwork. A brush attached to a hose gives a steady supply of clean water for rinsing off. Waxes are available either as a paste or spray and give good protection for various lengths of time. The spray waxes are easier to apply, though you must take care to avoid spraying areas that you do not want waxed.

Which type of polish?

If you use wax polish, you should polish your car thoroughly a minimum of every three months. With polymer sealants, the job must be done every four months. Both types of polish have their advantages and disadvantages. Wax polish does not last for as long as sealant and is generally harder to apply. However, it is cheaper and gives a uniform shine. Polymer is longer-lasting

and easier to apply, but it is more expensive and can cause streaks to appear on dark paintwork. It can also discolour rubber trim.

Special mild polishes are available for metallic paint. Polish chrome with a good non-abrasive cleaner. If the chrome is particularly rusted, try rubbing it down with kitchen foil. This will restore some of the original shine. Clean the inside

and outside of the windows and all mirrors with a proprietary glass cleaner. Alternatively, rub the windows down with a damp cloth and then polish them with newspaper.

Carpets should be swept with a vacuum cleaner to remove dirt and particles of grit. Tackle upholstery – whether vinyl, leather or fabric – with the type of cleaner recommended for the particular material.

Interiors

Vacuum the carpets and seats whenever you wash the car, as grit and dirt will cause them to wear quickly. There are a number of proprietary cleaners available for use on leather, vinyl and cloth upholstery.

Windows

Use a proprietary glass cleaner on the windows or alternatively, wipe the windows with a damp cloth, then polish them with newspaper.

Vinyl roofs

These should be washed with warm water and polished with a proprietary cleaner.

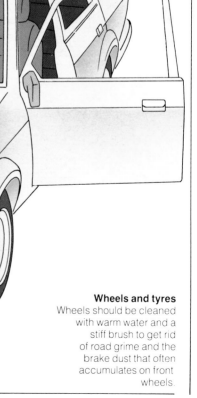

Chrome trim

If chrome-cleaning liquids fail, stubborn rust spots can be removed by rubbing with aluminium kitchen foil.

Under the bonnet

Engine cleaner can be sprayed or brushed on and the grime removed with a high pressure water hose.

Wheels and tyres

Wheels should be cleaned with warm water and a stiff brush to get rid of road grime and the brake dust that often accumulates on front wheels.

Restoring the shine

Age and road grime will eventually make paintwork patchy or dull. In such a case, normal cleaning and polishing will have little effect and the paintwork will need special treatment to restore its original shine.

The first steps

After washing and drying the car thoroughly *(see p.24)*, the paint must now be compounded with a cutting compound. Like some conventional polishes, cutting compounds come in liquid form, but, unlike polishes, they contain solvents and are slightly abrasive in their action. What they are designed to do is to remove stubborn layers of road dirt from the paintwork – plus an extremely thin layer of paint, so that clean paint is exposed.

Do not compound the car in bright sunlight. If you do, you could be faced with streaks or smears that are virtually impossible to remove. Apply the compound with a soft clean cloth – ideally, you should use mutton cloth. Do not use rough material or cloth with buttons or zips attached to it. Work in small areas on one panel at a time, rubbing the compound firmly on to the paint with a circular motion. Press firmly and ensure that each section is thoroughly coated.

Check the manufacturer's instructions to see whether or not the compound should be left to dry. Some compounds must be buffed off immediately after application. Buff the area with a soft, clean cloth, making sure that all traces of the compound are removed and the area is shiny when you have finished.

Continue the process of compounding and buffing until the work on the panel is completed, working on adjoining areas. If there are any smears or streaks, apply another thin layer of compound over the panel and then buff it off as before, working fairly quickly to ensure that the compound does not dry out. If, after this, there are still slight streaks, lightly buff the panel again with a clean cloth.

Compounding a complete car may take several hours and can be hard work. Be patient and take your time. It is far better to complete the job over a period of days – compounding one or two panels a day – than rushing through the job to finish it in one go, even if this means washing the car more than once.

Check the finish you are working on as well. If you are compounding metallic paint, you need to work more carefully, because it is easier to damage than a conventional solid-paint finish. In the former case, it is better to compound each panel twice, using the lightest possible coatings of compound, as cutting too deep will cause noticeable changes in colour.

Polishing the finish

You can buy polishing or buffing machines suited to all types of paintwork and powered by the car battery or mains-powered. The former work at low speeds and are relatively gentle, but the latter need careful handling. If excessive pressure is used, or if they are held in one place for too long, they can cut through paint extremely quickly. If you are using one for the first time, try it out on an old panel, or another painted surface, to accustom yourself to handling it.

You can use liquid cutting compound to restore the shine, if the paintwork is not too badly ingrained with dirt. Apply it with a dry cloth in small circular patches and cover an area of about a foot square at a time.

Dealing with awkward areas

You may find that some areas of bodywork, such as the door sills and front and rear valances beneath the bumpers, will not respond to conventional cutting compound. If this is the case, treat them with paste compound instead, as this is more abrasive. Paste compound is also particularly useful for removing minute scratches, or the tiny traces of alien paint that can be left after a scrape with another car.

Apply the paste in exactly the same way as you would the liquid, rubbing it into small areas at a time and then buffing it off. However, because the paste is so abrasive, you must take care not to cut right through the paint to the primer. Ater applying it, go over the area again with liquid compound.

Finishing off

Even after compounding the entire car, you may still find obstinate spots of tar on the

If the paintwork of your car is very dull, use cutting compound in paste form to restore it. This is abrasive and should be applied with a damp cloth, using only slight pressure. Work the paste on to the bodywork in small circular patches, covering an area of about a foot square at a time. Try to keep the pressure constant. When the paste has dried, polish it off with a clean cloth.

When the compound has dried, polish it off with another cloth. You will notice that the colour of the car will appear on the cloth – this is because the compound removes a very thin layer of paint with the dirt.

When you have restored the paintwork to its original shine, it must be protected against the elements with a coat of wax.

bodywork. Remove these by dabbing them with a soft cloth, soaked with white spirit, turpentine, or petrol. Do not use any other form of solvent or paint thinners. Any other blemishes, such as stone chips, should be dealt with as quickly as possible (see p.184). Remember, too, that, since all compounds are abrasive, they expose the paintwork, so, after compounding, the bodywork must be polished (see p.28).

The rest of the body

Once the paintwork has been restored, turn your attention to the other parts of the car where poor condition could ruin the car's general appearance. Vinyl roofs, for instance, fade and stain with age. You can clean a vinyl roof successfully with a suitable proprietary cleaner, but you should never try to polish or compound it.

Thoroughly rusted chrome cannot be restored satisfactorily. However, surface pitting can often be removed using abrasive chrome cleaner in paste form, or paste cutting compound. Once again, work in small areas and buff off with a clean cloth. Follow up by applying a good quality chrome cleaner – this will seal the surface and give added protection.

If your wheels are particularly grimy, you can clean them with a proprietary wheel-cleaning kit – this comes complete with special solvents and a stiff brush. Normally, however, conventional washing is enough (see p.24).

Special solvents can also be used to smarten up your tyres and the rubber sections on bumpers and trim. On tyres, you can use black boot polish as a cheaper, but effective, alternative. Apply it with a brush to cover scuffs – it will dry to give a semi-shiny finish.

Rust proofing

Rust damage is potentially dangerous, can be expensive to repair and will considerably reduce your car's second-hand value. When you buy your car, it will probably have been rust-proofed by its manufacturer, but additional treatment will give it extra protection. You can get this done professionally, or do the job yourself for a fraction of what a professional will cost.

However, note that rust-proofing is only worthwhile if the car is in good condition. Repairing rust damage (see p.176) is a professional job,

especially if it affects structural strength.

Preparing the car

In the majority of cases, corrosion starts from inside and spreads up to the surface. It attacks wings, wheel arches, doors, chassis box sections – in fact anywhere that has the ability to trap moisture.

Before you get down to the actual job, the car's underside must be cleaned thoroughly. Either get it steam-cleaned professionally – this is quite cheap – or do it yourself, which

will take a couple of hours. Wear goggles and gloves to protect yourself against flying debris and support the car firmly on axle stands or wheel ramps to gain access to the floor pan and chassis box sections. Rub down the whole of the underside with a stiff wire brush.

To clean the underside of the wings, remove the wheels and get to work with a sharpened piece of wood and garden hose, with the water pressure set as high as possible. Keep scraping and squirting until there is no mud left.

WHERE TO TREAT

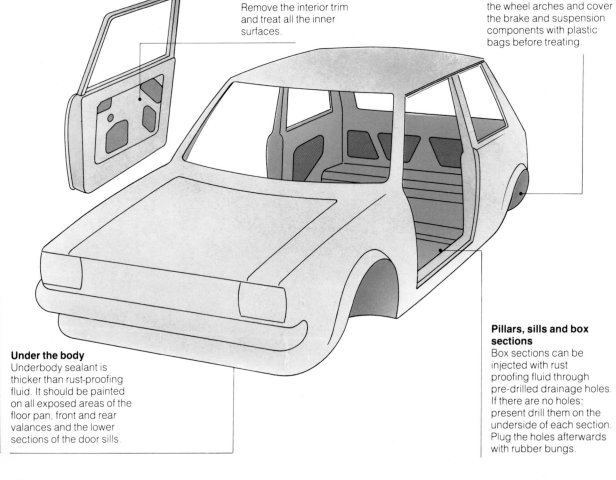

Doors
Remove the interior trim and treat all the inner surfaces.

Wheel arches
Clean off any mud within the wheel arches and cover the brake and suspension components with plastic bags before treating.

Under the body
Underbody sealant is thicker than rust-proofing fluid. It should be painted on all exposed areas of the floor pan, front and rear valances and the lower sections of the door sills.

Pillars, sills and box sections
Box sections can be injected with rust proofing fluid through pre-drilled drainage holes. If there are no holes; present drill them on the underside of each section. Plug the holes afterwards with rubber bungs.

Using a rust-proofing kit

You can buy rust-proofing kits from garages or car accessory stores. The kits contain a can of rust-proofing agent – the majority of these are a mixture of wax and oil – a hand pump and an extension probe. The probe is used to inject the box sections of the bodywork with the agent, as injection is the only effective way of protecting them. About four litres of rust-proofing agent will be needed for a thorough job.

Box sections are usually pre-drilled with a series of drainage holes. If not, you will have to drill your own and plug them at the end of the job – plastic or rubber bungs are supplied with the kit for this purpose. When you start work, push the probe into the sections as far as it will go and then slowly withdraw it. As you do this, operate the pump continuously, so that the whole of the internal area is covered by the probe's 360° spray. Allow any excess fluid to drain off before plugging the hole. Gain access to door sills by drilling holes into them from below, if necessary, but otherwise use the access holes inside the car.

Use the extension probe to treat the underside of the wings as well, particularly the underside of the front wings, because of the limited access behind the headlights. Brake assemblies should be covered with old plastic carrier bags to protect them from the spray.

The simplest way to rust-proof doors is first to remove their inner trim. You can then spray all of the inner panels and sections freely without covering the window-winder mechanism, or door-mounted radio speakers, with spray. Door and windscreen pillars should be injected in the same way as before, as should the hollow-section edges on bonnets and boots.

Sometimes, you may find that the pump clogs, or that the agent is proving difficult to spray. Clean the pump regularly with the solvent recommended by the manufacturer. If you are rust-proofing on a cool day, immerse the container in boiling water – this will thin the liquid and make it easier to apply.

Rust-converters

If your car is more than three years old – or second-hand – you may find that you have to cope with existing rust, rather than simply preventing rust from developing. If so, you will need a more advanced kit. Such kits consist of a rust-converter – this stops more rust developing on the rusted areas – and a sealer; alternatively, you can use the rust-converter on its own and follow it up with conventional rust-preventative treatment.

Remember, though, that rust-converters cannot deal effectively with extensive rusting on structual components, such as box sections, and should be used only to deal with light surface rusting in such circumstances. If the rust has spread extensively, or if you are in doubt, consult an expert.

Underbody sealant

Although it is impractical to inject underbody sealant – this is usually bitumen-based – into box sections and other double-skinned areas, it is well-suited to protecting areas at risk from flying stones and grit. It can be used to treat front and rear wheel arches, the insides of the front and rear valances, the whole of the exposed underpan and the lower sections of the door sills. It is tough, cheap, reasonably easy to apply and can be sprayed to match practically every existing paintwork (see p.186).

Make sure the metal to be sealed is thoroughly clean and dry before applying the sealant, as otherwise it will soon peel off. Normally, it is applied with a brush, using a stippling action to make sure that it sticks to the surface and that all the affected metal is covered.

The full job

For really thorough protection, it is best to use rust-preventative and underbody sealant in combination. Inject all enclosed and hollow sections with the fluid and treat all the other vulnerable areas with underbody sealant. At the same time, you can fit inner wing guards. These are made of plastic or aluminium and can be fixed in place underneath the wings with either blind rivets or self-tapping screws. The guards stop the grime thrown up by the wheels from reaching the wheel arches. It is also a good idea to fit a set of mud flaps on all four wheels.

Even a car that has been completely rust-proofed needs regular inspection. Every so often, hose inside the wings and up and down the underside of the car to remove road dirt and grime. Inspect the metal for signs of cracking or lifting underbody sealant and check that there are no areas where the surface of the fluid has been broken, exposing the metal. If you find any bare patches, touch-in as required.

Anatomy of the Car

Many people find cars mechanical puzzles that are hard to understand, let alone solve. As far as most drivers are concerned, what happens after they get into their car and start the engine is an almost total mystery. Technical manuals are of little help – simply because they are technical. So, apart from regularly filling the fuel tank and checking the oil, water and battery fluid levels, most drivers adopt the philosophy of leaving well alone.

Not surprisingly, neglect eventually leads to mechanical breakdown. Almost inevitably, this happens at the most inconvenient moment.

Breakdowns can be caused by extra mechanical stress – an exceptionally hot summer's day, or a winter snap freeze, will expose any weaknesses in the car's cooling and starting systems, for instance. Yet, in many instances, such incidents need never occur. By spending a minimal amount of time once a week making a few basic checks, you will often be able to spot potential problems before they arise, rather than having to cope with their consequences.

Remember, all cars share the same basic mechanical components and engineering systems, even though layout and specifications vary between makes and models. Once you have grasped the basic mechanical and electrical principles governing your car's operation, you will be able to keep your car in tip-top condition. You will also be much more confident in your dealings with a garage. You will know what a mechanic is talking about, rather than being blinded with science; in turn, you will be able to explain any problem clearly to your garage.

The heart of your car

At the heart of every car lies the engine, together with its supporting fuel, ignition, lubricating and cooling systems. In the majority of cars, the engine is mounted at the front, although some models are rear-engined. Whichever the case, the engine's task is the same – to convert fuel into mechanical energy.

To work, the engine needs electricity just as much as fuel. The basic power source is a self-contained battery. This is essential to starting the car; when the engine is running, it drives a generator – a dynamo or an alternator – which powers the ignition, and the rest of the electrical system and its components.

The fuel is stored in a petrol tank – this is usually positioned at the opposite end of the car to the engine to minimize any fire risk – and reaches the engine via the fuel pump and carburettor. Fuel and air mix inside the latter to create an explosive mixture, which is ignited in the cylinders to power the engine. Depending on the type of carburettor, the amounts of fuel or air in the mixture can be adjusted to ensure that the engine is running at optimum efficiency. The speed at which the engine runs is controlled by the car's accelerator pedal, which is mechanically linked to the carburettor and alters the amount of the fuel/air mixture entering the engine.

Inside the cylinders, the explosive fuel-and-air mixture is compressed by the pistons, and then ignited by an electric spark from the spark plugs, the high-voltage current required for this being fed from the coil via the distributor. The latter, as its name implies, distributes the current to each spark plug in a pre-determined order. The force of the expanding gases produced by the combustion pushes the pistons down the cylinders to rotate the engine's crankshaft.

This process produces considerable heat, which, in turn, means that the engine needs an effective cooling system. In most cars, this is provided by a water-based coolant, which circulates through channels bored in the engine block and then through the radiator at the front of the car, where the large surface area of the radiator's fins dissipates the heat. Some engines, however, are air-cooled. In these, the hot air cools as it flows through fins cast on the engine block and cylinder head.

Lubrication of the engine's moving parts is similarly vital to reduce friction and keep wear to a minimum. This is provided by a constantly-circulating supply of oil drawn from the sump, a reservoir under the engine, and pumped at high pressure to all the engine's moving parts.

Transmitting the power

As the crankshaft is rotated by the pistons, it passes its power to the gearbox, bolted to the engine, through the clutch assembly, which bridges the gap between the constantly running engine and the sometimes stationary transmission. The assembly consists of a spring-loaded disc, faced with a special friction material that bears down tightly against a metal flywheel on the end of the crankshaft.

When there is no pressure on the clutch pedal, the clutch disc rotates with the flywheel and transmits this rotation to the other components of the transmission system. When you depress the clutch, you break this connection by sliding the disc back from the flywheel with a cable- or hydraulically-operated lever linked to the pedal.

The gearbox's job is to make the best use of the available engine power by allowing you to vary the speed at which its drive shaft turns in relation to the speed of the engine. This means, for instance, that the engine can turn very quickly – so developing a large amount of power – though the wheels are only turning slowly to overcome the inertia of the car, as when climbing a hill or starting off. By selecting the appropriate gear with the gear lever, you can maintain the most economical engine speed to suit driving conditions. The faster you are travelling, the higher the gear should be.

Some cars are fitted with automatic transmission systems, which dispense with the clutch assembly in favour of a torque converter permanently attached to the crankshaft. Filled with a special fluid, the converter uses centrifugal force to engage the drive when the engine reaches a specific speed. It also drives a pump, which forces the fluid through various valves to change gears automatically in line with the engine revolutions.

In a conventional front-engined, rear-wheel-drive car, the gearbox drives a long propeller shaft connected to the rear axle. There, a set of gear wheels turns the drive through 90°, passing its impetus to the rear wheels through a series of short drive shafts. This assembly, known as the differential, also allows the drive wheels to rotate at different speeds. This is necessary when turning a corner, as the outer wheels have a larger radius to cover and therefore must rotate faster than the inner ones.

In front-wheel-drive cars, the gearbox has the differential built into it, and may be mounted in front of, or below, the engine. With rear-engined cars with rear-wheel drive, the entire assembly is at the opposite end of the vehicle.

Steering, stopping and handling

Your steering wheel is attached to a long shaft, at the end of which a simple gear mechanism converts the shaft's rotary motion into lateral motion to move another shaft from side to side. At each end of the shaft, rods, attached to the pivoting front-wheel assemblies, push the wheel to left or right, depending on which way the steering wheel is turned.

All cars have four braking units – one for each wheel. All four are hydraulically operated simultaneously by the brake pedal. The units are either fitted with shoes, which are pushed outwards against a rotating drum, or pads, which are pushed against either side of a rotating disc. The cable-operated hand brake allows the rear brakes to be locked on to prevent the vehicle moving.

A car's handling ability – that is, the way it performs when cornering, accelerating and braking – is also very important. If the wheels were mounted solidly to the car's body, you would find the car ricocheting from one bump to another. The suspension system overcomes this problem with springs fitted between the wheels and the body to absorb road shocks. In most cases, the springs are made of metal, though some cars have special rubber springs, or can be fitted with a pressurized gas suspension system. Dampers, commonly known as shock absorbers, are fitted to stop the spring continuing to oscillate after absorbing the force of a bump.

Since tyres need only minimal maintenance, they are often overlooked, though their job is of critical importance. Their tread patterns are carefully designed to provide the best grip in all possible conditions, but, at best, can be a compromise. This is why some tyres may seem to work efficiently on a dry road, but pass their limit of adhesion very quickly in the wet. Remember that, during an average rainstorm, each individual tyre must pump over a gallon of water clear of the road to maintain its grip, assuming a driving speed of 60mph (96.5kph).

Taken one at a time, the systems described here are not as complicated as they might seem at first. In the following pages, you will find descriptions of all the major individual mechanical systems, with details of their components, how they work, what their weaknesses are and what to look for, so that you can check that they are operating at the peak of efficiency.

The engine

In the majority of cars, the engine is mounted at the front of the vehicle. It usually drives the rear wheels, though front-wheel-drive designs are becoming increasingly popular. These have two main advantages. Because the weight of the engine is positioned over the wheels it powers, better traction is provided, while there is also no need for a tunnel in the floorpan for the propellor shaft.

There are also some rear-engined, rear-wheel-drive cars, though this arrangement is not absolutely satisfactory. This is because it does not provide the best weight distribution for driving stability.

How the engine works

All petrol engines work by internal combustion – that is, they produce mechanical movement by burning fuel mixed with air inside closed cylinders – and all operate on the four-stroke principle. The four-stroke cycle gets its name from the four strokes – two up and two down – that each piston makes in each of the engine's cylinders during the cycle. These strokes are termed the induction, compression, ignition/power and exhaust strokes respectively.

Each piston is connected to the engine crankshaft, where its vertical motion is translated into a rotary one. The principle is the same as that of pedalling a bicycle. The rotary motion is then transferred to the driven wheels through the gearbox.

The four-stroke cycle

Modern car engines normally have four, six or eight cylinders, the cranks of the crankshaft being arranged to ensure that,

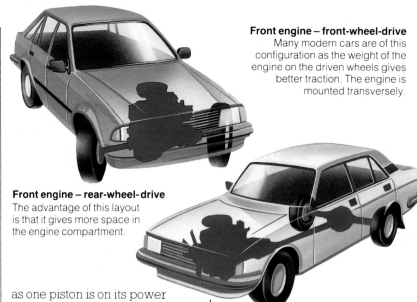

Front engine – front-wheel-drive
Many modern cars are of this configuration as the weight of the engine on the driven wheels gives better traction. The engine is mounted transversely.

Front engine – rear-wheel-drive
The advantage of this layout is that it gives more space in the engine compartment.

as one piston is on its power stroke, a second will be on its exhaust stroke, a third on its induction stroke and so on. Such an arrangement means the crankshaft rotates constantly, being helped in this by a system of counterweights and a heavy metal disc – the flywheel – bolted to one end of the shaft. The momentum created by the flywheel keeps the shaft turning smoothly.

At the beginning of the four-stroke cycle, the piston is positioned at the top of the cylinder, starting to move downwards. As it does so, it sucks in a charge of fuel-and-air mixture through a valve housed in the cylinder head. When the piston reaches the bottom of the stroke, the valve closes. This completes the induction stroke.

The piston then rises to compress the fuel-and-air mixture – the compression stroke. Just before the piston reaches the top of the cylinder, however, an electrical spark from the spark plug fitted into the cylinder head ignites the mixture. The force of the explosion forces the piston back

down the cylinder on its power stroke. Finally, the piston travels upwards again to expel the burnt gases through a second valve in the cylinder head. This is the exhaust stroke, at the end of which the exhaust valve closes, the inlet valve opens and the whole cycle begins again.

Inside the engine

Every engine consists of two basic units – the cylinder block/crankcase and the cylinder head. These may be made from cast iron or aluminium, though in some cases the use of the two metals is mixed – the block being of cast iron and the cylinder head of the lighter aluminium.

The cylinder block also carries a number of externally-mounted components. These are the starter motor, the water pump, the distributor, the oil pump and, in some cars, a mechanical fuel pump.

Cylinders and pistons

The cylinders are usually bored directly from the metal of the

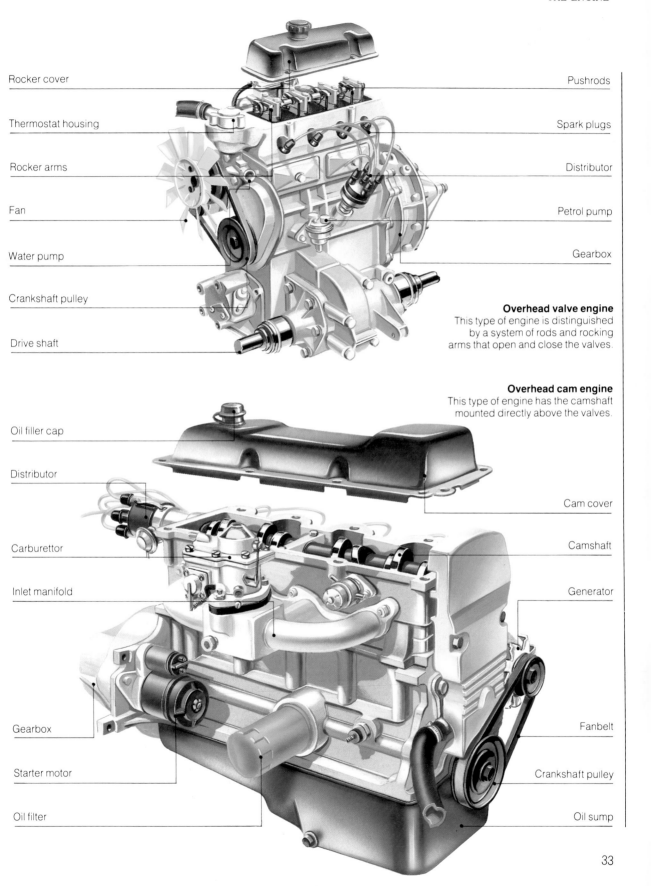

Rocker cover

Thermostat housing

Rocker arms

Fan

Water pump

Crankshaft pulley

Drive shaft

Pushrods

Spark plugs

Distributor

Petrol pump

Gearbox

Overhead valve engine
This type of engine is distinguished by a system of rods and rocking arms that open and close the valves.

Overhead cam engine
This type of engine has the camshaft mounted directly above the valves.

Oil filler cap

Distributor

Carburettor

Inlet manifold

Gearbox

Starter motor

Oil filter

Cam cover

Camshaft

Generator

Fanbelt

Crankshaft pulley

Oil sump

33

Engine/checklist

block, though sometimes, if the block is made from aluminium, the bores are lined with steel. They may be arranged in line, one behind another, in two rows in a V-shape, or flat. In the last two cases, the engine will have two cylinder heads.

The pistons must fit the cylinders tightly to stop any of the expanding gases escaping, with consequent loss of power. Naturally, the piston would wear very quickly against the cylinder if there were no gap at all between them, so a slight clearance is allowed between the piston and the cylinder wall. This, however, must be sealed to minimize any gas loss. This is achieved by a number of sprung metal rings fitted to each piston, which push outwards against the cylinder walls to ensure a gas-tight seal. The rings also stop the lubricating oil from the cylinder bore getting into the cylinder's combustion chamber.

Crankshaft and camshaft
Each piston is connected to the crankshaft by a tapered connecting rod. The top end of this rod fits around a pin – the gudgeon pin – driven through the piston. The bearing fitted here is known as the small end. The bottom end of the rod is clamped to the crankshaft and lined with a wear-resistant metal bearing. This bearing is the big end.

The crankshaft runs longitudinally through the crankcase. It is clamped to the block in several places by semi-circular metal caps, which also contain wear-resistant bearings. The back end of the crankshaft carries the flywheel. This is fitted with a toothed ring gear that meshes with the starter

motor. The flywheel also links up to the transmission through the clutch assembly, which is bolted to the flywheel's rear face.

The front end of the crankshaft is fitted with a gear wheel. This drives a second shaft – the camshaft – by means of a chain, a toothed rubber belt, or a second, larger, gear wheel.

The camshaft operates the valves in the cylinder head. It gets its name from the lobes (or cams) running along its length. These are are egg-shaped in profile and it is their rotation that opens and closes the valves. In many engines, the camshaft is contained within the cylinder block, though in most high-performance engines, it is positioned directly above the valves in the cylinder head. When the camshaft is in the block, the engine is defined as OHV (overhead valve); when the cam is in the cylinder head, it is known as OHC (overhead cam).

If the engine has its camshaft in the cylinder block, the rods that bear on the cam lobes – pushrods – move up and down as the camshaft rotates. A shaft – the rocker shaft – runs down the centre of the head, between the pushrod and valve positions. This carries a number of double-ended lever arms – the rocker arms – which pivot on the shaft. One end of each rocker arm bears against the top of the valve stem and the other bears against the top of the pushrod. By moving upwards the pushrod makes the rocker arm push down on the corresponding valve stem, opening the valve.

If the engine has its camshaft in the cylinder head, however, the need for pushrods is eliminated. In this instance, the

camshaft may operate the valves through a set of rocker arms, or may bear directly on special cam followers, fitted to the tops of the valve stems. Such an arrangement reduces the weight of the valve gear and the number of moving parts. As a result, less power is needed to operate it.

The cylinder head
The cylinder head is bolted to the top of the cylinder block and covers the top of the cylinders, where the valves are located and combustion takes place. The top of the head is concealed by a metal cover, which is screwed on to it. This protects the valve gear, or overhead camshaft, and keeps the circulating lubricating oil inside the head. The cover is fitted with a removable cap, so that the oil level can be topped up when necessary.

The head itself carries the valve assembly (and sometimes the camshaft); the spark plugs; and the inlet and exhaust manifolds, which take the fuel-and-air mixture from the carburettor to the cylinders and the exhaust gases from the cylinders to the exhaust pipe respectively. It also contains the cooling system outlet, plus its controlling thermostat.

Special passages, called ports, run from the side of the cylinder head to the valve openings. The inlet and exhaust ports can be on either side of the head – if this is so, the engine is known as a cross-flow engine – or both may lie along one side of the head. Both cylinder head and block are also cast with special internal passages to allow coolant to flow through them. These passages are collectively termed the water jacket.

Inside the head, each valve consists of a thin round stem that broadens out sharply to form a large round head with a chamfered edge that seals against a similar chamfer on the edge of the valve opening. The valves are kept closed by strong springs, which pull them firmly against their seatings to form a gas-tight seal.

What gaskets do
Wherever the engine's components are bolted together, it is essential to create and maintain gas-tight, oil-tight and water-tight seals. This is achieved by inserting a device called a gasket betwen the adjacent mating surfaces.

Gaskets are made from a variety of materials, depending on their position in the engine. The cylinder head gasket, fitted between the cylinder head and cylinder block, has to contain the pressure and heat of combustion, as well as sealing the coolant passages from the block to the head. For this reason, it is fairly thick and is faced with a thin copper sheet. The gaskets used to form a seal against oil – between the sump and block, for instance – are usually made of cork, while gaskets sealing water or petrol connections are normally made from thick compressed card.

Understanding lubrication
The bottom of the cylinder block is closed off by a metal pan – the sump – which contains the oil needed to lubricate the engine. It reduces friction between moving parts and helps to keep them cool.

The oil is forced around the engine at high pressure by a pump, bolted to the block and powered by a shaft linked to either the camshaft or the crankshaft. After the oil has been collected by a pick-up tube, it is first pumped through a filter, screwed to the side of the cylinder block and then passed through tiny channels – the oil ways – in the cylinder block and cylinder head to reach the bearings and valves. During the process, a mist of oil forms in the crankcase to lubricate the cylinder walls.

The amount of oil in the sump is measured with a dipstick, a long removable metal rod located in a tube in the side of the cylinder block and protruding into the sump. The sump is also fitted with a threaded plug at the bottom, so that the oil can be drained when necessary. Changing the oil regularly is essential, as the tiny particles of metal and dirt picked up by the oil in its journey through the engine gradually deprive it of its lubricating qualities. The oil filter should also be replaced when the oil is changed.

Engine checklist
When checking over the engine, do not smoke or work with a naked flame nearby.

Check all round the engine for signs of oil leaks resulting from blown gaskets or failed seals.

date checked ☑

Check the oil filter is tight on its mounting boss.

☐

Check the sump drain plug, making sure it is tight.

☐

Check to see whether or not the oil filler cap incorporates a breather and wire filter; if it does, make sure that the wire filter is not clogged.

☐

Check for coolant leaks, paying particular attention to the joint between the cylinder head and cylinder block, the joint between the water pump and cylinder block around the pump shaft and all hose connections.

☐

Check that both inlet and exhaust manifolds are secure with all their mounting bolts in place and tight. Similarly check the security of all engine accessories, such as the generator, distributor, fuel pump and water pump.

☐

Check the engine mountings low down on each side of the cylinder block. Make sure the securing nuts and bolts are tight and that the mounting rubbers are in good condition, showing no signs of perishing, softening or splitting.

☐

The ignition system

The battery

Your battery is your car's primary electrical power source. It has positive and negative terminals, the latter normally linked to the bodywork to act as an earth – all other metal components are also earthed in this way. In most cars, a single thick heavy-duty lead links the live terminal to the starter motor. The majority of batteries have a 12-volt output.

The starter motor

The current needed to turn the starter motor comes directly from the battery and is controlled by an electro-magnetic switch, called a solenoid. This is operated by the starter/ignition switch.

There are two types of starter motor – inertia and pre-engaged. The inertia type is fitted with a Bendix gear, in which the spinning motor shaft moves a pinion along a screw thread until it engages the flywheel. When the engine starts, the pinion spins back to its original position. The solenoid is mounted separately in the engine bay and acts as a switch or relay to control the current flow. With the pre-engaged type – fitted to modern cars – the solenoid is mounted on the starter. As well as regulating the flow of current, it triggers a lever that engages the starter gear with the engine flywheel before turning, disengaging it when the ignition key is released.

The coil

The coil boosts the low voltage supplied by the battery to the high voltage the spark plugs need to create their spark. It consists of two coils of copper wire – the outer is termed the primary winding and the inner the secondary winding – arranged around a soft iron core. Current flowing through the primary winding generates a magnetic field. When the flow of current is interrupted by the action of the contact breaker points within the distributor, the magnetic field collapses, causing the secondary winding to produce a pulse of high-voltage current.

The distributor

The distributor, usually mounted on the side of the engine, directs

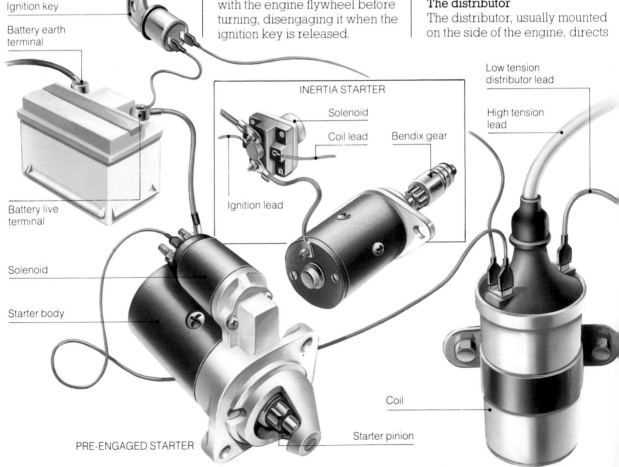

Ignition key

Battery earth terminal

Battery live terminal

Solenoid

Starter body

PRE-ENGAGED STARTER

INERTIA STARTER

Solenoid

Coil lead

Bendix gear

Ignition lead

Low tension distributor lead

High tension lead

Coil

Starter pinion

the current from the coil to the spark plugs. The current passes through a set of electrical contacts, called the contact breaker points. These are opened and closed by the action of a rotating cam to make and break the circuit, so creating a series of high tension pulses.

The cam is mounted on a shaft within the distributor, the shaft being driven from the engine. The position of the lever is set in relation to the cam to ensure that the contacts open at a precise point in the pistons' cycle. This allows the spark plugs to ignite the fuel fully before the pistons start to descend. This is the ignition timing, which can be adjusted when necessary (see p.128).

The gap between the points is critical and should be checked regularly (see p.122). If it is too narrow, the flow of current will not be broken; if it is too wide, the contacts will not stay open for a sufficient length of time. A condenser prevents electricity arcing across the points.

The high-tension pulses pass through a central electrode in the distributor cap to a rotor arm on top of the distributor shaft. As the rotor arm spins, the current is passed along it to electrodes fitted around the inside of the distributor cap at the ends of the flexible high-tension leads.

As the engine runs faster, so the moment at which the spark is created to burn the fuel must occur earlier in each piston's

stroke. This is regulated automatically by centrifugal weights inside the distributor and vacuum from the engine. Both systems turn the base plate of the points to advance their opening. As the engine slows, springs return the plate to its original position.

The spark plugs

Each cylinder has its own spark plug, screwed into the cylinder head and reaching through to the individual combustion chambers. The top of each plug is connected to a high voltage lead from the distributor cap. Pulses of electricity reach the tip of each electrode and then jump the gap to an earthing electrode, thus creating the spark. The electrode gap is crucial; if it is too narrow, the spark might not be large enough, but, if it is excessive, the current might not be able to jump the gap.

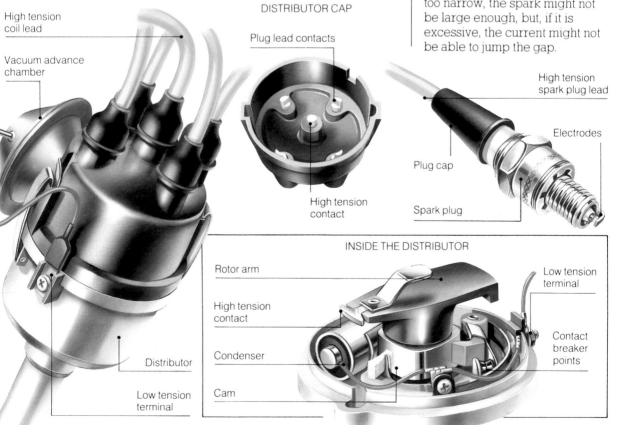

High tension coil lead

Vacuum advance chamber

Distributor

Low tension terminal

DISTRIBUTOR CAP

Plug lead contacts

High tension contact

INSIDE THE DISTRIBUTOR

Rotor arm

High tension contact

Condenser

Cam

High tension spark plug lead

Electrodes

Plug cap

Spark plug

Low tension terminal

Contact breaker points

Ignition system/checklist

When checking the components of the ignition system, work around the engine compartment in a logical order. Throughout, make sure that all wiring is in good condition. It should be clean, free of nicks or other insulation damage and, where appropriate, held firmly in clips; it should not be strained, kinked, or chafing against any sharp metal projections. All connections should be clean and free from corrosion.

It is important to establish the polarity of the electrical system in your car – that is, whether earth is positive or negative. To find this out, look at the wiring connections at the battery terminals. Most cars have negative polarity, in which case the red 'live' wire will be connected to the positive battery terminal (marked +). The black earth wire will run from the negative terminal (marked -) to a nearby position on the car's bodywork. With a positive polarity system, however, the wiring arrangement is reversed.

Check the battery. This is is usually mounted in a tray at one side of the engine compartment and held in place by a clamp, which may run along one of the battery's top edges or bear against a lip near the bottom of the battery casing. Make sure the clamp is squarely located against the battery and that the restraining nuts or bolts are tight; the battery must be stable, as otherwise it may topple and spill its corrosive contents. Check over the battery tray for rust or other damage that would make the mounting insecure.

date checked _____ ✓

Check the casing of the battery, looking for cracks or other damage that could allow the electrolyte it contains to leak.

_____ ☐

Check the battery terminals, which are set at each end of the battery top. Make sure that the connections are tight and clean. If the battery terminals are dry, coat them with a little petroleum jelly to keep them free of corrosion. Ensure that socket-and-clamp fittings are pushed home fully over the terminals and that their retaining screws or bolts are in place.

_____ ☐

Check the earth wire, making sure it is in good condition and that the bolt holding it to the bodywork is tight and uncorroded.

_____ ☐

Check the level of electrolyte in the battery. If the car is fitted with a 'sealed for life' battery, check this visually through the semi-transparent case. If not, remove the filler caps and check each cell individually. The electrolyte should just cover the tops of the lead plates. If necessary, top up with distilled or de-ionised water – never use tap water. Make sure that the filler caps are undamaged and clean and that their breather holes are not blocked. Replace the caps so that they are no more than finger tight.

_____ ☐

Check the starter motor. This is usually fitted on the same side of the engine as the battery to keep the wiring between the two down to the minimum. The starter motor itself is mounted low down at the rear of the cylinder block, where it is connected to the gearbox/clutch housing. It should be held in place by two or three bolts. Make sure that all of these are fitted tightly enough to hold the starter motor squarely against its mounting flange.

With an inertia starter motor, the solenoid will be mounted nearby on the engine compartment bulkhead, or the inner wing. Check the security of the mounting screws and inspect the heavy-duty leads that run between battery and solenoid and solenoid and starter motor. Make sure that they are in good condition and their connections are clean and tight. Also check that the two thin leads (one from the ignition switch and one to earth) are connected securely to their terminals on the solenoid.

With a pre-engaged starter motor, the solenoid will be mounted directly above the starter motor. Check it in the same way.

_____ ☐

Check the coil. This is usually mounted to one of the inner wings with a simple U-clamp. Make sure that the retaining screws are tightly in place and that the clamp itself is in good condition.

Inspect the coil's three wiring connections – the central connection for the thick high-tension lead that runs to the centre of the distributor cap and the thin low-tension leads on either side of it. The high-tension lead may simply push into the raised portion of the coil's top, with a rubber cap over the connection, or it may be held in place by a threaded plastic collar. Make sure the end of the lead is pushed fully home together with its protective cap, or that the screw connector is tightened correctly. The low-tension leads are connected by push-on 'spade' connectors – make sure these are pushed fully home, clean and tight.

_____ ☐

Check that the low-tension leads are connected correctly – on a negative-polarity system (*see p.36*), the lead from the ignition switch runs to the coil's positive terminal, while the lead to the distributor is connected to the negative terminal. In a positive polarity system, this arrangement is reversed.

One of the low-tension leads from the ignition switch may run through a porcelain resistor, which will be fitted close to the coil. Make sure that this resistor is secure, uncracked and free from all other signs of damage.

_____ ☐

Check the distributor. This is usually located at the side of the cylinder block, though, on some OHC- and V-engines, it may lie on top of the engine block. Make sure that it is held securely by its clamp, which is located at the base of its body.

_____ ☐

Check the narrow plastic vacuum pipe running between the inlet manifold and the vacuum capsule at the side of the distributor. Make sure that it is not kinked or damaged and that its ends are pushed fully home on its connector pipes. Some cars may be fitted with a rigid metal vacuum pipe, with screwed unions at either end. Make sure that these are tight.

Remove the distributor cap by levering away the spring clips, or releasing the retaining screws. Inspect the rotor arm fitted to the top of the distributor shaft, looking for signs of wear, damage or pitting. Make sure that the arm is clean.

_____ ☐

Check that the low-tension leads are connected securely to the contact breaker points and that the heel, which bears on the cam of the distributor shaft, shows no sign of excessive wear. Check the gap between the contact breaker points with a feeler gauge (*see p.126*).

_____ ☐

Check the inside of the distributor cap, looking for cracks or other signs of damage. Make sure that the contacts inside the cap are in good condition. The central contact may be spring-loaded, in which case it must be free to move up and down. Wipe around the inside of the cap with a clean cloth and then replace it, making sure that the clips or screws are fully home and that the cap sits squarely on top of the distributor.

_____ ☐

Check that the high-tension leads between coil, distributor and sparking plugs are all pushed fully home in the distributor cap, or held tightly by their screw caps. Make sure that the protective rubber caps are pushed home fully and are in good condition.

_____ ☐

Check that the low-tension lead from the coil is securely attached to its terminal on the side of the distributor.

Follow each sparking plug high-tension lead in turn, making sure that it is clean and free from damage and that it is held securely in any separator that may be fitted.

Pull off each plug lead – holding the cap, not the high-tension lead, as you do so – and inspect it, checking that it is firmly attached to the lead and not cracked or damaged in any way.

_____ ☐

Check the tops of the plugs, making sure that the contact screw is fitted tightly and that the porcelain insulator is clean. The plug itself should be screwed home tightly, while the depression around it should be free of oil and dirt.

Refit the plug caps, pushing them in until you feel or hear the spring connectors in them snap home.

_____ ☐

_____

The cooling system

As a result of the combustion of fuel and the friction generated between the engine's moving parts, a car's engine naturally generates a great deal of heat. To get rid of this unwanted heat, a coolant – usually a mixture of water and anti-freeze – is pumped through the engine block and cylinder head. Narrow passages channel the coolant past all the hot points within the engine. It is then pumped through the radiator, where the unwanted heat is released.

Some cars have air cooling instead. In this case, the engine has fins cast on to the block and cylinder head, giving a larger area through which heat can be dispersed. Air is channelled over the engine to cool it, usually with the assistance of an engine-driven fan.

The radiator

In most cars, the radiator is mounted at the front, so that is receives a steady flow of cooling air as the car moves. Its core consists of a number of copper tubes, surrounded by a block of thin copper fins. The large surface area this gives means that a considerable amount of heat can be dissipated. Brass tanks at the top and bottom of the core act as reservoirs for the coolant.

The thermostat is positioned at the coolant outlet on the engine. Its temperature rating– that is the temperature at which it opens – is stamped on the top ring.

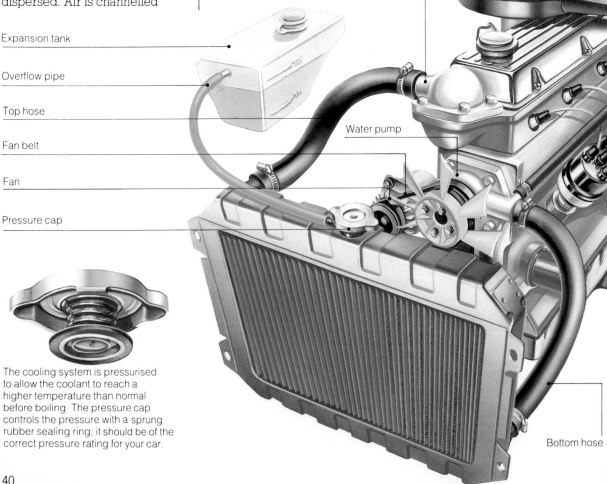

Thermostat housing

Expansion tank

Overflow pipe

Top hose

Water pump

Fan belt

Fan

Pressure cap

The cooling system is pressurised to allow the coolant to reach a higher temperature than normal before boiling. The pressure cap controls the pressure with a sprung rubber sealing ring; it should be of the correct pressure rating for your car.

Bottom hose

The coolant flows between the engine and radiator through a network of rubber hoses, the system being designed to ensure that the hot water enters the radiator's top tank, flows down through the core – where it cools – and flows back to the engine through the bottom tank.

The connections between the rigidly mounted radiator and the contantly vibrating engine must be flexible. As the hoses age, they become brittle and

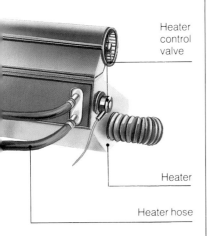

Heater control valve

Heater

Heater hose

Some cars are fitted with an electric fan, mounted directly on the back of the radiator. As opposed to an engine driven fan, which runs all the time and uses up some engine power, an electric fan operates only when the coolant reaches a certain temperature, controlled by a thermostatic switch, and is driven by its own electric motor.

eventually split. This makes them the weakest part of the system and, as a result, they should be checked regularly *(see p.114).*

To reduce the risk of the coolant boiling, the system is pressurized. This has the effect of raising the boiling point of the coolant. A relief valve in the filler cap regulates the pressure, allowing coolant to escape through an overflow pipe if both temperature and pressure become excessive. In older cars, this pipe may simply discharge coolant on to the road; in modern cars, it leads to a separate expansion tank, which retains the overflow until the pressure in the system drops.

The water pump
The water pump is designed to force coolant around the cooling system. The metal body houses a shaft, which has an impeller at one end and a pulley at the other.

The pump is bolted to the front of the engine, so that the impeller protrudes into the water jacket. The fan belt is fitted between the pump pulley and a similar pulley on the end of the crankshaft to provide the necessary drive – the belt may also drive the alternator or dynamo.

If the fan belt breaks, the coolant ceases to circulate. This means that the engine will overheat within a matter of minutes. For this reason, it is always advisable to carry a spare fan belt, which can be fitted quickly *(see p.110).*

The weakest point of the pump itself is the sealing gasket fitted between it and the engine. If this fails, coolant will be lost, with overheating as the result. The shaft bearings are also

prone to wear if the drive belt is too tight, so this, too, should be checked regularly *(see p.112).* If the pump starts to squeal, lubricating the bearings may help cure the problem. Since this cannot be done in the normal way, additive should be mixed with the coolant to lubricate the pump.

The fan
When your car is moving slowly, or is stationary, the cooling system cannot rely on the natural flow of air through the radiator carrying away enough of the excess heat. Here, help is provided by a fan, which draws air through the radiator core.

In many cars, this fan is bolted directly to the water pump's pulley and is driven by the same rubber belt that turns the pump. The drawback here is that the fan is being driven constantly by the engine, even when it is not needed. This wastes fuel. To overcome this, some fans are equipped with an electro-magnetic clutch, operated by a temperature sensor, which allows the fan blades to freewheel when the coolant is at optimum temperature.

Some vehicles dispense with an engine-driven fan altogether in favour of one driven by an electric motor. This type of fan is usually mounted directly on the back of the radiator and is also controlled by a temperature sensor, mounted close to the thermostat housing.

The thermostat
For the engine to run at peak efficiency, it must be kept at its optimum operating temperature. The thermostat, located at the engine's coolant outlet, not only ensures that the coolant reaches

Cooling system/checklist

its correct operating temperature as quickly as possible by blocking off its flow to the radiator; it also regulates the flow to suit all driving conditions. During winter, for instance, the thermostat will remain closed for longer, ensuring that the engine is not over-cooled and that there is enough heat for interior heating.

The thermostat operates by means of a rubber diaphragm, which has a rod attached to it. The base of the rod is surrounded by wax in a sealed container. As the surrounding coolant heats, the wax melts and expands, pushing the rod up and opening the diaphragm to allow the coolant to flow.

The car must be fitted with a thermostat of the correct temperature rating. Otherwise it may open too soon, or too late – if at all – and the engine could be damaged as a result.

The heater

The engine's cooling system also provides heat for the interior of the car. Small-diameter rubber hoses run between the engine and a heat-exchanger – a smaller version of the radiator, mounted beneath the dashboard. Hot coolant from the engine flows round this circuit and air drawn in from outside passes over the heat exchanger to carry the warmth to the inside of the car. Most cars have an electric fan to boost this flow.

The air temperature is controlled by a cable-operated valve, which regulates the amount of coolant flowing through the heat-exchanger. Cable-operated flaps also allow the warmed air to be directed to various parts of the interior, such as the windscreen and the floor.

Cooling system checklist

Check that the radiator mounting bolts are all tightly in place and that the mounting flanges are not parting company with the radiator itself. Inspect the front panel for signs of rust damage around the radiator fixing points.

Check both sides of the radiator core to make sure that none of the passages between the fins are blocked by dirt, leaves or dead insects.

Check the seams between the top and bottom tanks and the core for signs of coolant leakage. Also check the seams around the inlet and outlet stubs where they are soldered to the tanks. Look generally for signs of damage.

Check the level of coolant in the radiator. It should be about 25mm (1in) below the filler neck. If necessary, top up with the correct water/anti-freeze solution (see p.112).

Check that the system does contain anti-freeze – if this is the case, the coolant should be blue or green in colour.

Check that the filler cap is of the correct pressure rating; this will be marked on the cap and given in the manufacturer's handbook.

Refit the cap, making sure that it is turned fully home.

Check that the overflow pipe is fitted and correctly routed clear of the fan and other moving parts. On a sealed system it will run to the expansion tank; otherwise, it will be clipped to the side of the radiator and directed downwards towards the road. Make sure that the pipe is not kinked or blocked.

Check that the drain tap (if fitted) or the drain plug is tight and shows no sign of coolant leakage.

Check that all the bolts holding the fan to the pulley are in place and tightened fully.

Check the fan or drive belt tension, making sure that it is not too loose. You should not be able to deflect the belt by any more than 13mm ($\frac{1}{2}$in) when applying moderate thumb pressure at the centre of its longest run. Make sure that it is properly seated in all its pulleys and inspect its overall condition, looking for cuts, nicks or fraying. The belt should be replaced if damage is found.

Check that all the pulley retaining bolts are in place and that they are tight. Also check that the pulleys are not damaged in any way and that the flanges are not distorted. If they are, the drive belt could be 'thrown' or damaged.

☐

If the car is fitted with an electric cooling fan

Check all the wiring connections, making sure that they are tight and fully home. Make sure that the wires are clipped out of harm's way and that they are not chafing against sharp edges. The fan's thermostat will be attached to the radiator top tank; make sure that it is secure.

☐

Check the seam between the pump body and the engine block for signs of coolant leakage, resulting from a blown gasket. If present, this will probably show as rust-coloured streaks below the pump and around the front of the engine where the coolant has been blown back by the fan.

☐

Check around the end of the pump shaft behind the drive pulley for signs of coolant leakage, which indicates that the shaft seal has failed.

☐

Check the join between the thermostat housing and the cylinder head (or manifold, on V-engines) for signs of coolant leakage, which either indicates that the bolts are loose or that the gasket has failed.

☐

Check all of the cooling system's rubber hoses, including those that run from the engine to the heating system inlet and outlet stubs at the engine compartment bulkhead. Make sure that the hoses are fully home on their stubs and that their retaining clips are tight, but not cutting into the rubber. The clips should not be heavily rusted.

☐

Check each hose for signs of perishing, cuts, splits or any other damage that could cause coolant leakage. Make sure that none of them is strained or chafing against any sharp edge and that none of the hoses is touching the exhaust manifold.

☐

Check the heater control levers, making sure that they move freely.

☐

Engine running and at normal operating temperature

Check the cooling system hoses – often, a split will be undetectable when there is no pressure in the cooling system, but, once the engine is running and pressure builds up, a fine spray of coolant will be ejected. Listen for any hissing sounds and look for signs of steam escaping.

☐

Check that the fan is turning freely and that the fan belt is not slipping (indicated by a loud squealing sound, particularly when the engine is revved).

If the engine is fitted with an electric fan or a belt-driven fan with a viscous clutch unit, make sure that the fan cuts in as the coolant temperature rises.

☐

Check for signs of coolant being forced out of the joints between the water pump and cylinder block, and the thermostat housing and cylinder head (or manifold).

☐

Check that the thermostat opens when the engine has reached its normal operating temperature. This can be done by feeling the top and bottom radiator hoses. If the thermostat is working, both hoses will feel hot; if not, the bottom one will be hot and the top one cool.

☐

WARNING When checking components of the cooling system with the engine running, keep your hands and all items of loose clothing well clear of the fan and fan belt. Never wear a tie, which could become trapped in the fan. Similarly, keep hands and clothes well clear of a thermostatically operated fan, which could begin to rotate when you least expect it.

The electrical system

If your car is to run efficiently, it is just as important that you fully understand the workings of the electrical system as those of any other. However, because the electrical system needs little maintenance, it is easy to overlook.

By making regular routine checks on the battery (see p.108) and the fan belt (see p.110), you will usually be able to forestall trouble. If the generator is not working at peak efficiency, the ignition light on the dashboard should give you ample warning – it will start to glow faintly when several electrical components are operating at once.

The battery

The battery produces electricity through a chemical reaction between two sets of lead plates and the sulphuric acid solution – known as the electrolyte – in which they are immersed. The reaction occurs whenever a circuit is formed between the two battery terminals.

The reaction also causes lead to be removed from one set of plates and deposited on the other. If this was allowed to continue unchecked, one set of plates eventually would be exhausted. The chemical reaction would stop and the battery would be dead. To overcome this, an engine-driven generator – either an alternator or dynamo – provides a flow of current back to the battery to reverse the discharging process and so restore the lead to its original set of plates. In this way, the chemical reaction can be repeated time and time again.

The strength of the electrical current the battery provides is measured in amperes (amps for short) and the force which drives this current round the circuit is measured in volts.

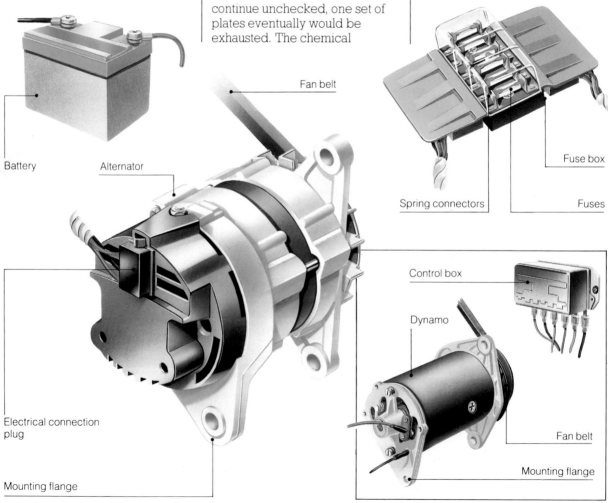

Battery

Alternator

Fan belt

Fuse box

Spring connectors

Fuses

Control box

Dynamo

Electrical connection plug

Mounting flange

Fan belt

Mounting flange

Practically all cars are fitted with 12-volt batteries, their capacities being measured in amp/hours. This is the number of hours a battery can deliver a steady current of 1 amp before becoming discharged.

How the current flows
The current flows from the 'live' battery terminal along the positive lead to the component being powered and then back to the 'earth' terminal via the car's body. Using the body as an earth return in this way saves considerably on the amount of wiring required.

The battery terminal used to earth the system determines what is termed the system's 'polarity'– in most cases, the negative terminal is used, thus producing negative polarity. This is an important point to bear in mind when buying electrical accessories for your car, since these will be designed to work with a particular system of polarity and so may be seriously damaged if connected into another system.

The generator
All cars are fitted with some form of generator – in modern cars, usually an alternator, but, in older ones, a dynamo – to keep the battery charged and the electrical system running. Both alternator and dynamo do the same job, using the same basic principles, both being driven by a rubber V-belt from a pulley on the end of the crankshaft. However, the former is lighter and more efficient than the latter.

An alternator contains an electromagnetic rotor, which turns inside a fixed set of copper wire windings. These are called the stator. A small amount of current is drawn from the battery to energize the electromagnet rotor. As the latter rotates past the windings of the stator, it generates a much greater amount of electricity in the windings.

The current thus produced is alternating current (AC). To convert it to direct current (DC), it is fed through a rectifier, which only allows current flow in one direction, before it is passed on to the battery.

A dynamo works on the same basic principle. In this instance, though, the electromagnets, called field coils, are stationary and mounted around the inside of the dynamo casing. The windings are carried on a rotating shaft inside the field coils. This assembly is called the armature.

Electricity is generated in the armature as it passes the field coils and is picked up from the end of the shaft by spring-loaded carbon brushes, which press against a segmented ring called the commutator. The windings are connected to the commutator in such a way that the latter delivers direct current, so that, unlike an alternator, a rectifier is not required.

Since the generator is being turned constantly by the engine at varying speeds, some sort of control device must be incorporated to prevent it supplying an insufficient or an excessive amount of current to the battery. The alternator controls the current flow through a transistorized regulator. Usually mounted internally, this senses the battery's requirements and controls the alternator output accordingly by varying the amount of voltage supplied to the electromagnetic rotor.

With a dynamo, the regulator is normally mounted separately on a bulkhead within the engine compartment. It usually incorporates three relays in the form of electromagnetic switches to stop excessive charging, stabilize the dynamo voltage and prevent the battery discharging when the dynamo is turning too slowly to charge it.

Both systems are monitored by a red warning light on the dashboard. When this lights up, it indicates that the battery is not being charged. In addition, some cars are fitted with an ammeter to indicate how much electricity is being generated, or a battery condition indicator to show the battery's state of charge.

The fuses
Electrical wiring is sized according to the current it has to carry – a thick wire can carry a higher current than a thin one. If a wire is forced to carry a current greater than its capacity, it will overheat and possibly melt and catch fire. This can happen for two reasons. An electrical accessory may need more current than the wire connecting it to the battery can handle, or a live wire and the car's body or some other metal component can come into contact, leading to a short circuit. If the latter occurs, a surge of current can flow along the wire, with potentially disastrous results.

To guard against these dangers, protective fuses are fitted to the various electrical circuits. A fuse is basically a thin piece of wire matched to the current rating of the circuit

Electrical system/checklist

wiring. It may be housed in a glass tube or on a ceramic holder, both with metal end caps, and clipped between two sprung metal contacts set in the wiring circuit. If a current higher than the fuse's rating is passed through it, the wire melts, breaking the circuit and so protecting the wiring from serious damage.

The car's electrical system is divided into a number of sub-systems, with a fuse controlling each one. This means that, if one fuse should fail or 'blow', only the appropriate part of the system will be affected. Practically all the fuses are housed together in a fuse box – this is usually located in the engine compartment – to make them readily accessible. Some components, however, may be fitted with their own 'line fuses', which are contained in plastic holders in the wiring itself.

The wiring

A car contains hundreds of feet of electrical wiring in a mixture of sizes – or current ratings – to meet the needs of all its various electrical accessories. The wiring is collectively called the 'loom'. To aid installation and to keep everything neat and tidy, the wires are bound together with tape, or moulded into a special plastic strip wherever possible. Individual wires emerge from the loom at the appropriate points to feed specific components.

To aid in circuit tracing when looking for faults (see p.137), the wires are colour coded, but the coding may vary from one manufacturer to another as there is no international agreement covering the colours to use. However, by refering to the manufacturer's handbook, you will soon come to understand the particular system.

In modern cars, the wiring behind the instrument panel has largely been replaced by printed circuits. These are much more compact and much less confusing than the old-fashioned wiring. Each circuit consists of a plastic panel with a number of copper strips on it. Each one is connected to a single point on the panel and so to the main wiring loom.

Electrical system checklist

When checking the components of the electrical system, work in a logical order. Start with the engine compartment, where the major components will be found, and then work round the car, inspecting wiring and fittings wherever they are accessible. Throughout the check, make sure that all wiring is in good condition – clean, free from nicks and damage to the insulation, not strained or kinked, not chafing against sharp metal edges, and held firmly by clips where appropriate. All connections should be clean, tight and uncorroded.

If you are unaware of the polarity of the electrical system in your car, look at the wiring connections at the battery terminals. Most cars have negative polarity, so the red 'live' wire will be connected to the positive terminal (marked +) and the black 'earth' wire will run from the negative terminal (marked –) to the car's bodywork. With a positive-earth system, the wiring is reversed.

Check that the battery is secure. It is usually mounted in a tray at one side of the engine compartment. It will be held in place by a clamp, which may run along one of the top edges of the battery, or bear against a lip near the bottom of the casing. Make sure that the clamp is squarely located against the battery and the restraining nuts or bolts are tight; the battery must be held firmly, as otherwise it could topple over and spill its contents.

date checked ☑

Check the battery tray for signs of rusting, acid corrosion, or other damage.

☐

Check the battery casing, looking for cracks or other damage that could allow the electrolyte to leak.

☐

Check the battery terminals. They are set in the battery top, one at each end. They may be round posts or square upright tags. In the former case, the wiring connectors may be clamps that fit round the posts, or special sockets fitting over the top of the posts. In the latter case, the wiring connectors are bolted through holes in the tags. Make sure that connections are tight and clean. Ideally, the battery terminals should be coated with petroleum jelly to keep them free from corrosion. Make sure the socket and clamp type fittings are pushed fully home over the terminals and that their retaining screws or bolts are in place.

☐

Check the earth wire, making sure that it is in good condition and the bolt holding it to the bodywork is tight and uncorroded.

Check the level of the electrolyte inside each cell of the battery – it should just cover the tops of the lead plates. If necessary, top up with distilled or de-ionised water – not tap water *(see p.108)*. Make sure the caps are unbroken, clean and that any breather holes in them are clear. When replacing the caps, make sure that they are no more than finger tight.

Some modern batteries are sealed for life and have transparent cases that allow you to see the level of the electrolyte inside them.

Check the generator. This may be an alternator or a dynamo, but, whatever the type, it will be mounted at the front of the engine on a pivoting bracket and locked in position by a bolt passing through a slotted metal strap. Make sure that both pivot bolts and the adjusting bolt are in place and tight *(see p.110)*.

Check that the pivot and mounting brackets are not cracked, broken or distorted.

Check that the generator pulley retaining bolts are in place and that they are tight.

Check that none of the pulleys are damaged and that their flanges are not distorted. If they are, the fan belt could be 'thrown', or damaged.

Check the fan or drive belt tension, making sure that it is fitted tightly enough not to slip *(see p.110)*. You should be able to deflect the belt by no more than 13mm (½in) when applying moderate thumb pressure at the centre of its longest run.

Check that the belt is seated correctly in its pulleys and then inspect its overall condition, looking for cuts, nicks or signs of fraying. If there is any sign of wear or damage, the belt should be replaced *(see p.110)*.

Check the wiring at the back of the alternator – this is usually contained in a single multi-pin plug. Make sure the plug is fully home. Dynamos are wired to individual terminals. Make sure that all these wires are in place, clean and tightly fitting.

Check the fuses. They are normally to be found in a box in the engine compartment, although in some cars they may be fitted below the dashboard. If in doubt, refer to the manufacturer's handbook. Remove the box cover (it may be held by screws or simply clip into place) and check that all the fuses are present and firmly

seated between their spring contacts.

Check the exposed type of fuse. Make sure that the thin strip of fuse wire is intact. Check all the wiring connections at the fuse box, making sure the connectors are pushed fully home on to their tags. Clean the fuse box cover and replace it. Make sure it is not cracked or damaged in any way.

Check all the car's electrical components and systems by switching them on, together with the ignition if necessary. Note if any fail to operate.

With the engine running

Check that the generator is being turned by the fan belt and that the fan belt is not clipping (indicated by a loud squealing, particularly when the engine is revved). Keep your hands and any items of loose clothing well clear of the fan belt and fan when making this check.

Check that the red charging light goes out when the engine is started.

The fuel system

The carburettor

No engine will run on neat fuel – what is needed is a mixture of fuel and air, with far more air than petrol in the mixture. The job of the carburettor is to mix both of these in the correct proportions. The driver controls the amount of mixture supplied to the engine through a cable linked to the accelerator. This adjusts the components within the carburettor and so regulates the speed of the engine.

From the fuel tank, fuel is pumped by an engine-driven mechanical pump, or an electrical pump, to a reservoir – the float chamber – within the carburettor body. A float inside this chamber operates a needle valve. As the level of petrol in the chamber rises, so does the float; when the chamber is full, the float closes the valve. As fuel is drawn off, the float drops and the valve opens to allow more fuel to flow into the chamber. Air reaches the carburettor through a filter and then enters the carburettor at the air intake tube.

From the float chamber, fuel travels through a tube to a small nozzle called a jet, set in the venturi portion of the air intake tube. The narrowness of the venturi causes the air that is being sucked into the engine by the action of the pistons to speed up its passage, so creating a low-pressure area. The pressure difference means that the fuel can be sucked out of the tiny hole in the jet as a fine spray to mix with the air stream. The mixture then flows from the carburettor through the inlet manifold and into the engine's combustion chambers.

The amount of mixture entering the engine is controlled by a round plate, or 'butterfly', mounted in the air intake tube on the engine side of the carburettor. This pivots on a spindle. If there is no pressure on the accelerator, the plate almost closes off the tube, allowing only a tiny amount of mixture through it – just enough to keep the engine idling. As the pedal is depressed, the plate rotates, opening up the air intake tube. This increases the suction from the engine and allows more of the mixture to enter the combustion chambers.

One simple fixed jet, however, could not meet all the engine's varying fuel requirements. When idling, for instance, the engine needs only the tiniest amount of fuel; a sudden burst of acceleration, on the other hand, needs a corresponding fuel surge. As a result, the carburettor will have more than one jet, or may be fitted with what is termed a variable jet, in which the size of

Variable jet carburettors

There are two main makes of variable jet carburettor fitted to cars. Both work on the same principle and both can be recognized by the domed cylinder of the vacuum chamber.

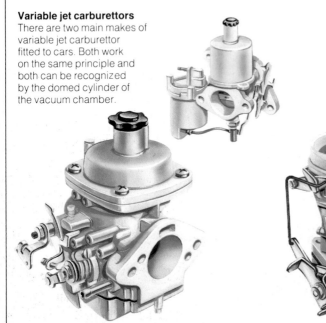

Variable jet carburettor

Fixed jet carburettor

Twin choke carburettor

Fixed jet carburettors

Many high performance cars are fitted with a twin choke, fixed jet carburettor. This has two barrels, each with its own jets, allowing more petrol to be drawn into the cylinders, thereby increasing the power of the engine.

the jet orifice can be varied. This is done by a needle valve, in which a tapered needle alters the jet size by moving in and out of the jet opening.

To meet the problem of starting from cold, when the engine needs more fuel than normal in the mixture, the carburettor is fitted with a choke control. A fixed-jet carburettor has a choke plate (similar to the throttle plate) at the top of its air intake tube. This is closed by pulling the choke control knob on the dashboard out, so reducing the amount of air flowing into the carburettor and producing a 'richer' fuel mixture as a result. Rather than feeding more petrol into the air stream, a

variable-jet carburettor lowers the jet in relation to its needle to make the jet opening larger. This has the same effect.

In some cars, the choke control is automatic. This is achieved by heat-sensitive metallic coils, which expand and contract to alter the position of the choke lever as the engine temperature changes.

ELECTRIC FUEL PUMP

Some cars are fitted with an electric fuel pump. It is usually mounted near the petrol tank.

The air cleaner
The air cleaner covers the mouth of the carburettor air intake. Its task is to ensure that incoming air is clean and free from small particles of dust and dirt. These would otherwise block the tiny passages in the carburettor and cause undue wear to the tightly-fitting components of the engine.

The air cleaner is a plastic or metal circular container, with a filter inside it. An air intake tube is set in the side. In modern cars, the filter is usually made of corrugated paper, but, in older models, a wire-gauze element soaked in oil may be used. The filter allows air to pass through it, but traps any foreign matter.

Over a period of time, the filter will become clogged, so reducing engine performance

Fuel pump
Most cars have a mechanical fuel pump. It is driven from the camshaft and is mounted on the engine block.

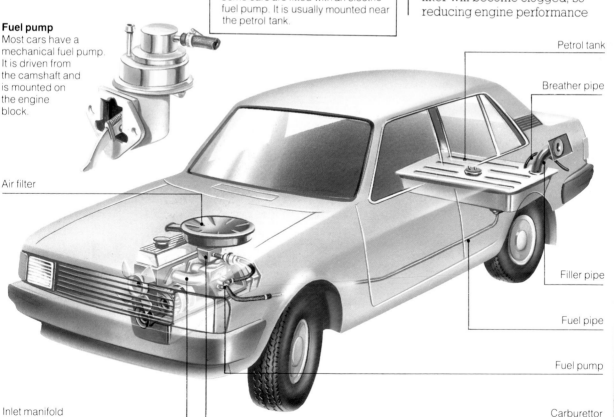

Petrol tank

Breather pipe

Air filter

Filler pipe

Fuel pipe

Fuel pump

Inlet manifold

Carburettor

Fuel system/checklist

by restricting the engine's 'breathing'. For this reason, a paper filter must be replaced at regular intervals, while a wire-gauze filter should be cleaned *(see p.116)*.

The pump

To ensure a steady flow of fuel from the fuel tank to the carburettor, a pump is fitted between the two. This may be driven mechanically by the engine, in which case it is mounted on the engine block, or electrically, when it is positioned near the fuel tank.

Both types of pump incorporate a rubber diaphragm and two one-way valves. A lever operated by the engine's camshaft, or, in an electric pump, a rod moved by an electro-magnetic switch, moves the diaphragm. As the diaphragm moves, it sucks fuel through the first one-way valve into the pump. A spring beneath the diaphragm then forces it upwards again and pushes the fuel out through the second valve.

If the carburettor's float chamber is full and its needle valve closed, the diaphragm remains in the 'down' position until the valve opens, when the spring is able to push the diaphragm up again. The operating lever can move the diaphragm only on a downward stroke; if the diaphragm is already in the 'down' position, they both idle.

The fuel line

Fuel is carried between the tank and the carburettor by a narrow-bore rigid metal pipe with flexible connections at each end. A filter – either a paper element in the pipe or a wire-gauze element at the outlet – is sometimes fitted to prevent any dirt and corrosion from the tank reaching the carburettor.

The tank

For safety reasons, the tank is usually fitted at the opposite end of the car to the engine. It may be set in the floor of the boot, or immediately behind the rear passenger seat.

Inside the tank, a float is connected to an electric 'sender' unit, which operates the fuel gauge on the dashboard.

The tank also incorporates a simple 'breather' tube to allow air to enter the tank as the fuel is pumped out. Otherwise the process would create a vacuum, which the pump could not overcome.

Fuel injection

Although modern carburettors are reasonably sophisticated, they do not always supply fuel to the engine in the most efficient or effective manner. If the throttle is opened fully very quickly, for instance, the carburettor will supply an excessive amount of fuel that cannot be used by the engine until its speed has actually increased. This is wasteful.

Many modern high-performance cars overcome the problem by using a system known as fuel injection to replace the conventional carburettor. In this, sensors measure the engine speed, the throttle opening and the air and engine temperature, passing the information to a central control unit. This controls a pump that supplies the exact amount of fuel required to suit any particular driving demand to injectors, mounted close to the inlet valves of each cylinder. These physically squirt the fuel into the cylinders.

Fuel system checklist

When checking your car's fuel system, remember to take the obvious sensible precautions against the risk of fire – do not smoke and do not let anyone else smoke nearby. Disconnect the battery to reduce the risk of accidental sparks.

Throughout, check visually for petrol leaks – the characteristic signs of these are stains on the road or bodywork as well as feel and smell. Where flexible pipes are simply pushed on to a stub, make sure that they are fully home; where they are held by a clip, check that the clip is tight and not biting into the pipe. Where rigid pipes are joined by threaded connectors, make sure that these are tight, but take care not to overtighten them as this may damage the pipes. Generally, make sure that the pipes are in good condition without any signs of damage, are not kinked, strained, or chafing and are clipped securely.

date checked _____ ☑

Check that the air cleaner is securely mounted. Any stays that are provided to steady it should be unbroken, with all their rubber grommets and mounting bolts in place. Make sure that the bolts are tight and free from corrosion.

_____ ☐

Check the air cleaner housing, looking for cracks or other damage. Make sure that the top cover is firmly attached and not distorted or damaged. If the top cover is held in place by one or more bolts, make sure that these are tightly in place.

_____ ☐

If your air cleaner has an adjustable air-intake trumpet with 'summer' and 'winter' positions, check that the trumpet is positioned correctly according to the season. In summer, it should be positioned to draw cooler air from the front of the engine compartment, but in winter it should collect warmer air from around the exhaust manifold.

_____ ☐

Check whether or not your car is fitted with a breather hose. If one is fitted, it will lead from the engine crankcase and will be attached to the side or bottom of the air cleaner. Make sure that the hose is fully home on its stub on the air-cleaner body and that any clip is tight. Check the condition of the rubber, making sure that there are no splits or cracks that would allow fumes to escape. Check also that the hose is not kinked.

If the hose is attached directly to the inlet manifold, check its full length, including the crankcase connection.

_____ ☐

Check that all the bolts holding the carburettor to the inlet manifold and the inlet manifold to the engine are in place and tight. This is essential to prevent air leaking into the manifold and unbalancing the fuel/air mixture supplied by the carburettor.

_____ ☐

Check that the cables or rods that operate the throttle and choke (if manual) are working freely.

_____ ☐

Check that the throttle linkage is firmly positioned in any mounting bracket and that the clips holding the linkage to the operating levers of the carburettor are secure.

_____ ☐

Check the condition and connections of the fuel pipe leading from the pump to the carburettor float chamber. In some cases, the pipe may be made of clear plastic. If this has become hard and brittle, the pipe should be replaced.

_____ ☐

If the car has a mechanical fuel pump

Check the pipe connections and make sure that the bolts holding the pump to the engine are all tightly. Make sure that the pump cover is secure and that there are no signs of fuel leakage from any of the seams.

_____ ☐

Before inspecting the fuel pipes beneath the car, check the throttle and choke controls inside it. Press the accelerator pedal down, making sure that it moves freely without any binding and that it returns to its original position when released. Inspect the cable connection, making sure that it is secure and that the cable shows no sign of fraying or kinking. Operate the

choke control, checking for full movement without stiffness or binding.

_____ ☐

Run the car up on to wheel ramps, or jack it up and support it on axle stands, so that the rear end – where the fuel tank is situated – is off the ground. Inspect the run of the fuel pipes, checking that they are securely held in their retaining clips and that there are no signs of damage or leakage. Inspect all pipe connections.

_____ ☐

Check electric pump connections, if visible, and make sure that the pump is held securely in place. Examine the wiring connections to see that they are pushed fully home, clean and tight.

_____ ☐

Check the fuel tank, if it protrudes through the floor of the car, for signs of damage or corrosion on its under surface. Inspect the tank mountings and the retaining bolts for security. Check the fuel pipe connections.

_____ ☐

Make sure that no breather pipe is blocked or kinked, and that any breather hole in the filler cap is clear. Check that the filler cap itself is properly fitted to the filler pipe.

_____ ☐

The hydraulic system

The brakes

On all modern cars, stopping power is provided by a hydraulically operated braking system. This allows the pressure on the brake pedal to be routed easily to the braking units and increased quickly when desired.

When the brake pedal is pushed downwards, it moves a piston within a master cylinder to force hydraulic fluid through narrow-bore pipes to the 'slave' cylinders at each braking unit. As the fluid enters the slave cylinders, it causes their pistons to move outwards and apply pressure to 'pads' or 'shoes', both of which are fitted with a special friction lining. It is the friction between these and the moving surface – either a metal disc or drum attached to the wheel – that slows and eventually stops its rotation.

These circuits are often duplicated to ensure that the brakes will still operate, even if the primary circuit fails. This is done by fitting a 'tandem' master cylinder with two pistons inside it, each of which feed a separate circuit. In some dual-circuit systems – as these are termed – a main circuit feeds all the brakes, the sub-circuit only backing up the brakes at the front; in others, both circuits feed one front brake and one rear brake each; and there are various other possible combinations.

As well as the all-wheel system, the rear wheels have a back-up system of their own. This is operated by applying the handbrake, which pulls a cable to operate the braking units on the rear wheels. In this case, levers on the brake units push the 'pads' or 'shoes' hard against the disc or drum, so locking the wheels.

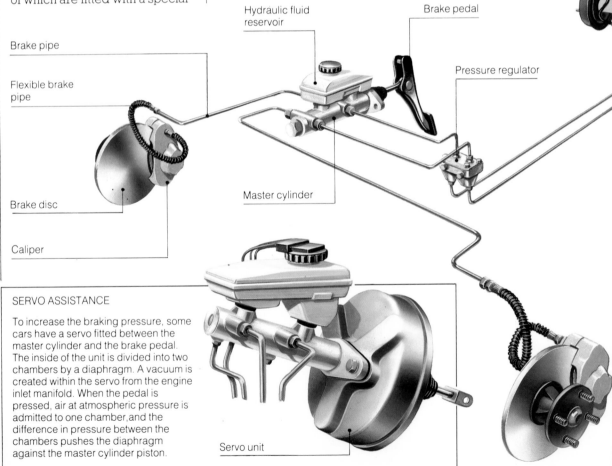

Brake pipe

Flexible brake pipe

Brake disc

Caliper

Hydraulic fluid reservoir

Brake pedal

Pressure regulator

Master cylinder

SERVO ASSISTANCE

To increase the braking pressure, some cars have a servo fitted between the master cylinder and the brake pedal. The inside of the unit is divided into two chambers by a diaphragm. A vacuum is created within the servo from the engine inlet manifold. When the pedal is pressed, air at atmospheric pressure is admitted to one chamber, and the difference in pressure between the chambers pushes the diaphragm against the master cylinder piston.

Servo unit

Servo assistance

Some types of brake unit need considerable pedal force to operate them, because of their large-diameter slave pistons. Here, the manufacturers help by providing 'power' assistance through a servo unit – this is usually fitted between the brake pedal and the master cylinder.

By making use of the vacuum in the inlet manifold, the servo provides extra pressure in the master cylinder piston when the brakes are applied. Its interior is

Brake drum

The handbrake is used for locking the rear wheels for parking or holding the car stationary when the clutch and accelerator need to be operated. It actuates the rear brakes by a cable pulling the shoes or pads against the drums or discs.

divided into two chambers by a flexible rubber diaphragm. The front chamber, nearest the master cylinder, is connected to the inlet manifold by a rubber hose.

When the brakes are 'off' (with the engine running), a valve at the centre of the diaphragm ensures that there is a vacuum in both chambers. When the brake pedal is pushed down, it moves a pushrod. This closes the valve between the two chambers and opens a one-way air valve serving the rearmost one. Air entering this chamber at normal atmospheric pressure makes the diaphragm move forward in response to the vacuum on the other side. The diaphragm moves the pushrod that operates the master cylinder piston.

When the brakes are released, the one-way air valve closes and the valve between the two chambers opens to equalize the pressure on both sides of the diaphragm. Then, a spring pushes the diaphragm back to its original position.

The servo system is fail-safe. If

a fault develops, the pedal pushrod comes into direct contact with the master cylinder pushrod. This means that the brakes are still operational.

Types of brake unit

There are two types of brake unit – the drum and the disc. The latter tend to be more efficient than the former, but more difficult to incorporate with the handbrake linkage. Therefore, most cars are fitted with a combination of the two – drums on the rear to make it easy to fit the handbrake and discs on the front to provide extra stopping power.

Drum brakes

A drum brake consists of an open-ended metal drum, which rotates with the wheel, and a fixed backing plate. This closes the open end of the drum and carries a pair of crescent-shaped brake shoes. The shoes, lined with a special hard-wearing friction material, are arranged on the backing plate with the slave cylinder between one pair of their adjacent ends. There is a fixed pivot between the other pair.

When hydraulic fluid flows into the slave cylinder, its pistons move outwards to force the shoes into contact with the inner surface of the rotating drum. This brings the drum to a halt. When the brakes are released, strong springs between the shoes pull them away from the drum and push the pistons back into the cylinder. Some drum brakes have two cylinders, one for each shoe.

With use, the lining material inevitably wears. This means that the pistons have to move

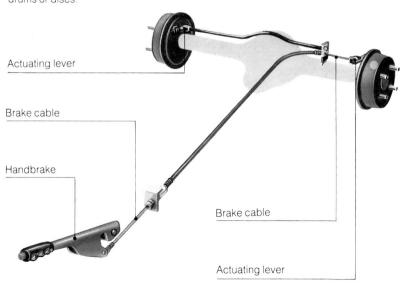

Actuating lever

Brake cable

Handbrake

Brake cable

Actuating lever

Hydraulic system/checklist

further to bring the shoes into contact with the drum – the immediate evidence of this is longer brake pedal travel. As a consequence, an adjuster is fitted to keep the linings close to the drum. This can be manually operated – in this case, it is located behind the backing plate – or an automatic mechanism, worked by a ratchet from the handbrake linkage.

Disc brakes
The disc brake works in the same way as a bicycle's brakes. A cast-metal caliper, containing one or more pairs of pads lined with friction material, straddles a steel disc, which rotates with the road wheel. When hydraulic brake fluid enters the caliper cylinders, it forces opposing pistons to push the pads into contact with the disc, so bringing it to a halt.

When the pistons move forward, the rubber seals fitted around them to prevent fluid leakage stretch slightly. When the pressure is released, they contract again. The contraction is enough to pull the pistons back until the pads are just clear of the disc. As the pad linings wear, however, the seals become less effective, so that the pistons are free to travel further forward. This lessens the system's efficiency and requires professional attention.

In some calipers, both opposing pistons move towards the disc; others, however, have only one moving piston located in a special sliding portion of the caliper. When this type of brake is operated, the moving piston pushes its pad into contact with the disc. As the cylinder fills with fluid, the sliding part of the caliper moves in the opposite

direction, bringing a fixed pad into contact with the other face of the disc.

With dual hydraulic circuits, two opposing pairs of pistons are used, each pair operating on a different circuit.

The clutch
Most modern cars are fitted with cable-operated clutches, though in some the clutch is worked hydraulically in the same way as the brakes. However, the clutch hydraulic circuit is completely separate from the brake circuits, having its own master cylinder and fluid reservoir.

The clutch transmits power from the engine to the gearbox through its 'driven' plate. This slides along the gearbox input shaft to be clamped tightly against the flywheel by a spring-loaded 'pressure' plate. The plate, in turn, is held in place by a diaphragm spring. When the drive has to be interrupted to change gear, the clutch release lever pushes a bearing into the centre of the diaphragm spring. The spring distorts to pull the pressure plate back from the driven plate, allowing the latter to slide back from the flywheel.

In a hydraulically operated system, a master cylinder is attached to the clutch pedal to operate a slave cylinder at the clutch release lever. When the clutch pedal is released, the diaphragm spring pushes back on the release bearing, forcing the release lever to push back the slave cylinder's piston. At the same time, the pressure plate is brought to bear on the driven plate and the drive is taken up again. Return springs are attached to the release lever and the clutch pedal to aid retraction.

Hydraulic system checklist
To inspect your car's hydraulic system, you will need to get underneath the body to examine the pipe runs, so make sure that you have a pair of car ramps or a jack and axle stands ready. Do not rely on a jack alone to hold the car clear of the ground and never support it on piles of bricks – these can easily topple over.

Throughout the check, search for hydraulic fluid leaks by sight and feel. Pay particular attention to the pipe connections at master cylinders, calipers, wheel cylinders and the clutch slave cylinder. Examine all hydraulic pipe unions and inspect all pipework and hoses carefully. Rigid metal pipes should show no signs of heavy corrosion, splits, cracks or other damage, and should be clipped securely in place. Make sure they are not strained or kinked. The flexible hoses at the front brakes and rear axle should not be chafing against any protrusions.

Start your check in the engine bay, where you will find the brake master cylinder and the clutch master cylinder.

Check that the nuts securing the master cylinder to the bulkhead are in place and tight and that the hydraulic pipes are secure.

Check the fluid reservoir cap. Wipe any dirt from around it. Some master cylinder reservoirs are transparent, allowing you to see the fluid level without removing the cap. If not, unscrew it and check the fluid level inside the reservoir. Top up if necessary with hydraulic fluid – check in your handbook to see which type of fluid is specified for the system. If the level of fluid in the reservoir has dropped below the outlet, there is probably a fault elsewhere in the system. This must be located, dealt with and the system completely refilled with fresh fluid. Replace the cap, making sure that its breather hole is not blocked.

Check the hydraulic pipe runs from the master cylinder to the front and rear brakes.

If a servo unit is fitted

Check that the vacuum hose between the inlet manifold and the servo is in place.

Check the hose for signs of splits, cracks or other damage. Make sure that it is not kinked.

Check the drum brakes to make sure that there is no fluid leaking from the bleed nipples.

Check all the hydraulic pipes, their unions and connections at brake and clutch units. To do this, run the front of the car up on ramps (or jack it up and support it on axle stands). Repeat the process with the rear of the car.

Check that the servo is operating correctly. With your foot pushing hard on the brake pedal, start the car. If the unit is working properly, the pedal will fall away slightly from your foot. If nothing happens, the vacuum hose may be blocked, or the unit itself is defective.

Check the front brake discs and calipers. This may involve removing the front wheels, though, on some cars, you can check the brakes visually through slots in the wheels.

Check the security of disc brake caliper mountings, making sure that the pad retaining pins and springs are fitted correctly and that there is no sign of fluid leakage from the bleed nipple.

Check the pad lining material – its minimum thickness should be 3mm ($\frac{1}{8}$in). Examine the disc itself – removing the wheels, if necessary – looking for signs of heavy scoring, distortion, cracks or other damage. The disc also must not be contaminated by oil, grease or hydraulic fluid.

Check for air in the system. Pump the brake pedal up and down a few times; if the resistance you feel through your foot seems to be increasing, there is air in the brake fluid. This must be removed by bleeding the system.

Check its mounting on the bulkhead.

Check the handbrake cables for signs of corrosion or fraying. Make sure that they are connected securely to the operating levers.

Check that the cables are routed correctly through their guides.

If a hydraulically operated clutch is fitted

Check that the slave cylinder is mounted securely and that its pushrod is firmly attached to the release lever. Make sure, too, that the lever return spring is in place and properly attached.

The suspension system

The suspension's job is to absorb road surface irregularities and provide a comfortable ride for the car's occupants. It is just as important that the system ensures the best possible adhesion between tyres and road at all times and under all road and driving conditions.

The suspension works by placing a dampened spring between each wheel hub assembly and the car body to act as a shock-absorbing device. In practice, the tyre acts as the first shock absorber, followed by the suspension and finally by the car seats, which absorb the last effects of road irregularities. To ensure the best possible tyre/road adhesion, the system is designed to alter the angle of the wheel in relation to the road

under different conditions – braking and cornering, for instance – when the body of the car may not be parallel to the road. It is also designed to ensure that the steering is self-centring – that is, to make sure that the drag on the front wheels will always push them straight on if the steering is released.

Front suspension

The types of suspension in common use not only differ from car to car, but also from front to rear axles. All modern cars are fitted with independent front suspension. This means that both front wheels are free to move up and down independently of each other. This is especially important for the front wheels, as bumps in the road will inevitably

affect the steering. To keep this to a minimum, the independent suspension system ensures that the action of one wheel does not affect the other.

The two commonest types of independent front suspension are the McPherson strut and the double wishbone system. The McPherson strut is a long telescopic tube mounted to the top of the inner wing and held in place at the bottom by two arms, attached to the car chassis. The tube has a coil spring around its top half, which is held between a plate on the strut and the inner wing surface. The bottom half includes an oil-filled damper. At the top of the strut a large

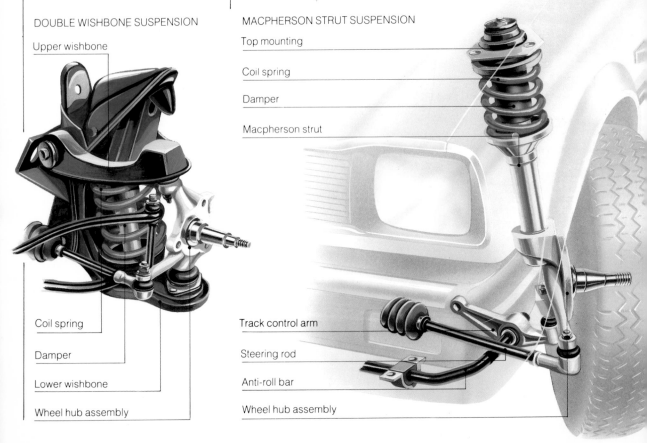

DOUBLE WISHBONE SUSPENSION

Upper wishbone

Coil spring

Damper

Lower wishbone

Wheel hub assembly

MACPHERSON STRUT SUSPENSION

Top mounting

Coil spring

Damper

Macpherson strut

Track control arm

Steering rod

Anti-roll bar

Wheel hub assembly

LEAF SPRING SUSPENSION

Mounting shackle

Damper

Leaf spring

Axle

INDEPENDENT REAR SUSPENSION

Damper

Universal joint

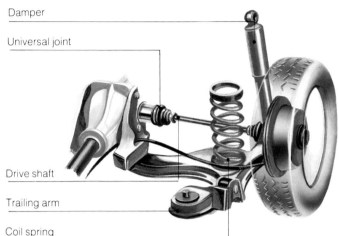

Drive shaft

Trailing arm

Coil spring

rubber bush allows for the small amounts of lateral movement that occur during the suspension's movement, while the wheel hub assembly is attached at the base. This pivots on a joint at the end of two arms attached to the chassis. These hold the assembly in place and allow the strut to move up and down as road undulations compress the spring.

The double wishbone system consists of two A-shaped arms – the wishbones – mounted one above the other and able to pivot up and down. The wheel hub assembly is mounted between the ends of each wishbone, ball joints enabling the wheel hub assembly to rotate for steering and remain vertical as the wishbones move.

Usually, the springing is provided by a coil spring, mounted at one end to the lower wishbone at one end, with the other bearing against a shaped housing on the chassis. A damper is mounted at the same points as the coil spring, where it follows the spring's movement, or to the upper wishbone and the body. The same system can be used with other types, of springing, such as torsion bars or rubber cones.

Rear suspension
The simplest form of rear suspension is leaf springs. These are mounted at either end of a solid beam axle. This is a solid casting, with the wheel drive shafts and differential gear contained within it and the wheels mounted at either end. Thus, the whole axle is affected by bumps to either wheel and, because of this, does not provide the best adhesion, especially during hard acceleration.

As well as absorbing the axle movements, the springs locate the axle on the car chassis and

stop it from moving forwards, backwards, or from side to side. If coil springs are used instead of leaf springs, locating arms – mounted at one end to the chassis, the other to the axle – are required to stop the axle moving in any direction other than up and down.

In an independent system, the differential gear, which transmits the drive from the propeller shaft through to the wheels, is mounted rigidly to the floorpan of the car. The drive shafts are not enclosed and have universal joints at each end, allowing them to continue to rotate – whatever their angle is in relation to the differential and wheel/hub assembly – as they move up and down with the suspension. Suspension arms, mounted to the wheel/hub assembly and the floorpan in front of the rear wheels, prevent movement fore and aft. A damper is mounted to the suspension arm or the wheel/hub assembly. Coil springs are most often used as the shock absorbers, though rubber cones, torsion bars or

Suspension system/checklist

hydraulic units can be fitted between the suspension arms and the floorpan to perform the same function, depending on the car model.

Types of spring

The oldest form of car springs are leaf springs. These consist of several long curved metal strips (the leaves) of varying lengths, clamped one on top of the other. The main leaf on the top is the longest and has its ends rolled over to form mounting eyes. The front end is mounted into a bracket bolted to the car's floorpan, the rearmost eye being linked to a pivoting shackle that is bolted to the floorpan as well. This arrangement allows for the lengthening of the spring as it flattens under pressure.

Coil springs consist of a thin strip of metal wound in a spiral. They are much lighter and more compact than leaf springs and last longer. Leaf springs eventually lose their springiness.

The springs stretch and compress as the wheel moves up and down. As this happens, the metal twists, the resistance to this twisting providing the springing. The more the metal twists, the stiffer the spring becomes.

A torsion bar is really just a coil spring that has been straightened out and it works in exactly the same way. It consists of a long metal bar, with one end mounted rigidly to the car's floorpan and the other attached to a moving suspension arm. As the arm moves, it twists the bar.

A rubber cone spring is basically a block of special rubber, which is compressed by the movement of the suspension arms. It is used only on light vehicles. On some suspension systems, rubber cones are included as well as a coil spring. These act as a final shock absorbing buffer, if the spring is pushed to maximum compression.

Hydraulic suspension, sometimes known as hydro-gas, is fitted to some cars. Each wheel/hub assembly has an oil-filled cylinder attached to it. A piston within the cylinder is connected to the suspension arm. As the arm moves upwards, it causes the piston to force fluid – either oil or a mixture of water and anti-freeze – against a diaphragm. This, in turn, compresses a gas to provide the springing; alternatively, the fluid can be forced against a rubber spring.

In this type of system, the pistons for each wheel are often interlinked by tubing. As one wheel is forced up, the fluid passing around the system pushes the pistons out, so raising the other wheels. This keeps the car level as the wheels move up and down.

Dampers

Popularly, but incorrectly, called shock absorbers, a damper's task is to resist the movements of the springs. Once compressed and released, a spring continues to oscillate unless it is stopped, like a rubber ball bouncing after it has been dropped. Thus, a car with no damping system would quickly loose its stability; each wheel spring would be oscillating at different times and rates. Similarly, a car with one or two worn, or inoperative, dampers can become fatally unstable, so it is well worth having all the dampers checked annually, once the car is more than a couple of years old.

Dampers reduce the 'bounce' of the springs and should stop them oscillating by the time the spring has been compressed, released, and has bounced once. A good test to check whether or not the dampers are working is to push one wing down and release it. It should bounce once and settle to its original position.

The commonest type of damper is the telescopic damper. It contains a piston, which moves up and down inside an oil-filled cylinder. As the piston moves, it forces the oil through valves and openings from one part of the cylinder to another. Through its natural resistance to this movement, the oil provides the damping force.

McPherson struts are fitted with a modified version of the standard telescopic damper. This is an integral part of the unit, so providing a combined spring/damper assembly.

The lever arm damper, which is fitted to some older cars, is similar in appearance to a hydraulic door closer. It, too, contains a piston in an oil-filled chamber, which has a swinging arm attached to it. The other end of the arm is attached to a moving suspension component, which is dampened by the effect of the piston pushing against the oil in the chamber. This type of damper is bulkier and less efficient than the telescopic damper.

Suspension arms

Often, particularly in the case of coil-sprung rear suspensions, the wheel assembly must be located rigidly to prevent it from moving backwards and forwards, though its up-and-down movement must not be impaired. This is done by fitting a suspension arm between the moving wheel assembly and the floorpan. Such arms are usually made from tubular steel or pressed-steel box sections and have rubber-bushed ends, so that they can pivot up and down on their mountings. A trailing arm runs from a point forward on the floorpan back to the wheel assembly, while a leading arm is mounted to the floorpan behind the wheel.

Some cars are fitted with what is known as a Panhard rod. This is a suspension arm, mounted parallel to a solid beam axle, with one end connected to the floor pan and the other to the axle. The rod stops the axle from moving laterally.

Anti-roll bars

An anti-roll bar is a long steel rod fitted across the width of the chassis between the suspension units and clamped to the floorpan by rubber blocks. Generally, the bar is fitted at the front end of the car. By acting like a longitudinal spring, it reduces the amount of body roll that would otherwise occur when the suspension on one side of the car is compressed, as in hard cornering.

Suspension checklist

To check your car's suspension system thoroughly, you must get underneath the car, so make sure that you have a pair of car ramps, or a jack and axle stands, handy. Many parts of the system will be caked in road grime, so arm yourself with a wire brush and some old rags to clean this off. You will also find a torch useful, plus a stout metal bar for levering against wishbones.

Begin by parking the car on level ground with its tyres inflated to the correct pressures – front and back – and a full tank of petrol. Crouch down and look at the car from the front, the rear and both sides, checking that the car is sitting level. Any appreciable difference from front to rear or from side to side should be investigated further; it may be due to a weak or broken spring, or a collapsed suspension mounting bracket.

date checked _____ ✓

Check all rubber, or plastic suspension brushes, looking for signs of softening, perishing, splitting or other damage.

Check from front, back and sides that the car sits level when parked on flat ground.

Check that the car only rebounds once or twice before settling at its normal ride height when each corner is pushed down firmly.

If the car is fitted with MacPherson struts

Check the condition of the strut top mountings on the inner wings.

Check that the retaining nuts are tight and that the metal around the mountings is not corroded.

Check the condition of the central rubber brush, making sure that it does not move as you bounce the car up and down.

Check any damper top mountings inside the boot, making sure that retaining nuts are in place and tight and that any rubber brushes are in good condition.

Check that mounting brackets are not corroded.

Check for dark stains or streaks on damper bodies. If present, this is a sign of fluid damage. Check the condition of mounting brushes by grasping the lower part of upper section and twisting. No movement should be possible.

Check that coil springs are seated properly in their cups and are not corroded or distorted.

Check that leaves of leaf springs are not cracked or flattened.

Check hydraulic suspension units for fluid leaks and the interconnecting pipework for signs of splits, cracks or other damage. Check that such units are mounted securely.

Tyres

Your tyres are one of the most important parts of your car. Yet, like many motorists, you may have failed to realize just how vital they are – not only to your car's performance, but also to your own safety. Though the amount of rubber in contact with the road is terribly small, it must be able to transfer the engine's power to the road and grip the surface when the car corners, or is braked hard. In bad weather, too, it must be able to displace surface water, snow or mud, so that the tyres can maintain their grip.

This is why you should treat your tyres with respect and look after them carefully. Regular inspection is essential to spot problems before they arise.

Tubeless and tubed

There are two basic types of pneumatic tyre – tubed and tubeless. The former contain a separate rubber inner tube, which is filled with compressed air through a one-way valve. The tube keeps the tyre in shape. The tubeless tyre relies on the seal between the bead, the inner edges of the tyre, and the metal wheel rim to keep the air inside it. A separate one-way valve is fitted to the wheel rim for inflation.

Because of modern advances in wheel design, tubeless tyres are now very common, although tubed tyres are still fitted to wire wheels. It has many advantages over its tubed rival – not the least of these being the fact that, when punctured, it tends to deflate more slowly. This is because its flexible inner lining has self-sealing properties. When a tubed tyre is punctured, it collapses immediately.

Radial tyres, due to their construction, reduce cornering wear. Also because they have less rolling resistance are more economical to run. Some radials incorporate steel cords to increase strength and lateral stability. Tread patterns vary from one tyre to another, although they all serve the same purpose.

How tyres are made

Tyres are made from a mixture of natural and synthetic rubbers, reinforced with layers of man-made fabrics or woven steel. These layers, called plies, give the tyre its shape and strength.

There are two common construction methods – cross ply and radial ply. These terms refer to the way in which the reinforcing layers are arranged inside the tyre. In the former, the plies run diagonally across the tyre from one bead to the other; in the latter, they run across the tyre at right angles to the beads, with additional reinforcing bands running around the circumference of the tyre beneath the tread. Both types have a steel wire moulded into them to form the bead.

Since radial ply tyres perform much better than cross ply tyres, practically all new cars are supplied with them as standard fittings. They grip the road better, last longer and reduce fuel consumption because they have less rolling resistance to the road surface.

What the tread does

Though tread patterns vary from one make and model of tyre to another, the tread serves the same purpose in each case. Its job is to clear water, mud and snow from the road at the point where the tyre makes contact with the surface. It does this by

A low profile radial tyre enables any given tyre size to accommodate a larger wheel and thus a larger and more efficient braking system. Handling characteristics are also improved.

forcing the water to flow through the tread grooves to the rear, where it is thrown off by centrifugal force. Tiny slits on the tops of the tread blocks absorb any remaining moisture.

It is vital that the tread is of sufficient thickness to do its job properly. If a tyre were allowed to become completely smooth, it would ride up on to a film of water across the road and you would loose all control of the car. For this reason, always replace tyres when the tread reaches the minimum legal thickness.

When you replace a tyre, you may be offered a 'remould' or 'retreat' version. The former are second-hand tyres that have had a completely new rubber covering bonded on to the original carcase, but the latter simply have a new section of tread bonded on to them. Both can prove a false economy unless chosen carefully and they should never be fitted to a high-performance vehicle.

Legal requirements

The law now stipulates that all tyres must meet minimum legal requirements. In addition to checking that the tyres are inflated to their correct pressures – not forgetting the tyre on the spare wheel – you must check them regularly to ensure that they are in good condition.

All four tyres must be able to grip the road in the wet, so you must check their treads regularly for wear and replace any that are badly worn. The legal requirement is for a minimum 1mm tread depth in a continuous strip across at least 75% of the tread, with at least the tread pattern still remaining across the remaining 25%. However, it is far better to replace a tyre once the tread depth reaches 2mm.

Never mix tyres of different constructions. Legally, you are allowed to fit cross ply tyres on the front wheels and radials on the rear ones, but you should then carry two spares, which is impractical. However, you cannot fit radials on the front wheels and cross ply tyres on the rear wheels, or a crossply and a radial on the same axle. The two handle differently and the car would soon become unmanageable as a result. It is safer and far more sensible to fit the same type of tyre on all four wheels – and the spare – and preferably of the same make and model.

Tyre sizes and marking

You must always fit tyres of the size specified by the car's manufacturer, since the suspension will have been designed to work best with these. The tyre size will be marked on the sidewall. The width and wheel diameter is marked on all tyres, but extra information is given on radials.

On cross ply tyres, the size is given in inches. A tyre marked '5.50 x 13' will be 5½in wide and fit a 13in-diameter wheel rim. You may find a letter 'S', 'H' or 'V' on the tyre as well. This indicates the maximum speed at which the tyre should be used. Consult your dealer if in doubt about this.

On radial tyres, a typical marking might be '155R13 78 S'. In this instance, the '155' refers to the tyre width in millimetres; the letter 'R' indicates that the tyre is a radial; the '13' is the wheel diameter in inches; the figure '78' indicates the maximum load grading; and the letter 'S' is the speed rating.

SIDE WALL SYMBOLS

1 Tubeless or tubed tyre. **2** 175 – width of tyre in millimetres. S – speed rating (113mph). R – radial, 14 – rim diameter in inches. **3** Tyre wear indicators. **4/5** Load and speed indicator. **6/7** Material and number of casing and tread plies. **8** Maximum pressure in pounds/sq.in. **9** Maximum load in lbs. per wheel. **10** Manufacturer. **11/12** Approval mark in accordance with Economic Commission for European standards. **13** DOT for Department of Transport (USA). – tyre confirms to US specifications. **14** Manufacturer's coding. **15/16/17** Wear resistance, traction capability and heat resistance classifications for tyres destined for USA only.

Problem diagnosis

When a car breaks down, there may frequently be an clear and easily-curable cause – a flat tyre, for instance – but it is just as likely that a breakdown will occur without such obvious visual clues. If this happens to you, a sound working knowledge of the way your car works can save the situation. It will enable you to trace the trouble to its source and apply the necessary remedy.

If you are unaware of what you are looking at or looking for, you will never get back on the road. So study the previous sections of this book carefully and apply the information they contain to your own car. Familiarize yourself with the layout of the fuel, ignition, cooling and electrical systems, study the owner's handbook supplied with the car and generally work at 'finding your way around' the vehicle.

The diagnostic charts in this section of the book are arranged in a simple easy-to-follow pattern that will allow you to establish what is causing a problem in the engine or in its ancillary systems quickly and to decide on what action is necessary to put things right. Study them carefully and read them again from time to time to refresh your memory. If you do, you will know where to start looking when you come to start your car on a cold frosty morning and it fails to turn over, when the engine begins to run roughly, or when all the lights suddenly go out.

Seasonal problems

Even a modern car is more likely to break down in winter than at any other time. Winter conditions can be extremely hard on the battery, which, in any case, is less efficient when the temperature drops. If the battery is already in poor condition or other electrical components have not been maintained properly, starting problems are almost inevitable. By paying a little extra attention to them during the winter months, the risk of breakdown will be reduced.

Low temperatures can cause other problems. If the correct quantity of anti-freeze has not been added to the cooling system, the water in the system may freeze solid, embedding the water pump rotor in ice and preventing its rotation. This, in turn, will stop the engine from turning over when you operate the starter. The fact that water inevitably expands as it freezes may lead to even more serious problems, such as cracks in the sides of the cylinder block. So take care at this time of year.

Failure to start

If the engine refuses to start, you should make some basic checks before looking for more complex reasons for the breakdown. Are you certain that the fuel tank contains enough fuel, for instance? The dashboard gauge itself may be inaccurate or even stuck. Unless you are really sure that the car cannot have used a tank of fuel since its last fill-up, check the level of fuel in the tank. You do this by removing the filler cap and rocking the car gently on its suspension; if there is fuel in the tank, you should be able to hear it sloshing about inside.

Dampness on the high tension leads, the distributor cap and the coil cover can affect the ignition and prevent the vehicle starting. Remove all of them – this will involve removing the plug leads as well – and wipe them dry and clean with a soft cloth. Wipe the inside of the distributor cap as well as the outside before you refit it. Take care not to confuse the plug leads when you replace them.

All these components should be kept free of dirt, as this can attract moisture. You can use various moisture-repellant aerosol sprays for this – it is a good idea to keep one of these in the car for use when it is damp.

Draining the battery

If the engine is reluctant to start, you will only compound the problem if you continually operate the starter. This drains a considerable amount of energy from the battery each time it is operated. If you operate it continuously for long periods, the battery will eventually flatten to the point when it cannot provide enough current to operate the starter motor at all.

If this occurs, switch off the ignition and allow the battery to recover for 20 minutes or so before you attempt to start the car again. If there is no underlying problem, the battery may have recovered enough to start the engine. Additionally, the constant turning over of the engine will have led to an excessive amount of petrol being sucked into it from the carburettor. This collects on the spark plug electrodes, preventing them from sparking. The characteristic sign of this problem – termed 'flooding' – is a strong smell of petrol.

If you flood the engine, leave it for 20 minutes or so to allow the petrol to evaporate and then try again. Do not operate the choke but, as you operate the starter, slowly depress the accelerator pedal, pressing it right to the floor and holding it there until the engine fires. When it does, you can pull out the choke and keep it out until the engine warms up. This is not necessary if the engine is already warm from previous running.

Isolating the cause
If the cause of a breakdown is not obvious, always approach the problem in a logical manner. Work through all the possible causes one by one, eliminating each in turn until you find the eventual reason for the fault. Establishing this may only involve a quick visual check of the relevant system or component in some instances; in other cases, a component may have to be at least partly dismantled.

In many instances, you will be able to correct the fault yourself, but, if you are not certain you know what to do, do not be afraid to call in an expert – particularly if your car is fitted with an advanced electronic ignition system or fuel injection. It is far better to for a competent mechanic to repair the car than for you to end up with a pile of bits and pieces and no idea of how to put them back together again.

The importance of servicing
Naturally enough, it is in your interests to do all you can to forestall the possibility of a breakdown by making sure that your car is regularly serviced in accordance with the manufacturer's service recommendations. You will find these in the owner's handbook,

or in the appropriate repair manual.

Regular servicing is essential, regardless of the car's age, mileage or value. If it is to run at peak efficiency for you, you must look after it accordingly. Even an old second-hand car still represents a reasonable investment and it is stupid to throw that away, as so many people unfortunately do. In addition, regular inspection of all the car's major systems, as described previously, will often throw up things that need attention. By having these tackled as soon as you find them – or, when you can, tackling them yourself – you will save money and aggravation in the long run.

Use your instruments
Monitoring the car's instruments and warning lights in a set pattern as you drive can also help in forestalling breakdowns. Depending on the dashboard layout, glance from left to right, right to left or top to bottom, taking in the readings of all the instruments and checking that no warning lights are flashing.

Remember, in this instance, that a glance means a glance, since you should not take your eyes off the road for more than a split second. Therefore, learn what the correct readings should be in advance, so that you can see instantly if a needle is in the wrong position. Even a minor deviation from normal may be the first warning of a serious problem and give you time to do something about it. If, despite these precautions, a sudden breakdown does take place, knowing what the instrument readings were at the time may also give you a good

idea where to start looking for the cause of the problem.

The instruments provided vary from car to car. At the most basic, they include a speedometer, a fuel gauge, a water temperature gauge and oil pressure and ignition charging warning lights. More complex dashboard lay-outs include speedometer, tachometer, oil pressure and water temperature gauges, an ammeter or battery state indicator, a fuel gauge and various warning lights. Whatever the level of instrumentation provided, make good use of all the information it supplies.

Listening to the car
A well-tuned ear is also useful. By listening to the car as you drive along, you can get used to the noise it makes. This makes it possible for you to notice quickly if any new noises crop up; some may just be simple squeaks in the seat springs, but others may have a more sinister meaning.

Any unusual noise should be investigated. You should never carry on driving regardless, as this may only make the problem worse.

Summing up
If you have followed a fault finding chart and have not resolved the problem, do not lose heart. Quite often, a fault will not manifest itself until another part of the system breaks down and though you may find the cause of that, the original problem may still exist. By familiarizing yourself with the sytems of the car *(see p.30)* you will be able to determine what areas you should investigate.

Dealing with a breakdown/1

Given the complexity of modern cars, it is surprising just how reliable they can be. But, though a minority of people take the trouble to keep their cars, serviced and well maintained, most people on the whole tend to take their cars for granted, expecting them always to start without fuss and assuming they will go on running with only a minimum of attention, except for keeping the tank full of fuel and the oil level topped up.

It is scarcely surprising that cars in this second category usually break down sooner or later, but even the best-maintained cars can suffer from breakdowns too. Though such a breakdown may only be minor – the result, say, of a puncture, a blown fuse or a burst coolant hose – all breakdowns are time-consuming annoyances. They inevitably occur when you least expect them and often at the most inconvenient moment. So, it pays to be prepared. Always have a survival tool kit to hand and familiarize yourself with the car's essential operating systems. This will enable you to tackle minor breakdowns yourself and also help you to explain any problem clearly, should you be forced to seek help from a garage.

The first essential is to know where to look to isolate the potential cause of a breakdown. The fault-finding charts (see p.70) will help you do just that. Find out how the various mechanical systems work by referring to the 'Anatomy of the Car' (see p.30), together with your owner's handbook. You will find that most breakdowns occur in the fuel, ignition or cooling systems and often the cure is quite simple. Always carry a few

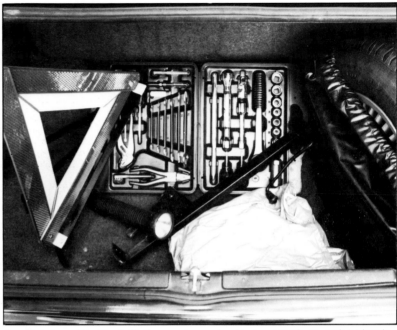

A well equipped boot is vital in the event of a breakdown. Apart from a good set of tools and a jack to suit your car, you should carry a torch, a warning triangle and something to kneel or lie on in wet weather.

spares, such as fuses, bulbs, contact breaker points and a fan belt; all are relatively small and will take up very little space in the boot. Make sure, too, that you always carry a spare wheel, fitted with a good properly-inflated tyre.

Safety first

When dealing with any breakdown, one of the most important priorities is safety – for your passengers, other road users and yourself. Your first task must be to get the car off the road, or at least as far away from the traffic as possible. A stationary car can be a serious obstruction and hence an accident risk, especially when visibility is poor. If this is impossible, you must take all possible steps to ensure that other road users are aware of its presence.

Motorway breakdowns

If you break down on a motorway, the first to do is steer your car towards the slow lane as quickly and safely as possible and then on to the hard shoulder, as far away as you can from overtaking traffic. Make sure that the whole car is clear of the road, as otherwise it could become a serious accident hazard. If the car is equipped with hazard warning lights, switch them on; if not, switch on the lights and nearside indicator to warn other road users that the car is disabled.

When you get out of the car, always use the nearside door – on no account get out on the offside, as you could accidentally open the door into the path of an oncoming vehicle or, worse still, step in front of one as you get out. Remember that motorway traffic generally travels much faster than traffic on other roads, so there is usually far less time and opportunity for other drivers to take avoiding action. If there are any passengers in the car, get them to stay where they are. If they have to get out, make sure they do not wander around and that they keep the car between them and the traffic. If you carry a red reflective warning triangle, set this up about 150 yards (137m) behind the car in the centre of the hard shoulder.

Unless the breakdown is simple enough for you to tackle yourself quickly – a puncture, blown fuse, or split hose, for instance – you should use an emergency telephone to call for help to tow the car off the motorway. These telephones are spaced at intervals along the hard shoulder. To find the nearest, look at the closest distance post; this will be marked with an arrow indicating the direction to take. Note the number and letter of the distance post before setting off, as these will enable the emergency services to locate you quickly.

On no account should you leave the car unattended for any reason other than going to the telephone. Do not take a short-cut across the motorway either, even though there is a telephone immediately opposite you. This is extremely dangerous and illegal.

Make a note of the symptoms of the breakdown and the cause, if you know it, and relay this – together with the make, model, date of manufacture and registration number of your car – to the telephone operator. If you are a member of one of the major motoring organizations,

mention this as well so that a motorway patrol can be routed to your aid. Otherwise a tow truck from the nearest local garage will tow you from the motorway, after which you can decide whether to get the garage to handle the problem or to sort it out for yourself. When making the call, do not replace the receiver until you are told to, as the operator cannot call you back.

Having finished the call, go back to the car car and wait for the tow truck to arrive. Do not forget to collect your warning triangle before you are towed away.

Breakdown on other roads
If you break down on a wide major dual carriageway, you should take the same safety precautions as you would on a motorway. On other roads, the situation varies. Many, for instance, will not have hard shoulders, but you must still make every effort to get the car clear of the carriageway, driving or pushing it on to a verge or into a lay-by.

If it is physically impossible to get the car clear of the road, park as close to the kerb as possible. Switch on the hazard warning flashers – or the lights and nearside indicators – and position a red warning triangle about 50 yards (48m) behind the car. You should not attempt a lengthy repair unless you are well clear of the road. If you are a member, 'phone the appropriate motoring organization – both the AA and RAC have their own telephone boxes along main roads for the use of their members – or, alternatively, a local breakdown service, if only to tow you to a

place of greater safety. Only work on the car if you know that by doing so you will not be a hazard to oncoming traffic – or yourself.

Breakdowns off the road
Breakdowns do not inevitably happen when you are on the road. They are almost, if not quite, as likely to occur when you try to start the car after it has been parked in a car park, or even in your own driveway. The results, however, are the same – you are stranded.

Off the road, you are likely to have more room in which to work on the car in safety, while, if you are at home, you will probably have better facilities available to help you in solving the problem. But, just as on a busy motorway, safety must come first.

You should never smoke while working on the car, nor anyone else close by – petrol fumes are all too easily ignited. If you need to work with the engine running, roll up your sleeves, take off your tie, or tuck it into your shirt, remove loose jewellery and tuck long hair up. Keep any loose clothing out of the way. These could all be trapped by the moving fan belt, the fan itself, or the various drive pulleys. Also remove a watch or a ring – if either accidentally come into contact with a live part of the electrical system, they can easily cause electric shocks, burns or short circuits. When using metal tools, take care not to bridge the battery terminals, or allow a tool to touch the live terminal and any earthed metal component for the same reason. If this happens, the result will be a short circuit and sparking. The latter could lead

Dealing with a breakdown/2

Changing a wheel

1 Remove any wheel trim or hub cap. They can be prised off with a flat-bladed screwdriver or the flat end of the wheelbrace usually supplied with the car's toolkit.

2 With the wheel still on the ground, loosen the wheel nuts slightly. They undo anti-clockwise, but do not undo them more than a quarter turn at this stage. If you find them difficult to release, try using foot pressure on the wheelbrace *(inset)*. Be careful the wheelbrace does not slip off the retaining nuts.

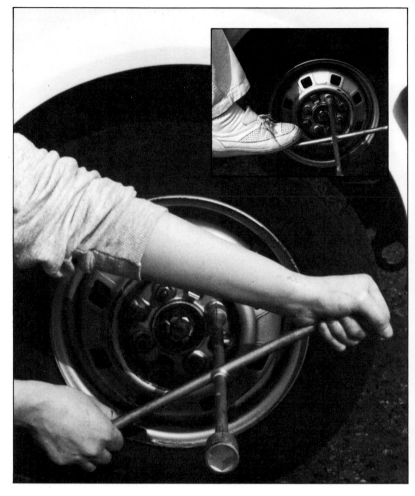

to electric shock, burns, and the ignition of petrol vapour – as well as damaging the tool.

Whenever possible, it is best to disconnect the battery completely to prevent any accidental short circuits. If one occurs, it may provide you with more remedial work that you originally bargained for. When dealing with wiring, take special care. If any wires have to be disconnected, label them, so that you can replace them correctly; wrong connections can seriously damage the electronic components fitted in modern ignition systems and

electrical accessories.

If the engine has been running, or is running while you are working on it, remember that the exhaust manifold and pipe will become very hot – enough to give you a severe burn. Make sure that you keep your hands and arms well clear of the exhaust system.

Similarly, take particular care if removing the radiator cap after the engine has been running, particularly if the breakdown is due to overheating. Steam will be released at high pressure – this could scald you badly. You

should allow the engine to cool for 15 minutes or so before removing the cap. Even then, muffle it with a heavy rag and only turn it to its first safety stop to allow any residual pressure to escape before taking it off completely.

Never crawl beneath a car if it is supported only by a jack. This is potentially dangerous, as the car could topple off its support if you rock it even slightly. Never support it on blocks of wood or piles of bricks either. If you have to work beneath the car, make sure it is supported on car ramps, or axle stands. These

3 Position the jack at the jacking point nearest the wheel to be changed (check this in the handbook). Ensure the handbrake is on if you are changing a front wheel, and place chocks at the front wheels if changing a rear wheel.

4 Raise the car on the jack until the wheel is free to rotate. Remember, an inflated tyre is larger than a flat one, so allow a little extra space for fitting the spare.

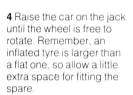

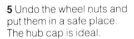

5 Undo the wheel nuts and put them in a safe place. The hub cap is ideal.

6 Remove the wheel and replace it with the spare. Replace the wheel nuts, making sure the cupped end of the nuts face towards the wheel and tighten them as much as possible. Lower the car and tighten the wheel nuts fully, working in a diagonal sequence around the wheel. Replace the hub cap or any rim embellishers.

should be positioned beneath chassis members or the rear axle, while the car itself should be standing on firm, level ground.

Changing a wheel

Probably the best-known problem that has affected – and infuriated – the majority of motorists at some time or another is a flat tyre. Changing a wheel is a straightforward business, but you will need to take care while you do so. This is because the car will be supported only by a single jack which, as previously explained,

can be precarious. However, there should be no problems, provided that the necessary precautions are taken.

Having got the car clear of the road, check which tyre is at fault and remove the spare wheel, jack, jack handle and wheel brace from the boot. Make sure that the handbrake is applied firmly, and, if the puncture is in one of the rear tyres, look around for something with which to chock the front wheels. This is an additional safeguard against the possibility of the car moving forwards or backwards. Make sure the car is parked on firm,

level ground.

If the jack has an arm designed to fit into a socket beneath the car, insert it into the socket nearest the flat tyre. Make sure that it is fully home. Check that the jack is not standing on soft ground, as, if so, it will sink into it and, as a result, the car may topple as you raise it. If the jack simply has a flat pad on top, place it beneath a substantial chassis member, or the axle concerned.

Before raising the car clear of the ground, remove the hub cap and any wheel embellisher – use the shaped handle of the

Dealing with a breakdown/3

wheelbrace to lever this off – and slacken the wheel retaining nuts. Considerable force may be needed for this, which is why it is sensible to do it while the car is still sitting firmly on all four wheels. If you are changing a front wheel, there also will be nothing to stop it turning once it is off the ground, since the handbrake operates only on the rear wheels.

Jack up the car sufficiently for the tyre to clear the ground – remember that the fully-inflated tyre on the spare wheel will need a greater clearance than the flat one. Finish unscrewing the wheel retaining nuts and lift the wheel from its studs.

Put the nuts somewhere safe – it is all too easy for them to roll away. If they do get lost, you can use one nut from each of the other three wheels as an emergency 'get you home' measure, but replace them as soon as possible.

Lift the spare wheel on to the wheel studs and fit the nuts finger-tight. Tighten them up further with the brace, holding the wheel firmly against the hub face. Work in diagonals, tightening first one nut, then its diagonally opposite number, then a nut on either side of this and finally the nut diagonally opposite that. In this way the wheel will be pulled evenly and squarely into place.

Lower the car to the ground and fully tighten the nuts, again working in diagonals. Refit the hub cap and the wheel embellisher, remove the jack and stow the tools and punctured tyre. Have the tyre repaired or replaced as soon as possible – driving without a serviceable spare tyre is foolhardy.

Coping with a flat battery

Another common problem, particularly in winter, is that of a flat battery. This may occur through neglect, or through a fault in the charging system.

Unless the battery is completely flat, there is a good chance that you can get the car going with a push or tow start. Alternatively, you can use a set of 'jump' leads connected to another car's battery and to yours to start the car.

You cannot tow or push start a car with automatic transmission, since the pump that operates the gearbox only works when the engine is running, so jump leads must be used. Such cars also should never be towed for any great distance – no more than 15 miles (24km) – or at speeds above 30mph (48kph), since towing can damage the transmission system.

If you are being tow started, make sure you use a proper tow rope, tied to some substantial part of the chassis, or to the bumper brackets. Do not tie it around the bumper itself – this may be quite flimsy and, if so, could easily bend.

You must get the car moving at a fast walking pace at least, so that, when a gear is engaged, the car's momentum will cause the engine to turn over as if the starter motor was functioning normally. Make sure you have the ignition key turned to 'on', with first or second gear engaged and the clutch pedal depressed. If the engine is cold and has a manual choke, pull out the choke knob.

When the car is travelling fast enough, release the clutch pedal. The car should start as the engine turns. Be ready for this, dipping the clutch pedal smartly to disengage the gear and remove the load on the engine, and – if you are being towed – applying the brakes to prevent the car running into the towing vehicle. Keep the engine running at high speed, so that the generator begins to charge the battery. You can tell this is happening if the red charging light on the dashboard goes out. Ideally, take the car for a long run to fully charge the battery.

If the battery is totally flat, use a battery charger to put some life back into the battery or start the engine with jump leads. These are very thick cables with crocodile clips at each end, one cable being black and the other red. When using them, position the two cars as close together as possible, but make sure that they do not actually touch, as there is the risk of a short circuit if their electrical systems differ in polarity.

Connect the negative terminals of the two batteries together with the black lead and the positive terminals with the red lead. Connect up to the dead battery first, taking care not to touch the ends of the cables together accidentally when making the connections.

Start the car with the good battery and run its engine at high speed while you operate the starter of the car with the flat battery. The current from the running car's generator will provide enough voltage to start the other vehicle's engine. Once this is running, disconnect the jump leads and keep the engine running to charge up the battery.

When you use jump leads, you must take particular care not to connect them up incorrectly, as a wrong connection could easily damage any electronic components in the ignition system. Indeed, some manufacturers specify that they should not be used because of this danger. If this is the case, remove the flat battery and connect it to the other car's battery with the jump leads. Run the car for 20 minutes or so to put some life in the battery and then replace it. This charging period should be enough to get the immobilized vehicle running again.

Replacing fuses and bulbs

If an electrical accessory suddenly stops working, the cause could be a blown fuse. To check whether or not this is the case, see whether other accessories on the same circuit are operational – check which these are in your handbook, as this usually shows both the fused circuits and which accessories are controlled by them. Alternatively, the information may be on the fuse box cover. If none of the other accessories work, then the fuse must be checked.

Switch off the ignition, disconnect the battery and remove the cover from the fuse box. Identify the fuse concerned. If it is a ceramic fuse – these fuses are fitted with exposed fuse wire – you will be able to see at a glance whether the wire has burnt through or not. Prise the fuse from its spring contacts and push another into place. Check the operation of the accessories on the affected circuit; if the fuse continues to blow, have the system checked by a garage.

In many cases, a blown fuse will not stop you from using the car. Some cars, however, are fitted with a circuit breaker,

which is designed to shut off the entire electrical system if the car receives a heavy blow. This is a precaution against fire should a short circuit occur. In this case, there is normally a reset button on the circuit breaker, which you simply push home to restore the power. Full details are given in your handbook.

It is equally simple to replace a blown bulb. Depending on the design of the unit, you may have to unscrew the lens to remove the bulb, or the bulb may be on a holder, which clips into the back of the light unit. In most cases, the bulb will be of the bi-pin type, needing slight downward pressure and a quarter turn to release it. Replace it in the same way.

'Get-you-home' repairs

You can repair a split coolant hose temporarily with PVC insulating tape. Bind the tape around the affected portion of the hose, taking it at least 25mm (1in) either side of the split and making sure that the surface is dry. If not, the tape will not adhere to it. Wrap several layers around the hose.

If the radiator is leaking, the problem is not as easy to solve. This can only be repaired by a garage and, if the leak is bad, the whole radiator may have to be replaced. However, you may be able to seal a small leak for a short time by adding a proprietary sealant to the coolant in the radiator.

After making either repair, you should top up the cooling system. Take care when removing the filler cap, remembering to muffle it with a heavy rag. Use warm water – not cold – unless the system itself is cold. Make sure, too, that the

heater controls are set to 'hot' to prevent an air lock forming in the heater matrix.

If the engine is overheating and you cannot repair – or locate – the cause, try turning the heater controls to hot and switching the booster on to full. This will take some of the heat away from the engine. If overheating continues, you should remove the thermostat (see p. 115). This will increase the flow of coolant through the radiator.

If your fan belt breaks, you can use a nylon stocking, or a pair of tights, as a temporary substitute. Knot the tights around the crankshaft and water pump pulleys tightly. You need not worry about the generator pulley, since there should be enough power in the battery to get you home.

If a fuse blows and you do not have a spare one available, you can remove a fuse from a 'luxury' circuit – the one controlling the heated rear window, or the heater fan, for instance – and use it as a temporary substitute. Make sure, though, that this fuse has the same rating as the blown one – if it is higher, the rest of the circuit could be damaged. Also check carefully that the circuit it controls does not contain any vital components, such as lights or indicators.

Many temporary repairs can be made with bits of wire, instant glue, adhesive tape and elastic bands, so keeping a few such items in the car is a good idea. Remember, however, that you are only making 'get you home' repairs. Any temporary repair must be made good at the earliest opportunity and any broken component replaced by a new one.

Engine starting

Nothing happens when you turn the ignition switch or key and lights and other electrical accessories will not operate	Cause	Action	
	1 Loose, corroded or dirty battery terminals and cable connections, stopping current flow.	Check cable connections at the battery. If necessary, disconnect it and clean and replace the connections, first smearing battery terminals with	petroleum jelly. Tighten all retaining bolts or screws fully. Also check condition of earth cable and its connection to car body. If necessary, disconnect, clean and refit.
	2 Completely flat battery.	Recharge the battery, or start engine with jump leads from another car. If the battery is	relatively new, have charging system checked at a garage.

Nothing happens when you turn the ignition switch or key, but lights and other accessories that operate with the ignition off work normally	Cause	Action	
	1 Faulty ignition switch.	Jog the key as you turn it. If there is a response, have the switch	checked and replaced if necessary.
	2 Blown ignition fuse.	Locate and check the ignition fuse.	

Nothing happens when you turn the ignition key or switch with the headlights switched on; there is no sound from the engine other than a slight 'click' and the headlights dim as the key is turned to the 'start' position	Cause	Action	
	1 Loose, corroded or dirty battery/starter motor cable connections, preventing current flow.	Check battery and starter motor cable connections. If necessary, disconnect it, clean connections and replace, first smearing battery terminals with	petroleum jelly. Tighten retaining nuts, bolts and screws fully. Also check condition of earth cable and connection to the car body. If necessary, disconnect, clean and refit.
	2 Battery charge low, or battery otherwise faulty.	Recharge battery, or start engine with jump leads from another car. If the battery is	relatively new, have the charging system checked.
	3 Starter motor pinion jammed against flywheel ring gear, or not meshing correctly due to a broken ring gear tooth.	Select top gear, release handbrake and rock the car gently to and fro. Alternatively, turn the square end of the starter motor shaft protruding through the back of the	motor with a spanner. Sometimes the pinion can be 'shocked' out of engagement by hitting the end of the shaft with a soft-faced hammer or mallet.
	4 Seized engine.	With the gear lever in neutral, remove the spark plugs. Turn the engine over with a	spanner on the crankshaft pulley retaining bolt. If this fails, seek help.

Nothing happens when you turn the ignition switch or key with the headlights switched on; the engine makes no noise other than a slight 'click', but the headlights remain bright as the key is turned to the 'start' position	Cause	Action	
	1 Broken or loose connection between battery and starter motor.	Check cable between battery and starter motor; if necessary, disconnect it, clean connections and replace, first smearing	battery terminals with petroleum jelly. Tighten retaining nuts, bolts and screws fully. If cable is broken, fit replacement.
	2 Faulty starter motor solenoid.	Check wiring connections at solenoid, making sure they are	clean and tight. If engine still fails to start, replace solenoid.
	3 Starter motor pinion jammed against flywheel ring gear or not meshing correctly due to a broken ring gear tooth.	Select top gear, release the handbrake and rock the car gently. Alternatively, turn the square end of the starter motor shaft, which protrudes through the	back of the motor, with a spanner. Sometimes the pinion can be 'shocked' out of engagement by tapping the end of the shaft with a soft-faced hammer or mallet.
	4 Faulty starter motor.	Replace the starter motor.	

Nothing happens when you turn the ignition key or switch with the headlights switched on; there is a whining sound from the engine, but the headlights remain bright when the key is turned to the 'start' position	Cause	Action	
	1 Battery insufficiently charged or otherwise faulty.	Recharge the battery, or start engine with jump leads. If the battery is relatively new, have charging	system checked. If battery will not recharge, fit a new one. The car may start with a tow or push.
	2 Starter motor drive pinion not meshing with the flywheel ring gear, or starter retaining bolts loose and motor assembly has moved forward.	Check tightness of starter retaining bolts; tighten if necessary. Otherwise, remove motor and replace with new one.	
	3 Flywheel ring gear teeth badly worn or broken.	Call in a garage to replace ring gear.	

When you turn the ignition key or switch, the engine turns over slowly, seems to get slower and slower and will not start; if the lights are switched on they glow only dimly	Cause	Action	
	1 Loose, corroded or dirty battery terminals and cable connections.	Check battery cable connections. If necessary disconnect them, clean and replace, first smearing battery terminals with petroleum jelly. Tighten	retaining bolts or screws fully. Also, check condition of earth cable and connection to car body. If necessary, disconnect, clean and refit.

Engine starting

Cause
2 Battery insufficiently charged, or otherwise faulty.

Action
Recharge the battery, or start the engine with jump leads. If the battery is relatively new, have the charging system checked. If the battery will not recharge, fit a new one. The car may start with a tow or a push.

---

3 Faulty starter motor.

Replace starter motor.

The engine turns over normally, but does not fire

Cause
1 If it is a particularly hot day, excessive heat in the engine bay can turn the petrol in the fuel line into a vapour, which cannot be pumped by the petrol pump.

Action
Switch off the ignition and allow the engine to cool down for 20 minutes or so. Open the bonnet to allow as much heat to escape as possible. If you can, wrap a rag soaked in cold water around the petrol pump.

---

2 Ignition fault. Check to see if there is a spark at the spark plugs.

Remove each plug in turn, fit it to its cap and hold this with a pair of insulated pliers so that the tip of the plug touches the metal of the cylinder block. Ask a helper to turn over the engine on the starter motor and watch for a spark between the central and side electrodes of the plug. Keep your fingers well away in case you get an electric shock.

The engine fails to start, but there is a spark at the plug electrodes

Cause
1 Sparking plug high tension leads connected in the wrong order, so that the plugs produce sparks at the wrong moment in relation to the piston and valve timings.

Action
Refit the high tension leads in the correct order.

---

2 Insufficient spark to ignite the fuel-and-air mixture. This may be caused by badly adjusted or faulty contact breaker points, or condensation on the high tension leads and distributor cap.

Remove the distributor cap and check the gap between the contact breaker points and their condition. If necessary, adjust the gap to the correct setting. Replace the points if they are pitted or badly burnt. In the latter case, fit a new condenser as well. Wipe the inside and outside of the distributor cap and the plug leads with a dry soft cloth before replacing them, or spray both cap and leads with a moisture repellant.

The engine will not fire and there is no spark at all at the plugs	Cause	Action	
	1 Oiled, flooded, pitted or incorrectly gaped plug electrodes.	If the spark plug electrodes are saturated with petrol, lay them aside to dry. If	they are covered in oil, wipe them clean. Check the gap between the electrodes.
	2 Faulty distributor.	Check the distributor body, together with the rotor arm on top of the distributor shaft for signs of hairline cracks or 'tracking' (streaks of dirt between the contacts inside the cap, which could cause short	circuits). If either are present, replace the affected component. If a carbon brush is fitted as the central contact in the distributor cap, examine it carefully for signs of wear or damage.
	3 Badly-adjusted or faulty contact breaker points.	Check the setting and condition of the contact breaker points, resetting the gap if necessary. Replace the points if they are badly pitted or burnt. Check that they open and close	properly and that there is a spark between them when they are open. Check the connections of the low tension lead between the distributor body and contact terminal.
	4 Dirty, loose or broken connections in either the low tension or high tension circuit between coil and distributor.	Inspect the high tension and low tension leads between distributor and coil for signs of damage, or dirty or loose connections. Replace any damaged leads and clean up the	connections before remaking them. Make sure that the ends of the high tension lead are pushed fully home in their sockets in the distributor cap and coil.
	5 Dirty, broken, or loose connections between the battery, ignition switch and coil.	Check the coil by disconnecting the low tension lead from the coil terminal. Switch on the ignition and touch the end of the wire	against the terminal. If the coil is working correctly, there will be a clicking sound as contact is made.
	6 Faulty ignition switch.	Inspect the connections at the ignition switch, making sure that they are clean and tight. Check the leads to and from the switch for signs	of damage or breaks. Replace any damaged wiring. Similarly, check the low tension lead from the battery to the starter motor terminal.

Engine starting

	Cause	Action	
If there is a healthy spark at the plug after these checks, but the engine still fails to start, check the fuel system, as fuel is probably not reaching the combustion chambers	1 Fuel tank empty.	Check the tank and fill up if necessary.	
	2 Faulty choke flap operation, causing a mixture that is too 'lean' to be supplied to the combustion chambers.	Remove the air cleaner assembly from the carburettor and check the operation of the choke flap as you operate the linkage. If the engine is cold, the	flap should be almost horizontal, closing off the carburettor air intake. If necessary, push it closed and hold it in place with a rubber band or piece of string.
	3 A blockage in the fuel lines or pump, preventing fuel from reaching the carburettor.	Check whether fuel is reaching the carburettor by freeing the petrol pipe from the carburettor and placing its open end into a small jar. If the engine has a mechanical fuel pump, operate the starter motor to start the pump. If the car has an electrical fuel pump, switch on the ignition. If a good, steady, flow of fuel is delivered, open the choke flap and look into the carburettor air intake while you operate the throttle linkage. If the venturi walls appear to be wet, the combustion chambers and plug are flooded. If they appear dry there is a fault	within the carburettor. If no fuel is pumped from the pipe – or only a trickle – check the fuel tank filler cap to see if the breather hole is blocked. Check the condition of the petrol pump filter and/or in-line filter to ensure that they are not blocked. If necessary, remove and clean them. If the filters are in good condition, inspect the petrol pipes and flexible hoses for splits or cracks, which could allow air to enter the system. If the pipes are undamaged, the fault lies in the pump itself, which should be overhauled or replaced.
	4 A blockage in the carburettor.	Seek advice from a garage.	
The engine fires, but will not run; it starts and runs smoothly for a moment, but then stops	Cause 1 Choke flap not closing fully due to badly adjusted linkage, or faulty automatic unit, so that the mixture is too 'lean'.	Action If you cannot smell fuel, remove the air cleaner from the carburettor and check the choke flap as you work the linkage. When the engine is cold, the flap should be almost	horizontal, closing off the carburettor air intake. If necessary, push it closed and hold it in place with a rubber band or piece of string while you start the engine.

Cause	Action	
2 Excessive use of the choke when the engine is hot, or during a prolonged attempt to start the engine. This will flood the carburettor and combustion chambers and a strong smell of fuel will result.	If there is a strong smell of fuel, let the engine stand for 20 minutes or so to allow the excess petrol in the combustion chambers to evaporate. Push the choke control fully home and operate the starter, slowly pushing the accelerator pedal to the floor and holding it there. If the car has an automatic choke, you may find it	necessary to remove the air cleaner and open and fix the choke flap in its vertical position first. If the choke appears to be operating normally, but the smell of fuel persists, the float chamber valve could be sticking, allowing a constant flow of fuel into the carburettor. This is a job for a garage.
3 A clogged air filter severely reducing the amount of air entering the carburettor.	Remove the lid from the air cleaner assembly and check the condition of the filter element. If the element is blocked and is of the disposable paper type, fit a new one. If the element is of	the oil-soaked wire gauze type, remove it, wash it thoroughly in paraffin, shake it dry and then soak it in engine oil before replacing it.
4 Blocked or defective crankcase emission valve.	This is a job for a garage.	
5 Insufficient fuel in the carburettor.	Check whether fuel is reaching the carburettor by freeing the petrol pipe from the carburettor and placing its open end into a small jar. With a mechanical fuel pump, operate the starter motor to start the fuel flow; with an electrical one, turn on the ignition. If a good, steady supply of fuel is delivered there is probably a fault within the carburettor, which is a job for a garage. If only a thin trickle of petrol is delivered, check the fuel tank filler cap to see if its	breathing hole has become blocked. This could create a vacuum in the fuel tank, which the pump cannot overcome. Check the condition of the petrol pump filter and/or in-line filter. If necessary, remove and clean them. If they are in good condition, inspect the petrol pipes for splits or cracks, which could allow air to enter the system. If the pipes are undamaged, the fault lies in the fuel pump, which should be overhauled or replaced.

Engine starting

When you operate the starter, the engine runs for a moment without firing on all cylinders and then stops	Cause	Action	
	1 Condensation on the components and leads of the ignition system, short-circuiting the current flow.	Wipe the inside and outside of the distributor cap, the plug leads and the other high tension and low tension leads	with a dry, soft cloth. Alternatively, spray them with moisture repellant.
	2 Incorrectly gapped or oiled spark plug electrodes, or dirty contact breaker points.	Remove the spark plugs, wiping off any oily deposit with a rag and filing any slightly pitted electrodes flat with an emery board or thin file. If the electrodes are heavily pitted, replace the plugs. Check the electrode gaps with a	feeler gauge and reset them if necessary. Check the contact breaker points. Clean them up with a points file or emery board if necessary. Check the gap with a feeler gauge, resetting if required. If the points are in bad condition, replace them.
	3 Loose, dirty, or broken connections in the ignition low tension circuit.	Check the wiring of the ignition low tension circuit, making sure that all connections are	clean and tight and that there are no broken wires.

When you operate the starter, the engine fires, but spits back through the carburettor, backfires or misfires and then stops	Cause	Action	
	1 Spark plug high tension leads connected in the wrong order.	Refit the high tension leads in the correct order.	
	2 Incorrectly set ignition timing, so that the spark plugs produce sparks either too early or too late.	Reset the timing according to the manufacturer's recommendations.	
	3 Air leak, at the inlet manifold, upsetting the balance of the fuel-and-air mixture.	Carefully inspect the inlet manifold for signs of cracks or loose retaining bolts. In the former case, the manifold must be	replaced; in the latter, tighten the bolts. If the car is fitted with a brake servo, check its vacuum hose connection at the manifold.
	4 Damaged or faulty exhaust system.	Check the exhaust system for signs of cracks, loose joints, or slack mounting and	retaining bolts. Replace any defective components and tighten any loose bolts.
	5 Burnt or sticking inlet or exhaust valves.	Seek expert help.	

Engine performance

When starting the engine from cold, it starts normally but stalls immediately the accelerator pedal is released and will not tick over	Cause	Action
	1 Full choke not applied or choke flap not closing fully due to faulty choke linkage or bad adjustment, causing too lean a mixture to be supplied to the combustion chambers.	On cars fitted with a manual choke, check that the choke control knob is pulled out fully. If this makes no difference, remove the air cleaner from the carburettor and check the operation of the choke flap. With the choke control knob fully out, the flap should virtually close off the carburettor air intake. Check that the flap operates correctly by having a helper move the control knob in and out. If necessary, adjust the linkage to allow the choke flap to move fully. If the carburettor is fitted with an automatic choke unit, the flap should be in the closed position when the engine is cold; if it is not, hold it closed with a rubber band or a piece of string and start the car. Allow it to warm up for a while on full choke, then release the choke flap.
	2 Idle speed set too low at the carburettor.	Set the correct idle speed in accordance with the manufacturer's instructions by adjusting the throttle stop or fast idle screw on the carburettor.
	3 Idle fuel mixture set incorrectly at the carburettor.	Seek advice from a garage.
After running for a while, the engine has warmed up but will not idle, stalling when the accelerator pedal is released	Cause	Action
	1 Choke control knob not pushed fully home on cars fitted with a manual choke, or the choke flap not opening fully due to a faulty linkage or automatic control unit, allowing too rich a mixture to reach the combustion chambers.	On cars fitted with a manual choke, make sure the choke control is pushed fully home. If this makes no difference, remove the air cleaner from the carburettor and check the operation of the choke flap. When fully open, it should be almost vertical. Check that the flap operates corectly by having a helper move the control knob in and out. If necessary, adjust the linkage to allow the choke flap to move fully. If the carburettor is fitted with an automatic choke unit, the flap should be in the fully open position when the engine has warmed up. If necessary, hold it fully open with a rubber band or piece of string and seek advice.
	2 Idle speed set too low at the carburettor.	Set the correct idle speed in accordance with the manufacturer's instructions by adjusting the throttle stop or fast idle screw on the carburettor.

Engine performance

	Cause	Action	
	3 Blocked air cleaner.	Remove the lid from the air cleaner assembly and check the condition of the filter element. If blocked and of the	disposable paper type, fit a new element; in an emergency the element can be left out to keep the car running.
	4 Blocked carburettor jet.	Seek advice from a garage.	
	5 Flooded carburettor.	This problem is probably caused by an inoperative needle valve	or float within the carburettor and is a job for a garage.
	6 Inlet manifold air leak, weakening the fuel mixture.	Look for signs of cracks in the inlet manifold and listen for any hissing sounds coming from the joints between the manifold, carburettor and cylinder head; the latter will indicate a blown gasket, which must be replaced. Check for any loose	mounting bolts or nuts – tighten any you find. Check the security and condition of the brake servo vacuum hose connection (if fitted) and also any crankcase breather pipe which may be connected to the inlet manifold.
After the engine has been run for some time and reached its normal operating temperature, it stops when the accelerator pedal is released and will not idle	Cause 1 Idle speed set too low at the carburettor.	Action Set the correct idle speed in accordance with the manufacturer's instructions by adjusting	the throttle stop or fast idle screw on the carburettor.
	2 Blocked pilot air jet in the carburettor.	To check the jet involves dismantling the	carburettor, which is a job for a garage.
	3 An air leak at the inlet manifold, upsetting the fuel mixture before it reaches the combustion chambers.	Carefully inspect the inlet manifold for signs of cracks or loose retaining bolts. In the former case, the manifold should be replaced; in the latter, tighten the bolts. Also,	listen for any hissing sound coming from the joints between the manifold, carburettor and cylinder head; this will indicate a blown gasket, which should be replaced.
As you drive along, the engine backfires, seemingly at random intervals and under all load conditions	Cause 1 Incorrectly set ignition timing.	Action Check the ignition timing and adjust if necessary in	accordance with the manufacturer's instructions.

Cause

2 A blockage or fault in the carburettor, fuel lines or fuel pump, preventing fuel reaching the combustion chambers in sufficient quantities and incorrectly mixed with air. Alternatively, the fuel may be contaminated by dirt or water.

Action

First determine whether fuel is reaching the carburettor or not. Do this by freeing the fuel pipe from the carburettor and placing its open end into a small jar or similar container. If the engine is fitted with a mechanical fuel pump, operate the starter motor to turn over the engine and work the pump. If the car is equipped with an electric fuel pump, simply turn on the ignition. If a steady flow of fuel is being delivered from the end of the pipe, the problem lies in the carburettor. Rectifying this is a job for a garage.

If only a thin trickle of petrol, or none at all, is delivered from the end of the pipe, inspect the fuel tank filler cap first to see if any breather hole in it has become blocked. This could cause a vacuum in the tank that cannot be overcome by the pump.

Check the condition of the fuel pump filter and/or in-line filter to ensure that they are not blocked. If necessary, remove the filters and clean them.

If the filters are in good condition, inspect the fuel pipes and flexible hoses for splits or cracks, which could allow air to enter the system.

If the pipes are undamaged, the fault is in the fuel pump which should be overhauled or replaced.

If the fuel system appears to be in order, check for fuel contamination by draining some of the fuel into a clean glass jar. Any particles of dirt in the fuel will be immediately obvious. If water is present it will settle to the bottom and form a clear layer with the darker coloured fuel above it. If dirt or water is present, the entire system should be drained to remove all of the contaminated fuel before the tank is refilled.

3 An air leak at the inlet manifold, upsetting the fuel mixture's balance before it enters the combustion chambers.

If the timing is set correctly and the fuel system is in good order, carefully inspect the inlet manifold for signs of cracks or loose retaining bolts. In the former case, the manifold should be replaced; in the latter, tighten the bolts.

Engine performance

	Cause	Action	
	4 Faulty distributor automatic advance-weight mechanism, upsetting the ignition timing.	If no other cause can be found, the problem may lie in a faulty distributor advance-weight mechanism preventing the automatic advance	of the ignition timing as engine speed increases. In this case, seek expert advice from a garage.

	Cause	Action	
After starting or running, the engine continues to idle when the accelerator pedal is released, but it appears to run roughly and unevenly whether hot or cold	1 A blocked air cleaner, upsetting the fuel mixture.	Remove the lid from the air cleaner assembly and check the condition of the filter element. If this is blocked and of the disposable paper	type, simply fit a new element; in an emergency the element can be left out to keep the car running.
	2 Faulty or incorrectly gapped spark plugs.	First, check that there is a spark at each spark plug. To do this, remove each plug in turn, fit it to its cap and hold the cap with a pair of insulated pliers, so that the tip of the plug is touching the metal of the cylinder block. Have a helper turn over the engine on the starter motor and watch for a spark between the central and side electrodes of the plug. Keep your fingers away from the plug in case of electric shock. If any plug fails to spark, fit it	into the cap of another high tension lead and try again. If it still fails to spark, replace. If a spark is produced, the first high tension lead is faulty and should be replaced. Inspect the overall condition of the plugs and replace them if the electrodes are badly burnt or pitted. Check the gaps between the electrodes carefully with a feeler gauge. If necessary, adjust the gaps to the correct setting.
	3 Faulty or incorrectly set contact breaker points.	Remove the distributor cap and check the gap between the contact breaker points and their condition. If necessary,	adjust the gap to the correct setting, or replace the points if they are pitted or badly burnt.
	4 Ignition timing set incorrectly.	Check and adjust the ignition timing if necessary, in	accordance with the manufacturer's instructions.

Cause	Action	
5 Idle speed set too low at the carburettor.	Set the correct idle speed in accordance with the manufacturer's instructions by adjusting	the throttle stop or fast idle screw on the carburettor.
6 Idle fuel mixture set incorrectly at the carburettor.	Seek advice from a garage.	
7 Flooded carburettor.	This is caused by an internal fault with the carburettor, and	rectifying it is a job for a garage.
8 An air leak at the inlet manifold, upsetting the fuel mixture's balance.	Look for signs of cracks in the inlet manifold and listen for any hissing sounds coming from the joints between the manifold, carburettor and cylinder head; the latter indicates a blown gasket, which must be replaced. Check for any	loose mounting bolts or nuts – tighten any you find. Check the security and condition of the brake servo vacuum hose connection (if fitted) and also any crankcase breather pipe connected to the inlet manifold.
9 Incorrectly set valve clearances.	Checking and adjusting valve clearances is a job for a qualified mechanic.	
10 Badly burned or incorrectly seating valve.	If the car still continues to idle roughly, it may be because a valve is failing to seat itself properly when it is	supposed to be closed, or because it is badly burned; seek expert advice from a garage.

	Cause	Action	
After driving the car, or running the engine for a while, the engine continues to fire on some or all cylinders for a short period after switching off the ignition	**1** Overheating of the engine, making the metal surfaces inside the combustion chambers so hot that they ignite the fuel mixture automatically.	Check the cooling system.	
	2 Ignition timing set incorrectly.	Check and adjust the ignition timing, if necessary, in	accordance with the manufacturer's instructions.

Engine performance

Cause	Action	
3 Idle speed set too high at the carburettor.	Set the correct idle speed in accordance with the manufacturer's instructions by adjusting	the throttle stop screw or fast idle screw on the carburettor.
5 Idle fuel mixture set incorrectly at the carburettor.	Seek advice from a garage.	
6 An air leak at the inlet manifold, upsetting the fuel mixture's balance.	Look for signs of cracks in the inlet manifold and listen for any hissing sound coming from the joints between the manifold, carburettor and cylinder head; the latter indicates a blown gasket, which must be replaced. Check for any	loose mounting bolts or nuts – tighten any you find. Check the security and condition of the brake servo vacuum hose connection (if fitted) and also any crankcase breather pipe connected to the inlet manifold.
6 Overheating spark plugs.	Check that the spark plugs are as specified by the car's	manufacturer. If they are not, replace them with the correct grade.
7 Heavy deposits of carbon in the combustion chambers.	If everything else appears to be in order, the fault could be caused by the build-up of excessive carbon deposits in the	combustion chambers. To clear means removing the cylinder head; seek advice from a garage.

	Cause	Action	
As you pull away from the kerb, or accelerate to a higher speed, the engine stops as the accelerator pedal is depressed	**1** Blocked air cleaner preventing an increased volume of air reaching the carburettor when the throttle is opened.	Remove the lid from the air cleaner assembly and check the condition of the filter element. If blocked and of the disposable paper type,	simply fit a new element; in an emergency the element can be left out to keep the car running.
	2 Badly adjusted or faulty choke mechanism, upsetting the fuel mixture.	On cars fitted with a manual choke, if the engine has just been started from cold, check that the choke control knob is pulled out fully. On the other hand, if the engine has warmed up, push the control knob home. If this makes no	difference, remove the air cleaner from the carburettor and check the operation of the choke flap. With the control knob fully out, the flap should virtually close off the carburettor air intake; when pushed fully home, it should lie

almost vertically, offering the minimum of disruption to the air flow. Check that the flap operates correctly by having a helper move the control knob in and out. If necessary, adjust the linkage.

If the carburettor is fitted with an automatic choke unit, hold the flap closed with a rubber band or piece of string. If you have only just started the engine from cold, allow it to warm up on full choke and then release the flap. If however, the engine has already warmed up, hold the flap fully open in the same way. Seek advice from a garage to cure the problem.

3 Inadequate fuel supply to the carburettor.

Free the fuel pipe from the carburettor and place its open end in a small jar. If the engine is fitted with a mechanical fuel pump, operate the starter motor to turn over the engine and operate the pump. If the car is equipped with an electric fuel pump, simply turn on the ignition. Check that the pump delivers a good steady stream of fuel. If only a trickle of fuel, or none at all, is delivered from the end of the pipe, inspect the fuel tank filler cap first to see if any breather hole in it has become blocked. This could cause a vacuum in the tank which cannot be overcome by the pump.

Check the condition of the fuel pump filter and/or in-line filter to ensure that they are not blocked. If necessary, remove the filters and clean them.

If the filters are in good condition, inspect the fuel pumps and flexible hoses for splits or cracks that could allow air to enter the system.

If the pipes are undamaged, the fault is in the fuel pump which should be overhauled or replaced.

4 Dirty, loose or broken connections in the distributor low tension circuit.

Remove the distributor cap and check the low tension wiring and connections to the contact breaker points.

Clean and tighten the connections and replace any wires that appear damaged.

5 Sticking piston in variable jet carburettors.

Repairing this involves dismantling the carburettor, and is a job for a garage.

Engine performance

	Cause	Action	
The engine performs normally until it faces a sudden load – such as climbing a hill or accelerating to overtake another vehicle – when it makes a rapid and high pitched metallic pinging or clattering sound. This is caused by the fuel mixture igniting too soon	**1** Wrong grade of fuel being used, with too low an octane rating.	Fill up with the grade of fuel specified in the handbook.	
	2 Ignition timing set incorrectly.	Check and adjust the ignition timing, if necessary, in	accordance with the manufacturer's instructions.
	3 Faulty vacuum advance-retard unit at the distributor, upsetting the ignition timing as load on the engine increases.	Check the operation of the vacuum-operated advance-retard mechanism together	with the vacuum pipe connections, making sure that the latter are secure.
	4 Overheating sparking plugs.	Check that the spark plugs are as specified by the car's	manufacturer. If they are not, replace them with the correct grade.
	5 Heavy deposits of carbon in the combustion chambers.	If everything else appears to be in order, the cause of the 'pinking' could be excessive carbon deposits built up in the	combustion chambers. To clear these means removing the cylinder head; seek advice from a garage.
When driving the car at medium to high speeds, the engine misfires constantly	**1** Blocked air filter element, preventing the required volume of air reaching the carburettor.	Remove the lid from the air cleaner assembly and check the condition of the filter element. If it is blocked and of the	disposable paper type, simply fit a new element; in an emergency the element can be left out.
	2 Dirty or burnt contact breaker points.	Remove the distributor cap and check the gap between the contact breaker points and their condition. If necessary,	adjust the gap to the correct setting, using a feeler gauge, or replace the points if they are pitted or badly burnt.
	3 Dirty, loose or broken connections in the low or high tension ignition circuits.	Check the low tension wiring and connections to the contact breaker points, between the distributor and coil, the coil and ignition switch, and the ignition switch and starter motor terminal. Clean and tighten the connections	and replace any damaged wiring. Similarly, inspect the high tension wiring between the coil and distributor, and distributor and spark plugs, making sure the ends of the leads are pushed firmly into their

respective sockets, or held securely by their screw-on collars. Look for damage to the insulation and replace any suspect leads.

4 Incorrectly gapped or faulty spark plugs.

First check that there is a spark at each plug. To do this, remove each plug in turn, fit it to its cap and hold the cap with a pair of insulated pliers, so that the tip of the plug is touching the metal of the cylinder block. Have an helper turn over the engine on the starter motor and watch for a spark between the central and side electrodes of the plug. Keep your fingers away from the plug in case of electric shock. If any plug fails to spark, fit it into the cap of another high tension lead and try again. If it still fails, replace it with a new one. If a spark is produced, the first high tension lead is faulty and should be replaced.

Inspect the overall condition of the plugs and replace them if the electrodes are badly burnt or pitted. Check the gaps between the electrodes carefully with a feeler gauge. If necessary, adjust the gap to the correct setting.

5 Dirt in the carburettor.

Free the fuel pipe from the carburettor and place its open end into a small jar or similar container. If the engine is fitted with a mechanical fuel pump, operate the starter motor to turn over the engine and work the pump. If the car is equipped with an electric fuel pump, simply turn on the ignition. Partially fill the jar with fuel and switch off the pump.
Examine the fuel in the jar for particles of dirt; if any are present the entire system must be drained to remove all the contaminated fuel before the tank is refilled. Also check the fuel pump filter and/or in-line filters to ensure that they are not clogged with dirt. If necessary, remove the filters and clean them.

Removing dirt from inside the carburettor means dismantling the component, and is a job for a garage.

6 Incorrectly set valve clearances.

Checking and adjusting valve clearances is a job for a qualified mechanic.

Engine performance

When running, the engine does not seem able to develop full power, leading to poor acceleration and an inability to reach normal top speed	Cause	Action
	1 Blocked air cleaner preventing an increased volume of air reaching the carburettor when the throttle is opened.	Remove the lid from the air cleaner assembly and check the condition of the filter element. If it is blocked and of the disposable paper type, simply fit a new element; in an emergency the element can be left out to keep the car running.
	2 Inadequate fuel supply to the carburettor.	Free the fuel pipe from the carburettor and place its open end in a small jar or similar container. If the engine is fitted with a mechanical fuel pump, operate the starter motor to turn over the engine and work the pump. If the car is equipped with an electric fuel pump, simply turn on the ignition. Check that the pump delivers a good steady stream of fuel from the end of the pipe. If only a trickle of fuel, or none at all, is delivered from the end of the pipe, inspect the fuel tank filler cap first to see if any breather hole in it has become blocked. This could cause a vacuum in the tank that cannot be overcome by the pump. Check the condition of the fuel pump filter and/or in-line filter to ensure that they are not blocked. If necessary, remove the filters and clean them. If the filters are in good condition, inspect the fuel pipes and flexible hoses for splits or cracks which could allow air to enter the system. If the pipes are undamaged, the fuel pump is faulty. It should be overhauled or replaced.
	3 The throttle not opening fully due to a badly adjusted operating linkage.	If a good supply of fuel is reaching the carburettor, check that the throttle plate in the carburettor air intake is opening fully when the accelerator pedal is fully depressed. Hold the choke plate fully open at the top of the air intake and look into the carburettor while a helper pushes the accelerator pedal up and down through its full movement. If necessary, adjust the throttle linkage to ensure that the throttle plate opens fully when the pedal is pushed to the floor.
	4 Fuel mixture set incorrectly at the carburettor.	Seek advice from a garage.

Cause	Action	
5 Blocked jets in the carburettor, preventing sufficient fuel mixing with the incoming air.	Clearing blocked jets involves disconnecting	the carburettor, which is a job for a garage.
6 Faulty carburettor accelerator pump, denying the engine the extra fuel it needs to run faster.	Repairing the carburettor accelerator	pump is a job for a garage.
7 Ignition timing set incorrectly, so that the plugs provide sparks at the wrong moment in relation to the piston and valve positions.	Check and adjust the ignition timing, if necessary, in	accordance with the manufacturer's instructions.
8 An air leak at the inlet manifold, upsetting the fuel mixture's balance before it enters the combustion chambers.	Carefully inspect the inlet manifold for signs of cracks or loose retaining bolts. In the former case, the manifold should be replaced; in the latter, tighten the bolts. Also,	listen for any hissing sound coming from the joints between the manifold, carburettor and cylinder head; this indicates a blown gasket, which should be replaced.
9 Incorrectly set valve clearances.	Checking and adjusting valve clearances is a job for a qualified mechanic.	
10 Worn cylinder bores causing a drop in compression at the combustion chambers when the pistons are at the top of their compression strokes.	If, after checking all the previous points, no cause for the lack of power can be found, it is likely that the cylinder bores are worn, particularly on a high-	mileage car. Ask a garage to check the compressions of the cylinders and to advise you on the best course of action.

Engine noise

A continuous light tapping sound comes from the top of the engine, speeding up and slowing down along with the engine	**Cause** 1 Valve clearance set too wide.	**Action** Adjusting the valve clearances is a garage job.
	2. The rocker arms, rocker shaft or cam shaft followers are worn.	Consult a garage.
A loud screeching sound comes from the front of the engine as the car is started. It then dies away, returning suddenly if the engine is revved	**Cause** 1 Loose or worn fan belt, or drive belt for a power-steering pump.	**Action** Check the fan belt and replace it, if worn or damaged. Check the fan belt tension. You should be able to depress the centre of its longest run under moderate thumb	pressure by no more than 13mm (½in). If necessary, adjust the tension by moving the generator on its bracket.
	2 The water pump has frozen solid, causing the fan belt to be dragged around its pulley by the crankshaft pulley.	Allow the cooling system to thaw out and check the engine for signs of leaks that may have been caused by the coolant freezing. Drain	the system and refill with the correct coolant/anti-freeze solution. Check the condition of the fan belt and replace it if necessary.
A continuous chirping or screaming sound comes from the front of the engine	**Cause** 1 Worn water pump bearings.	**Action** Replace the water pump.
A high-pitched metallic pinging or clattering comes from the engine when it is under a sudden load. This condition is known as 'pinking'	**Cause** 1 Wrong grade of fuel being used.	**Action** Fill up with the correct grade of fuel.
	2 Ignition timing set incorrectly.	Check and adjust the ignition timing in accordance with the	manufacturer's instructions.
	3 Faulty vacuum advance-retard unit at the distributor, upsetting the ignition timing as load on the engine increases.	Check the operation of the vacuum advance-retard mechanism together with the	vacuum pipe connections, making sure the latter are secure.
	4 Overheating spark plugs.	Check that the spark plugs fitted to the engine are of the grade specified by the	manufacturer. If not, replace them with the correct grade.

	Cause	Action	
	5 Heavy deposits of carbon in the combustion chambers.	If everything else is in order, 'pinking' could be caused by excessive carbon deposits in the combustion chambers.	To clear these requires the removal of the cylinder head. This is a garage job.
A constant and regular knocking comes from the engine, speeding up and slowing down with the engine	**Cause** **1** Worn crankshaft big-end bearings.	**Action** Seek garage advice. In addition to fitting new bearing shells, it may be necessary to regrind the crankshaft if this is worn	as well. In this case, it may be more economical to replace the entire engine with a reconditioned one.
A light regular tapping comes from inside the engine, speeding up and slowing down with the engine	**Cause** **1** Worn pistons or gudgeon pins, or a broken piston ring.	**Action** Seek the advice of a garage; worn or broken parts will need replacing, while the	cylinder block will probably need reboring and fitting with oversize pistons.
A tapping sound comes from the engine when it is first started, but disappears when the engine has warmed up	**Cause** **1** This is known as piston slap and is caused by worn pistons or cylinder bores. It may be accompanied by a general lack of power from the engine and increased oil consumption.	**Action** Seek the advice of a garage. Have the	cylinders rebored and/ or fit new pistons.
A low rumbling sound comes from inside the engine; this may be more apparent under load	**Cause** **1** Worn crankshaft main bearings.	**Action** Consult a garage. In addition to fitting new bearing shells, it may be necessary to regrind the crankshaft if this is worn	as well. If this is the case, it may be more economical to replace the entire engine with a reconditioned one.
A knocking sound comes from the rear of the engine when it is idling or during deceleration	**Cause** **1** Loose flywheel retaining bolts on cars fitted with a manual gearbox.	**Action** Have a garage check and tighten the flywheel bolts.	
	2 Broken driveplate on cars fitted with automatic transmission.	Have a garage or automatic transmission	specialist check the transmission.

Engine cooling

While the engine is running, steam appears from beneath the bonnet, the reading on the water temperature gauge rises considerably, or the water temperature warning light comes on. This may be accompanied by a moaning sound as the coolant boils under pressure

Cause

1 Low coolant level.

Action

Before topping up the coolant, wait for the engine to cool down for 20 minutes or so. Muffle the filler cap with a heavy rag, turn it to its first stop to allow any residual pressure to escape and then remove it. Top up the coolant level with the correct mixture of water and anti-freeze, or water and corrosion inhibitor, making sure that the water is warm.

In an emergency, the system can be topped up with water only, but the system should be drained as soon as possible afterwards and the correct coolant solution added. Never pour cold water into an overheated engine.

When topping up, make sure the heater controls are set to 'HOT' to prevent an airlock forming in the heater matrix. When the system has been topped up, start the engine to circulate the coolant; check for any obvious leaks that may have caused the coolant level to drop in the first place.

2 Gaps between the radiator fins blocked by dead leaves, insects or some other obstruction, preventing air flow through the radiator.

Inspect the radiator and spaces between the fins; flush out any blockages with a high-pressure hose, applying it to the radiator from the engine side.

Never poke bits of wire or sharp tools between the fins, as these may puncture the narrow tubes of the radiator core and aggravate the problem.

3 A coolant leak from the radiator or one of the cooling system hoses, reducing the coolant level.

Inspect the top and bottom tanks of the radiator, paying particular attention to the seams where the tanks are joined to the radiator core and to the seams around the inlet and outlet stubs. Inspect the core itself for damage and signs of leaks.

4 A leak from the pipe between the radiator and expansion tank (if fitted) or from the tank itself.

Inspect all the rubber hoses in the engine compartment and replace any that are found to be cracked, split, perished or damaged in any other way. In some cases, you may need to run the engine to detect splits since they may open up only when the system is under pressure. Look for stains on the hose, jets of water or jets of steam to pin-point a split.

Cause	Action	
5 Faulty radiator pressure cap, or one of the incorrect rating fitted.	Inspect the expansion tank pipe for signs of splits, cracks or other damage and, if necessary, replace it. Remove the radiator pressure cap and check the condition of its rubber seal; if it is damaged, perished or	badly worn, fit a new cap. If the seal appears to be in good condition, have a garage test its opening pressure. If necessary, fit a new cap, making sure it is of the correct rating for the system.
6 Loose or damaged fan belt, preventing drive to the water pump pulley.	Inspect the fan belt for signs of cuts, nicks or other damage that could cause it to stretch when being driven. If any damage is found, replace the fan belt. Also check the belt tension, making sure	that you can depress the midpoint of the belt's longest run under moderate thumb pressure by no more than 13mm (½in). If necessary, retension the belt.
7 Faulty electric fan (if fitted), preventing cooling air from being drawn through the radiator when the car is stationary or driven at slow speed and high engine speed.	Check the fuse controlling the fan circuit and replace it, if it has blown. Also check the condition of the fan wiring and connections. Make sure that none of the wiring's insulation is	damaged and that the connections are clean and tight. If the fuse and wiring are sound, check the fan unit by wiring it directly to the car battery.
8 Leaks from the water pump gasket or the pump itself.	Inspect the joint between the water pump and cylinder block; if any leaks are found, they may be due to loose retaining bolts or, more likely, a blown gasket. Tighten any loose bolts you find, but,	if all are tight, the gasket will need replacing. Check the pump itself for signs of cracks in its body or leaks from around the shaft. If either are found, replace it.
9 Leaks from the cylinder head or block core plugs.	Check all cylinder head and block core plugs to make sure that they are firmly in place and that there is no evidence of	leaks from any of them. If any leaks are found, have new core plugs fitted by a garage.

Engine cooling

Cause	Action	
10 Thermostat stuck in the closed position, preventing circulation of the coolant to the radiator.	With the engine warmed up, feel the top and bottom radiator hoses; if the top one is cool but the bottom hose hot, the thermostat is	stuck in the closed position. If this is the case, replace it with a new one, making sure it is of the correct rating.
11 A blockage somewhere in the cooling system, preventing circulation of the coolant.	Backflush both the radiator and cylinder block with a high pressure hose. To do this, disconnect the radiator hoses and insert the end of the hose in the radiator outlet (in the bottom tank), so that you flush it through in the opposite	direction to the normal flow. Similarly flush out the cylinder block and head by inserting the hose in the coolant outlet in the cylinder head. Make sure the heater controls are set to 'HOT' so that you flush out the entire system.
12 Leaks at the cylinder head gasket.	Inspect the joint between the cylinder head and block for signs of leaks. If none are found, remove the dipstick and look for water droplets on it, indicating an internal leak between the cylinders. Check the water in the radiator for bubbles when the engine is running – these mean gases from the combustion	chamber are entering the cooling system. If evidence of leakage is found, the gasket may be blown or the head warped. In the former case a new gasket should be fitted; in the latter, the head should be removed and either machined or replaced, depending on its condition – seek the advice of a garage.
13 Ignition timing set incorrectly.	Check and adjust the ignition timing if necessary.	
14 Ignition timing vacuum advance-retard mechanism not working properly.	Check the operation of the vacuum-operated advance-retard mechanism together	with the vacuum pipe connections, making sure the latter are secure.
15 An internal crack in the cylinder block or head.	Check the dipstick for signs of water droplets;	if any are found, consult a garage.

After two or three miles, when the engine should have reached its normal operating temperature, the temperature gauge on the instrument panel shows it to be running 'cold' and it fails to reach normal operating temperature for the rest of the journey

Cause

1 In extremely cold winter conditions, the problem may be due simply to the outside air temperature being so low that more heat than usual is being extracted from the coolant.

2 Thermostat stuck in the open position so that the coolant is circulating continuously, preventing the engine from reaching its normal operating temperature.

3 A faulty temperature sensor in the engine, or a defective temperature gauge, giving a false reading.

Action

In this situation partially blocking off the radiator opening may help. However, if you do this, take care not to block it completely and keep one eye on the temperature gauge to spot any signs of overheating.

Feel the top and bottom radiator hoses; if neither feels particularly hot, the thermostat may be stuck in the open position. Remove the thermostat and check its operation by suspending it in a bowl of water and heating the water to the thermostat's operating temperature. The thermostat should open. If not, fit a new thermostat, making sure it is of the correct rating.

If the thermostat appears to be working normally and there is no problem with extremely low air temperatures, the problem must lie in the temperature sensor or temperature gauge. First, inspect the wiring between the two components, making sure that the connections are clean and tight and that the insulation of the wires is not damaged. If the wiring is in order, either the sensor or the gauge is at fault; ask a garage to determine which it is and replace the faulty item.

Lighting/electrics

Lights are dim when the engine is running at speed	**Cause** 1 Loose or damaged fan belt, preventing the generator from turning fast enough to produce sufficient charging current for the battery.	**Action** Inspect the fan belt for signs of cuts, nicks or other damage that could cause it to stretch when being driven. If any damage is found, replace the fan belt with a new one. Check the	belt tension, making sure you can depress the midpoint of the belt's longest run under moderate thumb pressure by no more than 13mm ($\frac{1}{2}$). If necessary, retension it.
	2 A faulty generator or control unit not providing sufficient charging current.	Have a garage check the generator and its	control unit and repair or replace as necessary.
Lights are dim when the engine is idling	**Cause** 1 Loose or damaged fan belt preventing the generator from turning fast enough to produce sufficient charging current for the battery.	**Action** Inspect the fan belt for signs of cuts, nicks or other damage that could cause it to stretch when being driven. If any damage is found, replace the belt. Check the belt tension, making	sure that you can depress the midpoint of the belt's longest run under moderate thumb pressure by no more than 13mm ($\frac{1}{2}$in). If necessary, retension the belt.
	2 Battery in low state of charge.	Recharge the battery or start the car using jump leads from another car.	
	3 Faulty generator or charging circuit not providing enough charging current.	Have a garage check the generator and charging circuit.	
One particular light appears dim	**Cause** 1 The bulb is severely blackened by age or a bulb of inadequate wattage has been fitted.	**Action** Remove the lens cover or bulb holder from the light unit and inspect the bulb. If necessary,	replace the bulb with one of the correct wattage.
	2 The light's reflector is tarnished so that it does not reflect all of the bulb's output.	Inspect the condition of the light unit reflector; if	it is badly tarnished, replace with a new one.
	3 Dirty, loose or broken earth connection at the light unit.	Inspect the earth connection at the light unit, making sure the wiring is unbroken and	the connections are clean and tight. If necessary, replace any broken wire.

	Cause	Action	
	4 Dirty, loose or broken connection in the feed wiring to the light unit.	Check the feed wiring to the light unit, making sure the connections are clean and tight. Look for insulation	damage or a break in the wiring and replace any wires that are suspect.
With the engine running and the generator apparently charging the battery (ignition warning light out), the lights flicker constantly	**Cause** **1** Extremely high load on the battery, caused by too many electrical accessories operating at once.	**Action** Switch off any unnecessary electrical equipment. Consult a	garage about fitting a heavy-duty battery.
	2 Loose or damaged fan belt, preventing the generator from turning fast enough to produce sufficient charging current for the battery.	Inspect the fan belt for signs of cuts, nicks or other damage that could cause it to stretch when being driven. If any damage is found, replace the belt. Check the tension, making sure	that you can depress the midpoint of the belt's longest run under moderate thumb pressure by no more than 13mm ($\frac{1}{2}$). If necessary, retension the belt.
	3 Flat or faulty battery.	Recharge the battery or start the engine with	jump leads from another car.
	4 Dirty, loose or broken earth connection at the generator control box.	Inspect the generator control box wiring and its connections, making sure the latter are clean	and tight. Replace any damaged or broken wiring.
	5 Faulty generator control box.	Have a garage check the control box and	replace or repair parts as necessary.
A single or pair of lamps fail to light	**Cause** **1** Blown fuse.	**Action** Remove the cover from the fuse box and check the fuse controlling the lighting circuit in question. (Check this in the handbook). If necessary, fit a new	fuse, making sure that it is of the correct rating. If the fuse continues to blow, seek advice from a garage, as there is probably a short circuit in the system.
	2 Blown bulbs or loose or dirty bulb contacts.	Remove the lens cover or bulb holder from the lamps concerned. Remove the bulbs and check to see if they are	blown. Make sure the contacts inside the bulb holder are clean and unbroken.

Lighting/electrics

	Cause	Action	
	3 Dirty, loose or broken earth connection.	Check the earth connections at the lamp units, making sure any wires are unbroken and	that their connections are clean and tight. Replace any broken wires.
	4 Dirty, loose or broken connections in the wiring to the switch or between the switch and light units.	Check the wiring to the lighting switch and between the switch and lamps concerned, making sure all connections are clean	and tight. Look for any damaged insulation and breaks in the wires and replace any that are suspect.
	5 Faulty switch.	If everything else is in order, the fault must lie	in the switch, which should be replaced.
All lamps fail to work	**Cause**	**Action**	
	1 Loose, corroded or dirty battery terminals and cable connections, preventing current flow.	Check the cable connections to the battery. If necessary remove them, clean up and replace, having first smeared the battery terminals with petroleum jelly. Tighten the retaining bolts or	screws fully. Check the condition of the earth cable and its connection to the car body. If necessary, disconnect the cable, clean its end and the earth point on the chassis and refit it.
	2 Flat or faulty battery.	Recharge the battery, or start the car using a	pair of jump leads from another car.
	3 Loose, corroded or dirty connections in the wiring to the lighting switch; alternatively, a wire may be broken.	Check the wiring to the lighting switch, making sure that all the connections are clean and tight. Check for	damaged insulation and breaks in the wires and replace any that are suspect.
	4 Faulty main light switch.	If the battery, battery connections and lighting switch wiring all appear to be in order,	the fault must lie in the switch itself, which should be replaced.
With the ignition on, the direction indicators fail to work; nor does the repeater light on the dashboard	**Cause** 1 Blown fuse.	**Action** Remove the cover from the fuse box and check the fuse controlling the indicator circuit (check in the handbook to find the particular fuse). If necessary, fit a new fuse, making sure it is of	the correct rating. If the fuse continues to blow, seek advice from a garage, as there is probably a short circuit somewhere in the system.

	Cause	Action	
	2 Dirty, loose or broken connections in the feed wiring to the indicator switch, from the switch to the flasher unit or from the flasher unit to the indicators.	Inspect the feed wiring to the indicator switch, the flasher unit and the indicators, making sure that all the connections	are clean and tight. Check for damaged insulation or broken wires and replace any which are suspect.
	3 Faulty flasher unit.	Fit a new flasher unit.	
	4 Faulty indicator switch.	Fit a new indicator unit.	
With the ignition on, the repeater light on the dashboard flashes faster or slower than normal or remains illuminated	Cause **1** Blown bulb in one of the indicator units.	Action Operate the indicators, asking a helper to tell you which units are working – if any. Remove the lens cover	or bulb holder from the appropriate unit and check to see if the bulb has blown. If necessary, fit a new bulb.
	2 Dirty, loose or broken wiring connections at one or more of the indicator units.	If the bulb appears to be in good order, check the bulb contacts, making sure that they are clean and unbroken. Check the wiring to the	unit, making sure the connections are clean and tight and replace any damaged or broken wires.
	3 Faulty flasher unit.	If the indicator units themselves are working, the fault lies	with the flasher unit itself, which should be replaced.
With the ignition on, the windscreen wipers remain in the parked position when switched on	Cause **1** Blown fuse.	Action Remove the cover from the fuse box and check the fuse controlling the windscreen wiper circuit (check the handbook to find the fuse). If necessary, fit a	new fuse. If the fuse continues to blow, seek advice from a garage, as the problem is probably a short circuit in the system.
	2 Dirty, loose or broken connections in the wiper wiring circuit.	Check the wiring to the windscreen wiper switch and to the wiper	motor, making sure that all the connections are clean and tight.
	3 Faulty switch.	Fit a new windsceen wiper switch.	
	4 Faulty wiper motor.	Fit a new windscreen wiper motor.	

Reading instruments

Reading instruments

The number and type of warning lights and instruments fitted to the dashboard vary considerably from one make or model to another. As far as the manufacturer is concerned, the only instrument he is legally required to fit is a speedometer. Fortunately, all manufacturers provide more than this, so that you can monitor the car's vital operating systems and spot potential problems before they can develop into major disasters.

Get to know what the normal readings should be on all the warning instruments in your car and scan all of them briefly, but regularly, as you drive. By doing this, you will notice any variation immediately.

Depending on the car, the warning instrument package will include all, or some, of the following.

Ignition warning light
Fitted to all cars, this is a red warning light on the dashboard, which indicates whether or not the battery is being charged by the generator when the engine is running. It comes on as soon as you switch on the ignition, but should go out once the engine has been started.

If the light remains on, or flickers, after the engine has been started and will not go out even if the engine is revved	Cause	Action	
	1 Loose or broken fan belt, preventing the generator from turning.	Check and, if loose, retension the fan belt.	Replace a damaged or broken belt.
	2 Faulty wiring or connection in the charging circuit.	Check the wiring in the charging circuit, making sure all connections are	clean and tight. Replace any wires that show signs of damage.
	3 Faulty generator or control gear, preventing charging current from reaching the battery.	Have a garage or car electrical specialist	check the generator and control gear.

The ignition light remains lit when the engine idles, but goes out when it is revved	Cause	Action	
	1 Low electrolyte level in the battery.	Top up the battery, using distilled or de-ionised water.	
	2 Faulty dynamo or control gear.	Have a garage or car electrical specialist	check the dynamo and control gear.

The ignition light remains lit after the engine has been started and gets brighter as engine speed increases	Cause	Action	
	1 Faulty dynamo control box.	Check, clean and re-connect the earth connections at the control box. If these	appear to be in good condition, fit a new control box.

Oil pressure warning light
Also fitted to all cars, this is usually an amber light that indicates whether or not the oil pump is supplying enough pressure to the lubrication system to push the oil around the engine. It comes on as soon as you turn on the ignition, but goes out once the engine is running.

If the light goes out once the engine has started, but flickers on and off as the car takes a corner	Cause	Action	
	1 Low oil level in the sump, which means that the centrifugal force created by cornering forces the oil away from the end of the oil pick-up pipe momentarily.	Top up the oil level in the sump to the 'full' or 'max' mark on the	dipstick, using the recommended grade of engine oil.
The oil light remains lit after the engine has been started and is running at idling speed, but goes out when the engine is revved	Cause	Action	
	1 Faulty oil pump, or oil pressure switch.	Call in a garage and have the lubrication system checked. Have	any defective components replaced.
The light remains lit after the engine has been started, regardless of engine speed	Cause	Action	
	1 Low oil level in the sump.	Top up the oil level in the sump to the 'full' or 'max' mark on the	dipstick, using the recommended grade of engine oil.
	2 Faulty oil pressure switch.	Fit a new switch.	
	3 Faulty oil pump.	Have a garage check the pump and, if necessary, replace it.	
	4 Worn big end or main bearings.	Consult a garage. In addition to fitting new bearings, it may prove necessary to re-grind the crankshaft if this is	also worn. If this is the case, it may be more economical to replace the engine with a re-conditioned one.
The oil light comes on suddenly when the car is being driven normally in a straight line.	Cause	Action	
	1 Faulty oil pump.	Have a garage check the pump and, if necessary, replace it.	
	2 Failed big end or main bearing.	Consult a garage. In addition to fitting new bearing shells, it may prove necessary to re-grind the crankshaft if	this is also worn. In this case, it may be more economical to replace the engine with a re-conditioned one.

Reading instruments

Water temperature gauge
This shows the engine coolant's temperature

either in Centigrade, or as a simple low/normal/high reading. It is normal for the readings to fluctuate slightly as the thermostat opens and closes to vary the flow of coolant through the radiator.

If the gauge's needle begins to climb steadily above normal, indicating that the engine is over-heating

Cause	Action	
1 Low coolant level, possibly caused by leaks in the cooling system.	Allow the engine to cool and then top up the cooling system with the recommended water/anti-freeze or	water/corrosion inhibitor mixture. Check the system for leaks and repair as necessary.
2 Gaps between radiator fins blocked by dead leaves, insects, or some other obstruction, preventing air flowing through the radiator to carry away excess heat.	Check the radiator and remove any blockages by flushing it through	with a high-pressure hose from the engine side.
3 Faulty radiator pressure cap.	Replace the pressure cap with a new one of the correct rating.	
4 Loose or broken fan belt, which means that the water pump pulley cannot turn.	Check the fan belt and re-tension it, if loose.	Replace a damaged or broken belt.
5 Faulty electric fan (if fitted), preventing cooling air being drawn through the radiator when the car is stationary or being driven at slow speeds.	Check the fan wiring and connections, making sure the latter are clean and tight. If	the wiring is in good condition, replace the fan.
6 Thermostat stuck closed, preventing adequate circulation of coolant to the radiator.	Feel the top and bottom radiator hoses. If the thermostat has stuck in the closed position, the bottom one will be hot and the top one cool. If	so, replace the thermostat, making sure the replacement is of the correct temperature rating.
7 Blockage in the cooling system, stopping circulation of coolant.	Backflush the cooling system with a high-	pressure hose to remove any obstruction.

	Cause	Action	
	8 Ignition timing set incorrectly, or faulty vacuum advance-retard mechanism.	Check and set the ignition timing to the manufacturer's recommendations. Also check the operation of	the vacuum advance-retard mechanism, together with the vacuum pipe connections.
The gauge's needle fails to reach normal, even though the engine has been run for long enough to warm up	**Cause** 1 Extremely low outside temperature extracting too much heat from the coolant as the air passes through the radiator.	**Action** Partially block off the radiator opening, but keep a careful eye on	the temperature, in case the engine starts to overheat.
	2 Thermostat stuck open, so that coolant is circulating continuously, stopping the engine reaching its correct operating temperature.	Feel the top and bottom radiator hoses. If the thermostat is stuck open, neither will be particularly hot. If so,	replace the thermostat, making sure the new one is of the correct temperature rating.
	3 Faulty temperature sensor in the engine, or a defective gauge, giving a false reading.	Check wiring between temperature sensor and the gauge, making sure the connections are clean and tight. If the	wiring is in good order, have a garage check sensor and gauge and replace whichever is at fault.

Ammeter

This supplements the ignition warning light and shows the rate of charge being supplied by the generator to the battery. One half of its face is marked with a + to indicate a positive flow of current; the other half is marked with a - to indicate a battery discharge.

Under normal conditions, the ammeter should show a healthy rate of charge immediately after starting the engine, when the battery will be receiving a high current to replace the energy drawn from it by the starter motor. The needle should then drop back until it is just on the positive side of the central marking. This indicates the battery is receiving a trickle charge.

A very low charging rate, or a discharge, under different engine running conditions are caused by the same faults that lead to the ignition warning light coming on under the same circumstances. A very high charging rate indicates that the generator, or control gear, is faulty. These should be checked by a garage.

Battery condition indicator

Some cars are fitted with a battery condition indicator or voltmeter in place of an ammeter. Instead of showing the rate of charge being received by the battery, this shows the voltage present between the battery terminals. Immediately after starting, this will drop considerably, because the battery's charge is drained substantially by the demands of the starter motor. It will increase as the battery is recharged by the generator.

If the reading remains low – even if the ignition warning light is not activated – have the battery checked by a garage or car electrical specialist. A low reading and the appearance of the warning light means that you are suffering from one of the charging problems described previously. An abnormally high reading indicates that there is a fault in the generator or control gear. Both should be checked by a garage or car electrical specialist.

Driving noise

When the car is being driven, the tyres make a continuous noise as they come into contact with the road surface, regardless of the type of surface	**Cause** 1 Incorrect tyre pressures	**Action** Inflate the tyres to the pressures specified by the manufacturer.
	2 Incorrectly set front wheel alignment.	Have a garage check and realign the front wheels.
When the brake pedal is depressed to apply the brakes, a loud squealing sound comes from the brakes themselves	**Cause** 1 Worn disc pad retaining pins, or worn brake discs. 2 Faulty or missing anti-squeal shims in disc brakes, or faulty shoe retaining clips in drum brakes.	**Action** Have a garage inspect the disc brake assemblies.
	3 A build-up of brake lining dust in the calipers or brake drums.	Have a garage clean the dust from the calipers and drums as necessary.
Knocking sounds come from beneath the car as it is driven along, particularly when travelling over rough surfaces	**Cause** 1 Worn or perished rubber bushes at the ends of leaf springs, dampers, anti-roll bars or suspension arms, allowing the components to move about on their mountings. 2 Worn leaf spring shackles or shackle pins. 3 Loose or worn U-bolts holding the rear axle to its springs. 4 Slack upper mounting nuts on a MacPherson strut suspension unit. 5 Broken spring.	**Action** All these jobs should be handled by a garage.
On rear-wheel-drive cars, a thumping noise comes from the area of the back axle as the car is accelerated	**Cause** 1 Softened rear springs or worn dampers allowing the axle to hit the bump stops.	**Action** These should be replaced by a garage.

	Cause	Action	
A constant whine comes from the axle as the car is driven, rising in pitch as the car's speed increases	**Cause** 1 Low oil level in the axle.	**Action** Top up the axle with the recommended grade of oil.	
	2 Worn or damaged gears in the axle.	Consult a garage. It may be more economical to replace the entire axle	with a reconditioned one.
With the engine running, a noise comes from the clutch when the pedal is released	**Cause** 1 Incorrectly adjusted clutch operating linkage.	**Action** Check and adjust the clutch operating linkage in accordance with the	manufacturer's instructions.
With the engine running, a noise comes from the clutch when the pedal is depressed, but disappears when it is released	**Cause** 1 Worn or damaged clutch release bearing, or a dry flywheel spigot bearing.	**Action** Have a garage check the clutch and either replace the clutch	release bearing, or lubricate or replace the flywheel spigot bearing.
With the engine running, there is a thud as the clutch pedal is released after engaging gear	**Cause** 1 Excessive freeplay at the axle due to wear or some other fault.	**Action** Consult a garage. It may be more economical to	replace the axle with a reconditioned one.
With the engine running, the gear lever makes a rattling or buzzing sound	**Cause** 1 Gear lever loose in its mounting, or the gear lever damper (if fitted) may be loose or missing. 2 The remote control linkage connecting the lever to the gearbox is worn.	**Action** Consult a garage.	
With the car stationary and the engine running, a grinding noise can be heard as you try to engage gear	**Cause** 1 The engine idle speed is set too high.	**Action** Reset the idle speed in accordance with the	manufacturer's instructions.
When the car is being driven, there is a grinding noise from the gearbox as you attempt to change gear	**Cause** 1 Faulty clutch assembly, or worn synchromesh or bearings in the gearbox.	**Action** Consult a garage and have the clutch and gearbox checked. If necessary, have the clutch repaired. In some cases, it may be more	economical to replace the gearbox with a reconditioned one, rather than attempting to repair it.

Tyre wear faults

The tyres on your car are your only contact with the road. To to get the best from them, they must be properly looked after. There is nothing you can do to stop them wearing out, but, with care you can ensure that they give the maximum amount of of trouble-free, safe motoring.

Maintaining your tyres

To prolong the life of your tyres, you should always make sure that you check their pressures regularly and maintain them at the figures given in your owner's handbook.

Keeping the tyres at their specified pressures is essential if they are to do their twin jobs of supporting the car's weight and maintaining their shape, so that the full width of the tread is in contact with the road surface. If they are consistently over- or under-inflated, the tread will wear unevenly, producing less grip and reducing the tyre's useful life. Remember that tyre manufacturers often specify higher tyre pressures for prolonged high-speed driving, for towing and when carrying a full load.

Always wash the tyres whenever you wash the car to lessen the risk of harmful substances building up on them and damaging the rubber. Petrol, oil and tar, for instance, should be removed as soon as possible. Inspect the tyres carefully and remove any sharp objects which may have wedged themselves between the tread blocks before they have a chance to puncture the casing.

Driving style

How you drive can also considerable affect the way the tyres will wear. Tyre-spinning starts, hard cornering and heavy braking will all wear the tyre tread down very quickly and make tyre replacement necessary much earlier than normal. Bumping into the kerb or running up over it when parking will also severely damage the tyre sidewalls.

If a tyre is punctured, never continue to drive on it. Stop at once and replace it with the spare wheel. If you do this, you should be able to salvage the tyre with a simple repair, but driving for only a short distance on a flat tyre is disastrous. It will damage the sidewalls and generate a lot of heat inside the tyre. This will soften and weaken the rubber and the tyre may start to lose its tread or physically come apart.

New tyres need special treatment to break them in. Keep your speed down to below 50mph (80kph) for the first 50 miles (80km) or so. Drive carefully – not harshly – and keep the car load well below maximum capacity. Otherwise your new tyre may have an extremely limited working life. Remember, tyres are very expensive.

Inspecting the tyres

Regular inspection of the tyres – and the wheels – is essential if they are to be kept in good condition. Check them at least every two weeks on the car and remove them every few months for a thorough examination.

Begin by checking the tyre pressures, making sure that they are all correct (including that of the spare wheel). It is worth investing in your own pressure gauge, since the gauges on garage forecourts may not

If the tyre pressure is constantly too high, only the centre area of the tread will be in proper contact with the road and so will be excessively worn. If the tyre is under-inflated, both sides of the tread area will be worn. This is because there is not enough pressure in the tyre to stop the force on the sidewalls pushing the tread into a concave shape.

always be totally accurate due to years of misuse. If necessary, pump up the tyres to their correct pressures.

Check the tread for signs of wear and for any cuts, nicks or other physical damage that might cause tyre failure. Prise out any sharp objects, such as stones or road chippings, that may have lodged between the tread blocks. If any appear to be deeply embedded, monitor the pressure in the affected tyre. If this appears to drop relatively quickly, have the tyre checked for a puncture.

If a tyre appears to lose pressure faster than the others

A split like this in the tyre sidewall can easily be caused by mounting a curb, or hitting a large pothole. Even a small crack in the sidewall can be dangerous, as it can hide more extensive damage to the interior carcass of the tyre.

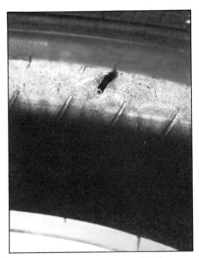

If the tread is penetrated by a foreign object, such as a nail, the tyre may not immediately deflate but extensive damage still could be caused to its interior. Check tyres regularly and remove any foreign body – however small – that is trapped in the tread.

Wear down one side of the tyre tread can be caused by a number of faults. If it is as bad as this, it is probably due to a fault in the steering or suspension, which has forced the tyre out of alignment with the direction in which the car is travelling. The alternative is continual hard cornering, which throws the car's weight on one edge of the tyre.

for no apparent cause, also have it checked. The pressure loss may be due to a faulty valve, a tiny puncture or a poor seal with the wheel rim.

Check the sidewalls for scuff marks, bulges or other damage. Scuff marks can result from a collision with the kerb, or rubbing on the bodywork or steering components. If these are present, there could be more serious damage inside the tyre, so you should have the tyre checked. If there is obvious signs of serious damage, such as the fabric showing through or bulges, the tyre must be replaced immediately.

Inspect the wheel rim for dents or buckling, which could damage the tyre or break the seal between tyre and trim. A damaged wheel rim also offers a visual clue to potential internal tyre damage.

Check the tread depth, preferably with a proper depth gauge. If this is less than the legal requirement, you must replace the tyre at once.

Identifying the cause of tyre wear

Unusual or uneven wear patterns on the tyres are often clues to the existence of mechanical or driving problems, which should be corrected before they have serious effects.

Prolonged driving with over-inflated tyres will show itself as a patch worn down the centre of the tyre tread. Driving with under-inflated tyres will wear strips along the edges of the tread, but leave the centre

relatively untouched. Extra heat may also be generated inside the tyre and the tread may separate from the carcass as a result.

Spinning the tyres as you accelerate away will throw off tread rubber and also generate excessive heat inside the tyre, with subsequent weakening of the rubber. Hard cornering will throw the majority of the car's weight on to the shoulders of the tyres, which will wear quickly as a result, while heavy braking will produce flat spots on the tread. In severe cases, heavy braking may even cause the tyre to wear through to the fabric below the tread.

Any uneven tread wear patterns indicate a problem with the steering or suspension alignment, or possibly some form of braking defect. Such problems should be investigated and put right by a garage.

Problem solving

Knowing why a breakdown occurs is one thing, but being able to do something about it is quite another. Having isolated the component, or components, concerned, what do you do next? Knowing, for instance, that your car will not start because the starter motor is jammed is all very well in theory, but is of little practical use to you if you do not know the easiest way to free it.

This section is the answer to this problem. It itemizes all the important components and systems and shows you how to correct basic faults in them, or when to replace defective items with new ones, getting you back on to the road with the minimum of fuss and in the least possible time. It shows you not only how to make permanent repairs; it is full of useful hints, tips and tricks of the trade, enabling you to make a temporary repair that will get you home, or to a garage, where a permanent repair can be made.

Isolating the problem

In many instances, dealing with a breakdown can be a reasonably simple matter once you have located the problem's cause. Knowing where to look to find particular components is obviously important, so finding this out and applying the information to your own vehicle is extremely valuable.

You will find your owner's handbook a mine of useful information. It will tell you, for instance, not only where the fuses are located, but their ratings and the circuits they control; the spark plug types and gap; the contact breaker points gap; the recommended grade of oil to use and the sump capacity; the capacity of the cooling system and the recommended anti-freeze mixture; and the bulb types and ratings for all lights. All of this information is essential to the efficient operation of your car and will help you cure any faults that may arise.

If you bought your car second-hand and there was no handbook with it, try and obtain one from a local main dealer. If it is no longer available, you can buy a specialist workshop manual, though these can be too technical for the novice.

The importance of maintenance

Breakdowns are most frequently caused by poor maintenance, so make sure that you inspect all of the car's essential systems regularly and follow the maintenance schedule given in your handbook or manual. Carry out all the necessary checks and clean or replace the items specified at the required intervals, or get a garage to do it for you. A weekly check on the tyres, oil and coolant levels, the battery electrolyte level, brake fluid level and lights can save you considerable trouble. When it comes to cars, remember that 'a stitch in time saves nine'!

Take tyres, for example. Punctures can be caused by sharp stones lodging between the blocks of the tyre tread and working their way through the carcass. If you check your tyres regularly, you can remove any sharp objects before they have the chance to do any damage. Ensuring the engine has an adequate supply of oil will keep everything moving smoothly. A lack of oil – or very old oil, which has lost much of its lubricating properties through picking up tiny metal fragments on its journey around the engine – can

lead to a build up of friction between the engine's moving parts. This generates heat and can cause a great deal of damage.

Similarly, the coolant in water-cooled engines must be kept at the specified level to prevent engine overheating. Check the cooling system regularly for leaks – these can occur in many places in the system, allowing coolant to escape and the level in the system to drop. The hoses between the radiator and engine and the engine and heater are particularly vulnerable. With age, these may become softened, or perished, or their retaining clips may have been over-tightened and be cutting into the rubber as a result. Cracks may occur, or the hoses may be chafing as a result of contact with parts of the engine. They can even melt if they touch a hot manifold.

Hose replacement is simple. If you do not have a spare hose to hand – if one springs a leak while you are on the road, for example – you can make a temporary 'get you home' repair. Bind the damaged area with insulating tape – this is something you should always carry in your tool kit – or apply a puncture repair patch. If the damage is at the end of the hose, you may be able to trim this portion off and refit the rest of the hose.

Whatever you do, never drive on with an over-heating engine, as this can result in serious damage. Stop, allow the engine to cool down, make the repair and top up the system before proceeding.

Eletrical maintenance

Looking after the car's battery is

extremely important as well, since this provides the power required to turn the engine over when you start it, to feed the ignition system and to operate ancillary systems, such as lights, horn, windscreen wipers and car radio. To work properly, the battery must be kept topped up with distilled or de-ionised water, so that the level of the electrolyte inside the battery is .always just above the tops of the lead plates in each cell. If the level of electrolyte is allowed to fall below this, the battery's output will suffer in the short term. In the long term, the battery can be damaged permanently.

Starting the car probably puts the greatest strain on the battery, since a large amount of current is drawn off by the starer motor. Unless the battery is in tip-top condition, it will not be able to provide this output for very long. If any of the components of the ignition system are not in good working order, so that the engine is reluctant to fire, prolonged use of the starter is quite likely to drain the battery as a result.

This is particularly likely to occur in cold weather, when the battery is unlikely to be in peak condition in any case. So it is in your own interest to keep both the battery and ignition system – points, spark plugs and leads – in a good state of maintenance and properly adjusted to ensure speedy starting.

If a battery is extremely old, it may fail to hold its charge. In such a case, replace it. If it is in reasonable overall condition and simply flattened – by . excessive use of the starter, say, or by accidentally leaving the lights on throughout the night –

you should usually be able to re-charge it with a proprietary battery charger.

Such chargers are inexpensive. They are merely simple transformers, which, when connected to the mains, pass an electrical current back through the battery in the reverse direction to normal current flow. Although, in some cases, it is possible to charge the battery while it is still connected up and in its normal position in the engine bay, it is wisest to remove it – or at least to disconnect it – to avoid the risk of accidentally damaging any of the electrical fittings during the charging process.

In use, the battery is kept charged by the car's generator. This is either a dynamo, or, on modern cars, an alternator. Both types of generator are driven by a rubber belt from a pulley on the end of the crankshaft. This is the danger spot here. To ensure the generator is driven at the right speed, the belt must be tensioned correctly, as, if it slips, the output of charging current will be erratic. In such a case, the battery would soon be drained of energy, causing starting problems and trouble in other parts of the electrical system.

The tension is normally adjusted by pivotting the generator closer to the engine, or further away from it. Some cars may be fitted with a screw tensioner, or a special type of split pulley, which increases the tension as its two halves are pulled together.

The drive belt itself is made from fabric-reinforced rubber. Since it is constantly spinning at high speed, it suffers considerable wear and tear.

Such belts are prone to stretch, so reducing their tension, and suffer from nicks and cuts. These stretch the belt even more and may even lead to it fracturing completely. Thus, the state of the belt should be checked regularly.

It is wise to carry a spare fan belt of the correct size in the car in case of emergency, but, if you are in difficulties, a nylon stocking or pair of tights can be tied around the pulleys to get you home, or to a garage. In common with all temporary repairs, though, this should be made good at the earliest opportunity. Never rely on a temporary repair for longer than necessary.

As well as the problems described above, many breakdowns are caused by problems elsewhere in the ignition system. For this reason, it is important to make sure that all the wiring connections between the various ignition components are clean and tight. Because the components are inter-related, a fault can be traced reasonably simply, provided you approach the problem methodically and logically, isolating the point where the current ceases to flow.

These examples demonstrate that the need to know your way round the components and systems of your car is of obvious importance in enabling you to find the cause of any problem quickly. By familiarizing yourself with the detailed information in the following section, you will find that you waste the least possible amount of time in curing any fault and getting your car back on the road and moving again.

Battery maintenance

Battery condition

If your car is fitted with a battery condition indicator, you can check its condition instantly. If not, a voltmeter, or a multimeter with voltmeter function, can be used. The best time to test the battery is just after it has been charged, or after the car has been running. Readings taken immediately after the battery has been topped-up are inaccurate.

Connect the meter to the terminals according to the manufacturer's instructions and check the reading – this should be 12 to 13 volts. If the reading is low, some of the cells are faulty, and the battery will not perform properly.

You can test the battery with a hydrometer. This measures the specific gravity – or density – of the electrolyte. A hydrometer is a type of syringe, fitted with a rubber bulb and containing a weighted float. This is marked with a graduated scale, usually reading from 1.10 to 1.30. In a fully-charged battery, the reading should be between 1.270 and 1.290, which means that the electrolyte is at least 1.270 times heavier than water.

Take a reading from each cell. If they are all low – 1.200, for instance – then the battery needs charging. If any one reading is significantly lower than the others, that cell is faulty. Be careful not to spill electrolyte on your skin or on the car bodywork.

Charging the battery

If the battery is flat for whatever reason, it will need recharging. Before doing this, check the electrolyte level and top it up if necessary. Make sure that your battery charger's output is set to

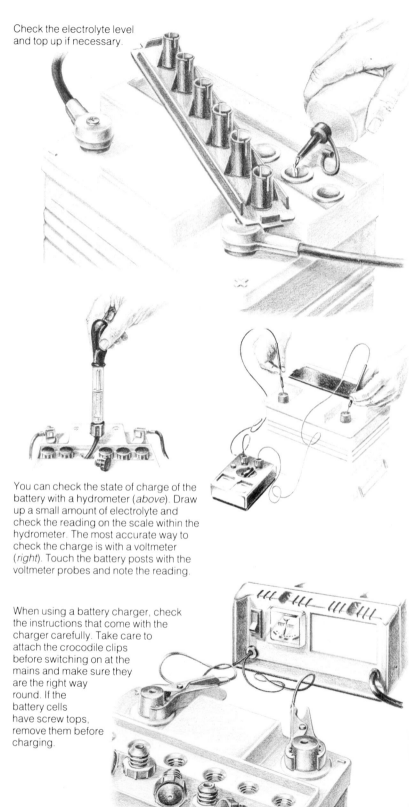

Check the electrolyte level and top up if necessary.

You can check the state of charge of the battery with a hydrometer (*above*). Draw up a small amount of electrolyte and check the reading on the scale within the hydrometer. The most accurate way to check the charge is with a voltmeter (*right*). Touch the battery posts with the voltmeter probes and note the reading.

When using a battery charger, check the instructions that come with the charger carefully. Take care to attach the crocodile clips before switching on at the mains and make sure they are the right way round. If the battery cells have screw tops, remove them before charging.

suit the battery – normally it should be 12 volts – and connect the charger's clips to the battery terminals. Ensure the clips are the correct way round. Plug the charger into the mains and switch on.

It takes between 12 and 18 hours to fully charge a flat battery. When the charger's meter indicates the battery is fully charged, turn off the mains, remove the plug and disconnect the charger leads, taking care not to cause a spark.

Maintaining your battery

To keep your battery operating at peak efficiency, you should check the electrolyte level at least once a month, unless your battery is sealed-for-life and thus requires no topping-up.

With translucent batteries, the electrolyte level is checked against a mark on the side of the battery; otherwise the cell caps, or trough cover, must be removed. In this case, look inside each cell and check that the fluid is just above the plates. If it is low, top up with distilled water. Never use tap water.

After topping-up, wipe the surface of the battery dry and replace the caps or trough, making sure that their vent holes are clear. These allow the gas produced by the battery to escape. This is explosive, so never bring a naked flame near the battery.

Check that your battery is mounted securely and that there are no leaks. Also check the terminals – if these are not clean and tight, you will experience starting problems. Disconnect both terminals every six months and clean them back to shiny metal with a wire brush. After reconnecting, smear them with

Remove a cup-type terminal by undoing the retaining screw. Pull off the terminal by gently turning it from side to side.

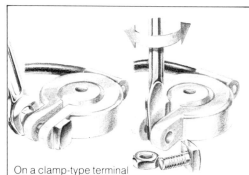

On a clamp-type terminal slacken the bolt. If it is difficult to remove, gently prise the clamp open with a screwdriver.

Remove any deposits from the inside of the cup with a thin file or emery paper.

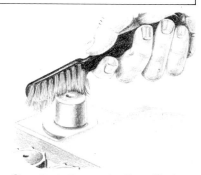

Clean the battery posts with a stiff wire brush.

If a clamp-type terminal is loose on the battery post, wrap the post with aluminium kitchen foil to get a tighter fit. If a screw hole in the post no longer holds the screw tightly, put a small piece of solder into the hole.

petroleum jelly to prevent oxidization.

Whatever job you are carrying out on your battery, never short out the terminals. It could cause an explosion.

Before refitting the terminals, smear the battery posts with petroleum jelly.

Fan belt maintenance

Checking the fan belt

You should check the tension and condition of the fan belt at least once a month. Ensure the ignition is off when working in the engine bay.

Check the tension on the belt's longest run between two pulleys. Hold a ruler against the belt to determine the midway point and push against the belt. Note how far it moves. The exact amount should be specified in your handbook, but generally it should be about ½in (13mm). If it is more or less, the belt requires adjustment. An over-tightened belt can damage the water pump and generator bearings.

Use a spanner on the crankshaft pulley to manually turn the engine over. Look carefully at the belt and feel for cracks or splits. Take care not to trap your fingers. To make a thorough, complete check, however, you must remove the belt completely. By bending it at a sharp angle, any defect will become apparent.

Adjusting the fan belt

All dynamos and alternators are secured to the engine by a bracket on which they pivot. A slotted strap at the top of the generator is provided for adjustment.

Slacken the two lower pivot bolts and then the bolt securing the slotted strap. If the belt is loose, place a piece of wood between the generator body and the engine block and gently lever the generator away from the engine until the correct tension has been established. Tighten the slotted strap bolts and re-check the tension. Tighten the two lower pivot bolts. If the belt is too tight,

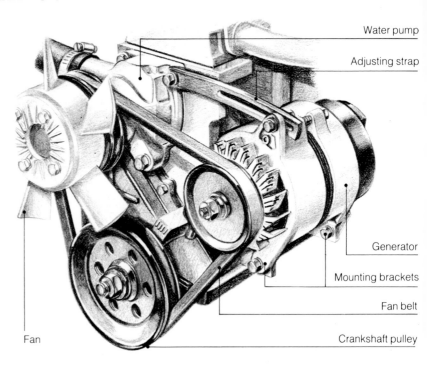

Water pump

Adjusting strap

Generator

Mounting brackets

Fan belt

Crankshaft pulley

Fan

Always check the tension of the fan belt along the longest run between two pulleys. If this is not possible, check it between two other pulleys, making an allowance for the shorter run of the belt.

Any splits or cracks in the fan belt will be more obvious if you bend the belt into a tight loop, or twist it. The belt will have to be removed completely to make these checks.

follow the same procedure, but gradually push the generator towards the engine.

Some cars have an idler wheel with its own slotted adjusting strap. Retension the belt following the same procedure.

Replacing a fan belt

To remove the old fan belt, slacken all the bolts on the generator and push it towards the engine as far as it will go. Pull the belt off the topmost pulley and then remove it from the crankshaft and water pump pulleys.

If the engine is transverse-mounted, it may be necessary to feed the belt through the fan blades in order to remove it. On some models, you must also remove the cowling that shrouds the belt.

When fitting a new belt, always choose the type the manufacturer has specified for the car, and check its size against the old belt. Before fitting examine the grooves of the pulleys. They should be clean and free from any signs of damage. Check that the pulleys are all in line. If not, the generator has probably been wrongly fitted.

Place the new belt over the fan and locate it in the grooves of the other pulleys. If the belt cannot be pushed easily on to the water pump pulley, feed it on by rotating the pulley with the fan, if attached, or with a spanner. Once the belt has been fitted, check that it is sitting correctly on all the pulleys and is not twisted.

Adjust the tension of the new belt as described previously. After about 200 miles (321km), re-check the tension.

Points to remember

Always make sure that your fan belt is kept dry and free from oil. Never lubricate a squeaking belt. This will only cure the squeak temporarily; the belt will become swollen or sticky and eventually fail.

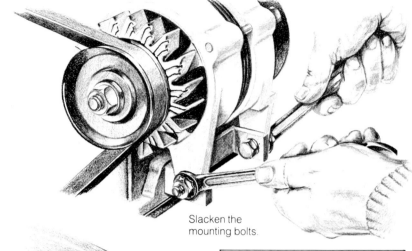

Slacken the mounting bolts.

Slacken the bolt on the adjusting strap.

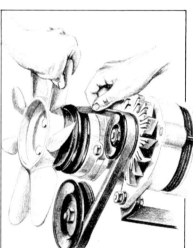

If you have trouble fitting a new fan belt over its pulleys, or the fan and water pump pulley are covered by a shroud, you can feed the belt on to the pulley by rotating it. If the fan is attached to the pulley, turn the pulley with this. If the pulley does not have the fan attached, turn it with a spanner on the retaining bolt.

Tension the belt by levering the generator away from the engine block, a hammer handle is the ideal tool, and tightening the bolt on the adjusting strap. Recheck the tension and, if it is correct, tighten the mounting bolts.

Cooling system maintenance/1

Checking the radiator

You should check the coolant level in your radiator once a week and always before starting a long journey. Check the water hoses regularly as well. With the engine cold, squeeze each hose along its length, looking for evidence of splitting, perishing, or cracking. Pay particular attention to curves and connections. Each hose should feel firm. If one feels soft, or if there are signs of swelling, the inner reinforcing fabric is damaged. This means that the hose will soon burst, or implode, under pressure, causing a blockage. Check that all hose clips are secure at the same time.

If the coolant needs continual topping up, check the system for leaks. These are not always easy to spot, since they may occur

only when the engine is running and the system is pressurized. Tell-tale signs are rust-coloured stains on metalwork, patches of damp on the road under specific areas of the engine, or splashes of anti-freeze in the engine bay.

Draining the system

The cooling system should be drained completely every two or three years. You will also need to drain some coolant to

add anti-freeze. With a non-sealed system, drain the coolant with the engine cold by unscrewing the radiator drain plug, or by removing the bottom hose from the radiator. Remove the radiator cap to speed up the process. After refilling the system, check that the heater blows out hot air. If not, there is an air lock in the system. Keep the heater control to hot and disconnect the bottom hose from

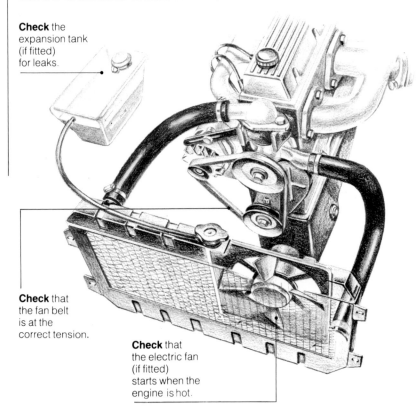

Check the expansion tank (if fitted) for leaks.

Check that the fan belt is at the correct tension.

Check that the electric fan (if fitted) starts when the engine is hot.

CHECK THE WATER PUMP

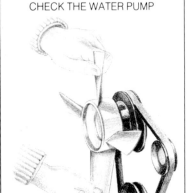

You can check the bearings in the water pump by gripping the top and bottom blades of the fan. Try to rock them backward and forward. If you feel any movement in the pulley, the water pump bearings are worn and the unit should be replaced. If the pump does not have a fan attached, carry out the test by gripping the pulley.

CHECK THE RADIATOR CAP

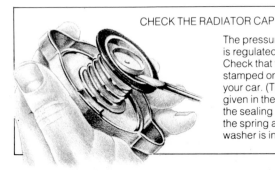

The pressure in the cooling system is regulated by the radiator cap. Check that the temperature rating, stamped on the cap, is correct for your car. (The correct figure will be given in the handbook). Check that the sealing ring moves freely against the spring and that the rubber washer is in good condition.

the engine, placing a container beneath it. Run the engine until it is warm, letting the coolant flow until all the air bubbles are expelled.

With a sealed system, not only must the engine be cold, but the heater control switched to hot before the system can be drained. Follow the same basic procedure, but loosen all the bleed screws on the hose and connections. When refilling, raise the car slightly on axle stands, so the top of the radiator is the highest point in the system. Pour coolant into the expansion bottle to about 25mm (1in) above the full line. Fill the radiator. After running the engine until it is hot, tighten the bleed screws and bleed the system, topping up after completing this.

Topping up

To top up the radiator, remove the cap and check the coolant level. If the engine has been running, take great care when removing the cap. Hot coolant under pressure may spurt out, so wrap a rag around the cap to protect you while you undo it.

The coolant level should be just below the bottom of the filler neck. If not, top up with water. If the radiator needs frequent topping up, or if the coolant level drops suddenly, consult a garage, but, before doing this, check the system for leaks and check the thermostat (see p.114). With a fully-sealed system, top up the expansion bottle to the level indicated.

Adding anti-freeze

Most garages will advise you to use a good quality anti-freeze in the cooling system all the year round. Anti-freeze does not only protect the engine in cold weather; it will also help stop the system becoming blocked. Dilute the neat anti-freeze as specified by the manufacturer – some recommend a 60/40 mix of water to anti-freeze and others a

If the engine has been running, always take care when removing the radiator cap. Wrap a rag around it, release it to the first stop and allow any pressure to escape before removing it.

50/50 one. Always use the anti-freeze recommended for your engine.

Remember, too, that anti-freeze has a lower viscosity than water and can escape through the tiniest of gaps. Whenever you add anti-freeze, run the engine until warm and then check for leaks.

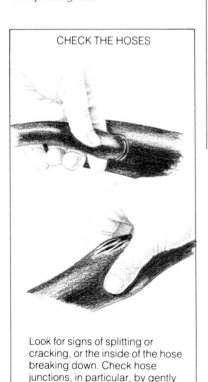

CHECK THE HOSES

Look for signs of splitting or cracking, or the inside of the hose breaking down. Check hose junctions, in particular, by gently pulling on one of the hoses.

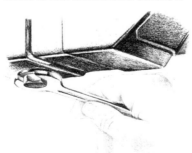

To drain the radiator, take off the cap and release the drain plug or tap at the bottom of the radiator. As this is exposed to road grime, you may find that the tap or plug is corroded and difficult to free. Take great care not to apply excessive force, as this could break the plug or tap away.

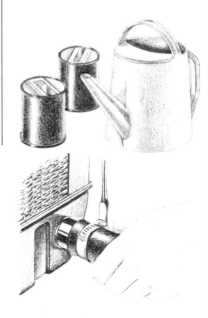

If you find the drain plug or tap difficult to undo, you can drain the radiator by removing the bottom hose. Release the clip and gently pull the hose off the radiator pipe. If the hose sticks, try twisting it gently at the same time as you pull it.

Cooling system maintenance/2

Replacing water hoses

Water hoses weaken with age and engine movement. Since a burst hose causes rapid overheating, which could damage the engine seriously, all hoses should be checked regularly and replaced, if defective. Make sure that you buy replacements of the correct size and shape.

After draining the cooling system (see p.112), unscrew the hose clips and slide them away from their connecting stubs. If the hose is stubborn, cut it off the stubs with a sharp knife.

Metal stubs corrode with age. Clean them with a wire brush. Replace old clips, preferably with worm-drive rather than wire ones, as the former have a larger contact area and are less likely to cut into the rubber. Gently work the hoses on to the stubs, smearing a little washing-up liquid inside them to make them slide on easily.

Tighten the clips, refill the cooling system and start the engine. Check for leaks once the engine has warmed up.

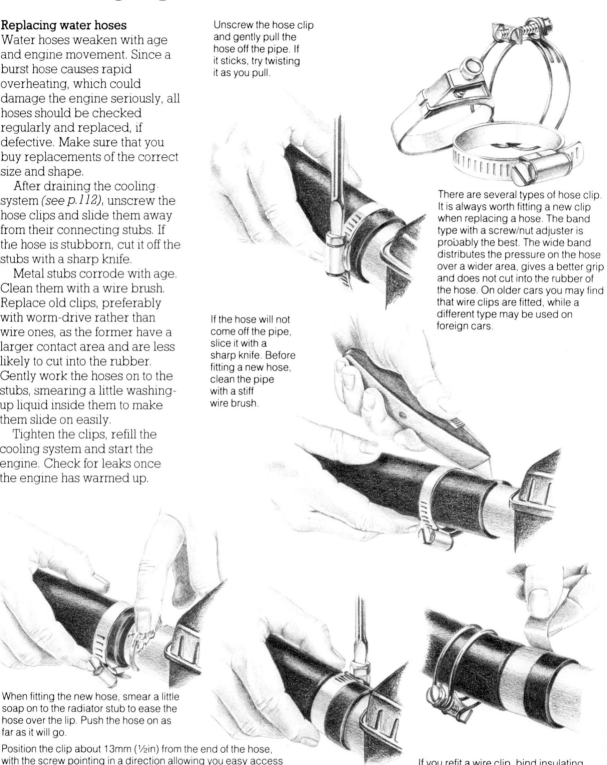

Unscrew the hose clip and gently pull the hose off the pipe. If it sticks, try twisting it as you pull.

There are several types of hose clip. It is always worth fitting a new clip when replacing a hose. The band type with a screw/nut adjuster is probably the best. The wide band distributes the pressure on the hose over a wider area, gives a better grip and does not cut into the rubber of the hose. On older cars you may find that wire clips are fitted, while a different type may be used on foreign cars.

If the hose will not come off the pipe, slice it with a sharp knife. Before fitting a new hose, clean the pipe with a stiff wire brush.

When fitting the new hose, smear a little soap on to the radiator stub to ease the hose over the lip. Push the hose on as far as it will go.

Position the clip about 13mm (½in) from the end of the hose, with the screw pointing in a direction allowing you easy access to do it up or to unscrew it. Tighten the clip to make it secure.

If you refit a wire clip, bind insulating tape around the hose to protect it.

Removing the thermostat

A common cause of overheating is a thermostat that has stuck closed. If a car has overheated badly, removing the thermostat is an effective emergency measure. This can be only temporary, however; the thermostat must be replaced, or the fault rectified, as soon as possible.

On most engines, the thermostat is housed on top of the cylinder head at the front. The top radiator hose usually leads straight into it. Before removing the thermostat, drain about two pints of coolant from the system. Remove the hose clip and pull off the hose. Undo the nuts or bolts holding the thermostat housing in place, unscrewing them alternately a little at a time to avoid distorting

the housing. Pull off the housing – if it sticks, tap it sharply with a piece of wood.

Lift out the thermostat and clean all traces of old gasket from the housing and its mating face on the engine, blocking the opening with rag. Fit a new gasket *(see p.136)* and refit the thermostat, making sure it is the right way around. Look for the marks saying 'front' or 'rad', or the arrow which should point towards the radiator.

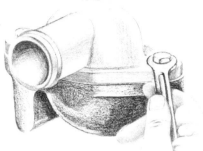

Undo the retaining nuts or bolts and lift off the thermostat housing.

Lift off the gasket. Fit a new one.

Checking the thermostat

You can carry out a spot check to see whether the thermostat is operating properly or not by feeling the radiator, or top radiator hose, after starting the engine from cold. Either of the two should stay cool for a few minutes and then warm up quickly. If the process is gradual, the thermostat is stuck open; if it is extremely slow – and the engine overheats – the thermostat is failing to open.

To check fully whether or not the thermostat is operating correctly, suspend it in a pan of heated water. When the water is within three to four degrees of the operating temperature normally stamped on the thermostat, it should open. When the thermosat is removed from the water and allowed to cool, it should close.

Suspend the thermostat in a pan of water and heat to the temperature at which the thermostat should open. (Check this in the handbook).

The thermostat should remain closed (*left*) to within two or three degrees of its opening temperature, when it will begin to open (*right*).

Lift the thermostat out of its housing and check to see.it is working correctly.

Before refitting, clean all traces of the old gasket from the engine block and the thermostat housing. Stuff a rag into the opening to stop bits of gasket getting into the cooling system.

Changing the air filter

The air filter's main job is to eliminate dirt to ensure that clean air is sucked into the carburettor. If the filter is dirty or choked, the carburettor mixture will be contaminated, causing the engine to run roughly and increasing fuel consumption.

On many cars, however, the air cleaner assembly has a second purpose as well. A hose

Filter casing

Filter element

Mounting bolt

Summer/winter flap

Fresh air intake

Hot air intake

Breather hose from engine

connected to the rocker cover, cam cover or engine block allows crankcase fumes to be recirculated through the system and passed out through the exhaust.

Types of filter
There are three types of air filter. Most modern cars have a replaceable paper filter fitted inside a metal or plastic pan, but some older models have an oil-bath, or wire gauze, filter. Both of these can be removed for cleaning. Whichever type of filter is fitted, it should be

checked every six months, or 6,000 miles (9,600km), and cleaned or replaced as necessary.

Replacing a paper filter
A paper filter can usually be lifted out without removing the air cleaner assembly from the carburettor. On metal assemblies, the top is held in place by a centre bolt, or wing nut. With the plastic type, the top is fixed with self-tapping screws

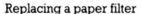

Filters are of different shapes and mounted in different positions, depending on the type of carburettor fitted.

The paper filter element, fitted to most modern cars, will be the same shape as the filter casing. If the filter is round and has a side intake, only one part of the filter will become dirty. It can be turned around so that a clean part of the filter faces the intake.

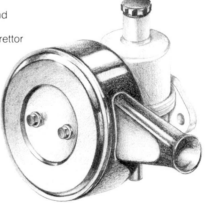

and sealed around the edge by a tight-fitting rim.

Remove the screws and look for an arrow on the cover. This indicates where the screwdriver should be inserted to prise it off. Do not try and prise it off elsewhere, or the plastic may crack.

If the cleaner assembly has a side spout, only one side of the element should be dirty. If the rest of the element is not choked with dirt, you can rotate it to ensure a clean section opposes the intake spout. If the filter is dirty overall, as is inevitable with a cylindrical air cleaner housing, a new filter must be fitted.

Always fit the replacement element specified for your car. Fitting the wrong type could upset the carburettor mixture by altering the air flow.

Cleaning other types of filter

A wire-gauze filter should be bathed in petrol and then allowed to dry. After this, a light coating of oil should generally be applied, but, if in doubt, consult your handbook.

With the oil-bath type, the whole of the assembly must be removed from the carburettor, thoroughly washed in petrol, refitted and then filled with oil.

If the air filter assembly has a rubber 'breather' hose from the engine, you may find a white, sticky substance is present, which can clog the element. This is caused by condensation mixing with oil vapour, and is a particular problem if the oil has not been changed for some time, or the car never has the opportunity to warm up thoroughly. The filter element must be replaced, the filter housing cleaned with petrol and the hose cleaned as well.

Undo the retaining nut or bolt on the top of the casing and lift off the filter lid.

If the filter casing is made of plastic, the lid may be held on by self-tapping screws and sealed around the edge by a tight-fitting rim. Once the screws have been removed, the lid is prised off with a flat-bladed screwdriver. There will be a mark on the lid and on the casing where the screwdriver should be inserted. Align these marks when replacing the lid.

Lift out the filter element and check that it is not clogged with dirt. If it is, replace it. The filter casing may be held to the carburettor by the bolt that retains the lid or by nuts on top of the carburettor. To remove it, undo the nuts, being very careful not to drop any down the mouth of the carburettor.

The casing may have a retaining stay attached to the side. This is either bolted on or is pressed on with a rubber plug which is levered off.

The breather pipe from the engine is attached to the underside of the casing and can be pulled off. Remember to re-attach it when replacing the filter casing.

Checking for fuel flow

A fault in the fuel system will impair engine performance at the least, or at worst, stop the engine completely. While the carburettor itself is a complex piece of equipment – any work on it should be carried out by a garage – there are basic checks and maintenance that you can carry out to ensure that problems do not suddenly arise.

The first component you should check is the air cleaner assembly *(see p.116)*. It is easily identifiable, being the highest point of the engine, and shaped rather like a frying pan. You should check the carburettor area over by eye, looking for signs of fuel leakage, or weeping from a gasket. The tell-tale signs of this are light brown staining on the carburettor body.

Operate the throttle and choke linkage to make sure that they are both working smoothly and opening and closing the throttle and choke flaps to their full extent. If the carburettor is fitted with an automatic choke, start the engine and check that the top flap is in the closed position. As the engine warms up, the flap should gradually move to an upright position.

Checking for fuel

If the engine splutters and coughs or you find it difficult to start, the problem could be caused by fuel not reaching the carburettor. With the engine switched off, disconnect the fuel pipe leading into the carburettor. Do not smoke when carrying out this test and take care that no fuel falls on to hot engine components. Hold the end of the pipe over a clean jar and ask a helper to turn the engine over with the ignition. Fuel should spurt from the pipe.

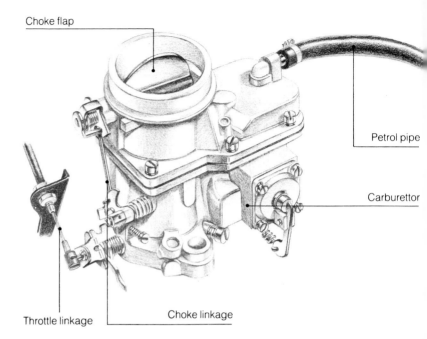

Choke flap

Petrol pipe

Carburettor

Choke linkage

Throttle linkage

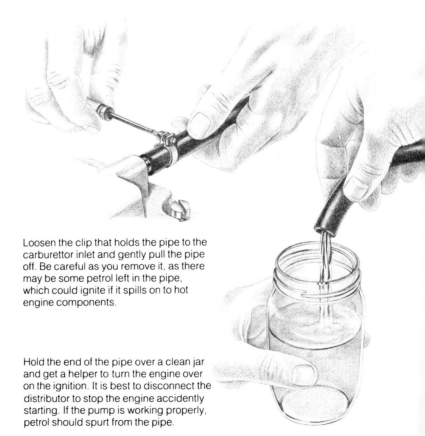

Loosen the clip that holds the pipe to the carburettor inlet and gently pull the pipe off. Be careful as you remove it, as there may be some petrol left in the pipe, which could ignite if it spills on to hot engine components.

Hold the end of the pipe over a clean jar and get a helper to turn the engine over on the ignition. It is best to disconnect the distributor to stop the engine accidently starting. If the pump is working properly, petrol should spurt from the pipe.

Petrol pump   Cap retaining scew

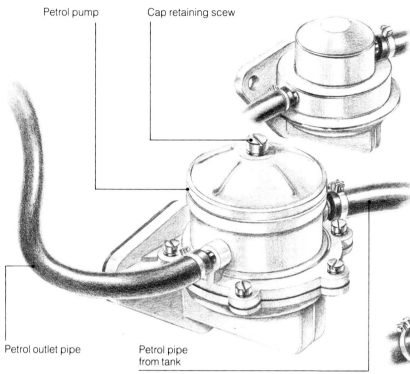

Petrol outlet pipe   Petrol pipe from tank

Sealed petrol pump

Many petrol pumps fitted to modern cars are sealed. If this is the case, you will probably find a filter fitted in the petrol pipe leading from the tank to the pump. This is known as an in-line filter and takes the form of a clear or translucent plastic case with a paper filter element inside. If you can see the filter element, check it is not clogged or discoloured. If the filter element is not visible, it is worth changing if the car is due for a major service. The petrol pipes will either push fit on to the filter or be held in place with clips. When replacing the unit, make sure that the arrow stamped on the case is pointing in the direction of the petrol flow.

In-line filter

Checking the fuel pump

If very little fuel or none at all appears at the carburettor, there is probably a fault in the fuel pump. Check the outlet pipe from the pump by disconnecting it and turning the engine over. If fuel flows from the pump, the pipe is blocked. If no fuel appears, the fuel pump filter may be blocked.

The gauze of which this filter is made can become clogged and so should be cleaned periodically, though this can only be done if the pump has a removable top. If you can remove the filter, wash it in petrol and clean off any dirt with a soft brush. If the pump on your car is sealed, a separate in-line filter will probably be fitted between the pump and carburettor. This should be replaced at regular intervals.

Unscrew the top of the petrol pump and lift it clear of the body.

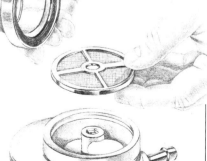

Check that the sealing ring around the base of the pump cap is in position and not distorted, perished or damaged in any way, as this will cause the pump to leak. Lift out the filter and clean any dirt from the gauze with a soft brush soaked in petrol. Be careful not to damage the gauze as this may allow particles of dirt to enter the pump or carburettor.

119

Accelerator/choke cable maintenance

If a worn throttle cable sticks with the throttle open, this can be dangerous. If you find the accelerator pedal stiff to operate, first check under the bonnet to see if the cable has become kinked. It should be routed in smooth curves – these should have as wide arcs as possible – away from any hot engine components.

The stiffness may also be caused by a fault in the carburettor. To check this, release the cable from the carburettor linkage. Once the cable is free, ask a helper to operate the accelerator pedal. Hold the inner cable in one hand and the outer cable in the other. You will feel if there is any stiffness in the cable, or if it is snagging. Confirm that the cable is at fault by operating the carburettor linkage by hand. It should move freely – if it is stiff, lubricate the linkage with light oil. If it is still stiff after this, get your garage to check the carburettor.

Removing the cable

A sticking cable must be removed for lubrication or replacement. Cables with a plain end at the carburettor – that is, with no nipple fitted – can be withdrawn from inside the car once the throttle linkage has been disconnected. Withdraw the cable through the eye in the accelerator pedal. The outer cable is then disconnected and pulled from its collar in the bulkhead.

If the cable has a nipple, or other attachment, at the carburettor, the inner and outer cables must be removed together. Disconnect the nipple from the accelerator pedal and withdraw the cable through the bulkhead into the engine compartment.

Examine the inner cable for signs of fraying or broken strands. In either case, it should be replaced. If the cable is intact, lubricate it.

To refit a plain-ended cable, thread the inner cable through the accelerator pedal into the engine bay. Feed it through the outer cable and attach it to the carburettor. Allow a small amount of slack, so the carburettor can close fully and the engine tick over correctly. Get a helper to depress the accelerator pedal and check that the throttle linkage can move fully. If not, adjust the cable accordingly.

To refit the other type of cable, push it through the bulkhead from the engine bay. From inside the car, pull the inner cable through and connect the nipple to the accelerator pedal. Connect the other end to the throttle linkage. Check for throttle movement and adjust it, if necessary.

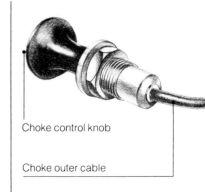

Choke control knob

Choke outer cable

Accelerator outer cable

Cable end nipple

Accelerator inner cable

Accelerator pedal

Outer cable retaining clip

If you are fitting a new inner cable, it will need to be lubricated. Hold the outer cable lightly between the jaws of a vice and build a cup around the top with plasticine. Pour light oil into the cup until it seeps out of the other end of the cable. Remove all traces of the plasticine from the cable end and work the inner cable in and out a few times to ensure the oil is spread evenly.

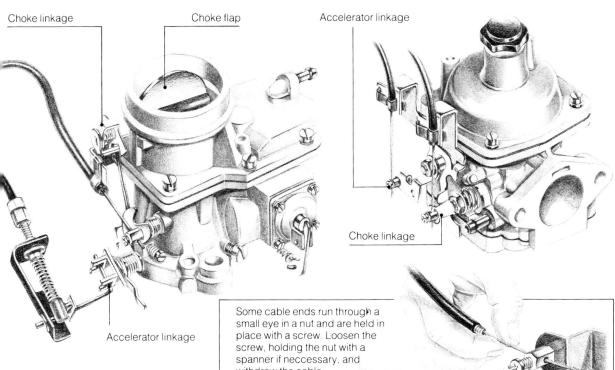

Choke linkage   Choke flap   Accelerator linkage

Choke linkage

Accelerator linkage

Checking the choke cable

To check the choke cable, get a helper to operate the choke and see whether the linkage at the carburettor can move fully. This may involve removing the air cleaner assembly in order to check the choke flap.

If the flap does not open fully, slacken the linkage at the carburettor and take up some of the slack on the cable. If the flap does not close fully, the cable requires more slack.

If you suspect the cable is at fault, check it in the same way as the throttle cable.

Most choke inner cables can be withdrawn from inside the car by pulling out the choke control knob completely. Inspect the cable for damage and replace it, if necessary.

Disconnect the outer cable from the dashboard and carburettor and pull through the bulkhead. It then can be

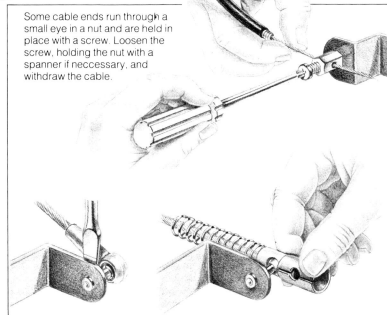

Some cable ends run through a small eye in a nut and are held in place with a screw. Loosen the screw, holding the nut with a spanner if neccessary, and withdraw the cable.

If the accelerator is controlled with a rod linkage, the two are normally linked by a ball and socket. To remove this, gently prise the rod and ball apart with a screwdriver.

Some ball and socket connectors are covered with a collar. Slide the collar away from the joint and pull the rod clear.

lubricated. Reverse the procedure to refit the cable. Adjust the cable at the carburettor to ensure that the choke can close fully.

Whenever fitting a cable, make sure that there are no kinks along its length. Tape or clip it away from hot engine components.

121

Spark plugs

Spark plugs should be cleaned and the plug gaps checked at each service interval. New plugs should be fitted as part of each major service.

Label each high tension lead according to cylinder numberand disconnect the leads by pulling firmly on the spark plug caps. Before removing each plug, clean around its base with a stiff brush.

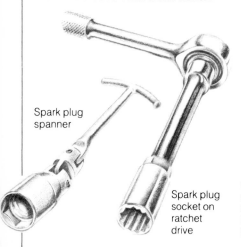

Spark plug spanner

Spark plug socket on ratchet drive

Use a plug spanner to unscrew the plugs, taking care that no dirt falls into the plug holes. Make sure that the spanner fits squarely on to each plug and is pushed firmly home.

Cleaning and replacing plugs

Hard deposits will build up on the electrodes, which, in time, will impair the spark. Use a wire brush to remove loose deposits and then carefully open the electrode gap with a pair of thin-nosed pliers. File back the faces of both electrodes to bare metal to clear all the deposits. Reset the gap.

Take care when refitting the plugs – if they are cross-threaded or over-tightened, the cylinder head could be damaged.

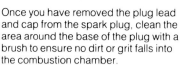

Once you have removed the plug lead and cap from the spark plug, clean the area around the base of the plug with a brush to ensure no dirt or grit falls into the combustion chamber.

Make sure the plug spanner is fitted squarely over the plug flats and unscrew the plug in an anti-clockwise direction. If the plug is tight, the arm of the plug spanner can be turned through 90° to give more leverage.

Checking for a spark

When looking for the cause of a starting problem, check whether or not there is a spark at the plugs. Disconnect all high tension leads and remove one plug. Reconnect its high tension lead.

With a pair of insulated pliers, hold the base of the plug against bare metal to earth it. Do this away from the carburettor and plug hole. Turn the engine over on the starter. If everything is working correctly, a bright spark should flash between the two electrodes. If no spark appears, double-check by connecting the plug to another high tension lead to see if it is the plug that is at fault.

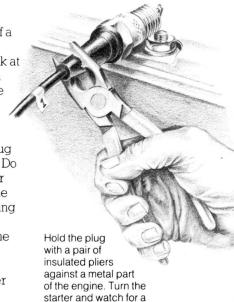

Hold the plug with a pair of insulated pliers against a metal part of the engine. Turn the starter and watch for a spark at the electrodes.

Checking and adjusting the gap

Remove the plug, taking care that no dirt falls into the engine. Check if the electrode gap is set to the manufacturer's recommendation. This is given in thousandths/inch, or hundredths/millimetre. If you cannot establish the exact setting, a safe average is 25 thou (0.6mm).

Slide the appropriate feeler blade between the electrodes to measure the gap – the blade should fit snugly. If the gap is incorrect, the L-shaped electrode can be adjusted with a pair of pliers.

Refit the plug, taking care not to cross the thread, or to over-tighten it.

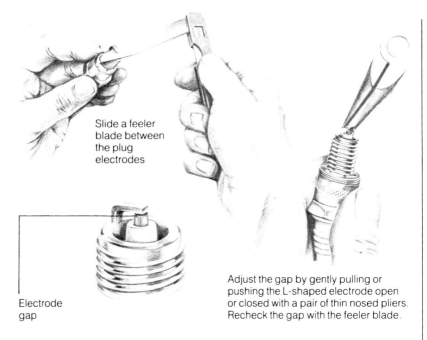

Slide a feeler blade between the plug electrodes

Electrode gap

Adjust the gap by gently pulling or pushing the L-shaped electrode open or closed with a pair of thin nosed pliers. Recheck the gap with the feeler blade.

Plug faults

The physical state of the plug electrodes can tell you a lot about the condition of the engine and help you to diagnose faults elsewhere in it. After use, the electrodes should be light brown. If they are sooty, the fuel mixture is too rich; white deposits on them indicate a weak fuel mixture, or an air leak; plugs fouled with oil signify worn valves or piston rings. If only one plug is affected, the problem is confined to the cylinder to which it was fitted, so keep the plugs in order when removing them.

If the plugs are not changed at the proper service intervals, the electrodes will deteriorate and the gap between them increase, reducing the spark and impairing engine performance.

Deposits that are left to build up on the electrodes will impair the spark and affect engine performance. If the deposit is very heavy, the plug should be replaced

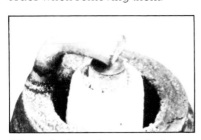

If the engine is running correctly, the plug electrodes will be light brown and free from thick deposits.

If the fuel/air mixture is too rich, a thick, black layer of carbon will build up on the electrodes. It should be cleaned off with a stiff wire brush.

Oil on the electrodes indicates that wear within the engine is allowing oil into the combustion chambers. If this is the case, consult a garage.

Distributor/1

Checking the distributor

At each service interval (6,000 miles (9,677km) or consult your handbook), you should carry out the essential basic checks on your distributor described here. First, remove the plastic distributor cap, which is held in place either with spring clips or two screws.

Clean the cap with a dry cloth and examine its inside for cracks or electrical tracking – minute burn marks that look like scratches. If there are any signs of damage, fit a new cap.

The cap will have either a carbon brush in its centre, which should move freely on its spring, or a fixed contact, which must be secure. If the plug contacts around the edge of the cap are burnt or corroded, a new cap should be fitted.

Find out which direction the rotor arm turns by turning the crankshaft pulley in the direction of engine rotation. In some cases an arrow on the rotor head will indicate this. Alternatively, push the car a short way in top gear. Then grasp the rotor and move it in the appropriate direction. It should turn a little with even resistance and spring back into position when released. This is a check on the centrifugal advance weights inside the distributor. A more accurate test is described later.

Remove the rotor arm and examine it for signs of cracks or electrical tracking. If it is damaged, you must fit a replacement. Grasp the central shaft and try to move it from side to side. A hint of play is allowable, but, if there is more than this, the distributor needs to be professionally overhauled or replaced.

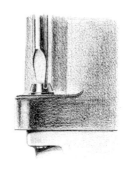

The distributor cap is held on by a pair of spring clips, which are pushed apart, or by two screws.

Check the high tension lead connections to the distributor. Pull them out and widen the metal contact to give a tighter fit if they are loose. Make sure that the plug leads are numbered for correct refitting.

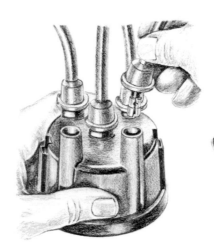

High tension lead connectors are either a push fit or screwed into the cap. With the screw type, check the lead is making good contact with the metal contact.

Check the rotor arm for cracks and signs of electrical tracking. If the contact on the end of the arm is dirty, clean it off by rubbing it against a tyre. Do not use emery paper to clean it.

Checking the vacuum advance

As an initial check on the vacuum advance unit, pull the pipe and rubber union off the stub on the vacuum diaphragm. Turn the baseplate, on which the contact breaker assembly is mounted, in the opposite direction to the rotation of the rotor. Hold the baseplate against the tension and place your thumb over the stub. Release the plate. It should not move until you take your thumb away, proving that the diaphragm inside the vacuum advance is undamaged. If the diaphragm does move, it is faulty, and the distributor should be overhauled.

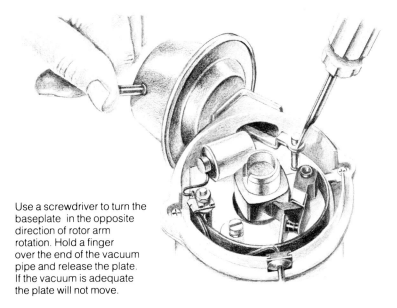

Use a screwdriver to turn the baseplate in the opposite direction of rotor arm rotation. Hold a finger over the end of the vacuum pipe and release the plate. If the vacuum is adequate the plate will not move.

Checking the contact breakers

Electrical current passing through the contact breaker points causes one face to burn away and the other to build up a peak of metal, while the fibre heel is gradually worn away by the cam on the rotor. For these reasons, the contact breaker gap should be checked periodically and the points themselves replaced every 6,000 miles (9,677km), or at each service.

Some distributors – those made by Lucas and Ford, for instance – are designed to make it extremely easy to reach the points. All you have to do is to remove the distributor cap and rotor arm. Other types have an aluminium plate covering the contact breakers. To remove this, you will have to unscrew two or three small screws.

If there are heavy burn marks on the contact surfaces, the condenser is faulty, as its job is to stop current arcing across the gap between the points. Since the component is inexpensive and easy to replace, being held in position only by a single screw, it is worth fitting a new one whenever you replace the contact breakers.

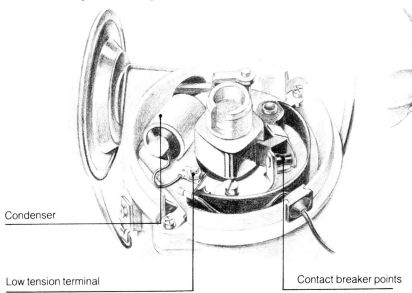

Condenser

Low tension terminal

Contact breaker points

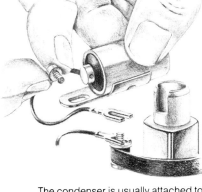

The condenser is usually attached to the contact breaker baseplate by a single screw. On some distributors though, it is mounted externally. To remove it, release the low tension lead from the low tension terminal, making a note of its position on the terminal, and undo the screw.

Distributor/2

Setting the gap

When setting the contact breaker gap, remove the spark plugs to make engine rotation easier. Turn the engine with a spanner on the crankshaft pulley, or put the car in gear and rock it, until the fibre heel of the points is on a cam peak and the contacts are fully open.

You should set the points to the gap specified in your car's handbook. Select the appropriate feeler blade and clean it thoroughly. Insert the blade between the contact breakers. If the gap is correct, the blade drags slightly as it passes through it.

On most distributors, you can adjust the gap by freeing the fixing screw and then sliding the entire assembly, or just one contact, around a pivot with a screwdriver blade. Other types are fitted with an adjusting screw. To adjust the gap in this case, insert the feeler blade and slide the assembly until you encounter a slight resistance. Tighten the fixing screw and re-check the gap.

After making the adjustment, smear a little high-melting-point grease on the cam lobes. If there is an oil pad in the top of the rotor shaft, coat it with a drop of light oil.

Using a dwell meter

Rather than use a feeler gauge, it is more accurate to set the gap with a special tool called a dwell meter. This measures in degrees how far the rotor has turned between each opening and closing of the contact breakers. This is the dwell angle. If, for example, the dwell angle specified in your handbook is 48° to 52°, the reading on the meter must be at

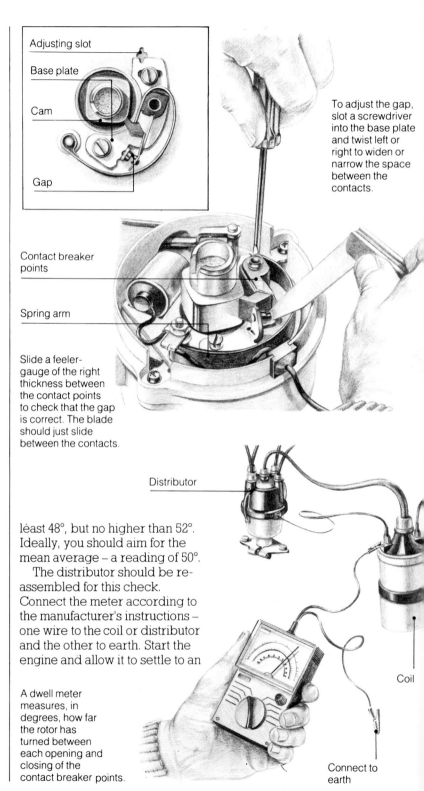

Adjusting slot

Base plate

Cam

Gap

To adjust the gap, slot a screwdriver into the base plate and twist left or right to widen or narrow the space between the contacts.

Contact breaker points

Spring arm

Slide a feeler-gauge of the right thickness between the contact points to check that the gap is correct. The blade should just slide between the contacts.

Distributor

Coil

Connect to earth

A dwell meter measures, in degrees, how far the rotor has turned between each opening and closing of the contact breaker points.

least 48°, but no higher than 52°. Ideally, you should aim for the mean average – a reading of 50°.

The distributor should be re-assembled for this check. Connect the meter according to the manufacturer's instructions – one wire to the coil or distributor and the other to earth. Start the engine and allow it to settle to an even tickover. The needle will flutter, but then should point to a firm figure. If, however, it continues to fluctuate by more than two or three degrees, the distributor is worn and should be overhauled.

If the figure is too high, the contact breaker gap must be widened. If it is too low, the gap must be lessened. Switch off the engine and adjust the gap accordingly. Then repeat the test, since it takes considerable practice to get it right first time.

Fitting new contact breakers

Though you can clean the contact faces of the contact breaker points with a file, this is a false economy at worst and a temporary measure at best. If the faces are severely worn, new points should always be fitted.

Start by disconnecting the two leads linked to the assembly – one will run from the coil and the other from the condenser. Both leads are usually held in place on the spring arm of the breaker by a small grub screw. Note their positions. The assembly itself is held by one screw, or sometimes by two. Remove the screw or screws and then examine the contact faces. It is normal for there to be a peak on one and a slight indentation on the other.

Before fitting new contacts, clean their faces with a solvent and lubricate the pivot with light engine oil. Smear the cam with high-melting-point grease.

Re-fit the assembly, making sure it is square with the baseplate. Re-connect the low tension and condenser leads in the correct order – this is important. Check the gap and reset it, if necessary.

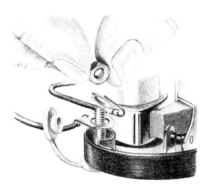

Undo the locknut holding the low tension and condenser leads. Remove the leads, making a note of the order in which they are attached and the position of any washers.

Lift out the spring arm together with the contact attached to the actuating arm.

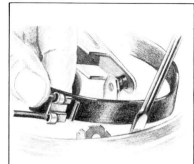

On some distributors the low tension leads slot directly into the end of the spring arm. Lever the arm up and out and slide out the connector.

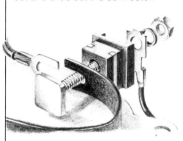

Other distributors have a square ended bolt holding the spring arm and low tension leads. When removing the leads, note the order in which you take them off and the position of any washers.

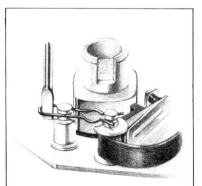

If the actuating arm is held to its post with a spring clip, lever the clip off with a screwdriver, and remove the arm and contact. Be careful not to drop it into the distributor body.

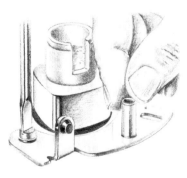

Unscrew the base plate and lift it clear. Be careful not to drop the screw, or its washer if fitted, into the body of the distributor.

Distributor/3

Timing the ignition

The timing should be adjusted whenever the distributor has been disturbed, or new contact breaker points fitted.

Most engines are timed statically – that is, with the engine switched off. The pistons are positioned by turning the engine over to the point at which the number one spark plug should fire. When the engine is in the position, marks on the crankshaft pulley will correspond with marks on the crankcase and the rotor arm should be pointing to number one plug lead. If it is not, rotate the engine another 360°.

Check in the car handbook to make sure that you can identify these marks and their positions correctly. After aligning them, connect a test lamp between the live terminal of the contact breakers (the low tension terminal) and a convenient earth. Switch on the ignition. Loosen the distributor pinch-bolt and turn the body in the same direction as the rotation of the rotor arm until the test lamp goes out. This happens when the points are just opening. Turn the body the other way until the lamp starts to flicker and then tighten the distributor pinch-bolt. If you do not have a test lamp, turn the body in the same way, but rely on your ears. The sound of the contact breakers making a small click, indicating that the circuit is broken, is a sign that the timing is now set correctly.

Stroboscopic timing

The most accurate way of timing the ignition, however, is by stroboscopic timing, as this can be done with the engine running. If a stroboscopic lamp

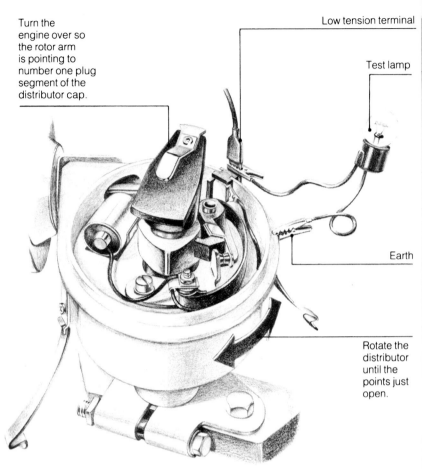

Turn the engine over so the rotor arm is pointing to number one plug segment of the distributor cap.

Low tension terminal

Test lamp

Earth

Rotate the distributor until the points just open.

TIMING MARKS

The timing marks for setting the ignition timing are usually on the engine block and are aligned with a notch or mark on the crankshaft pulley. They may be stamped on the block as a series of lines with figures showing degrees, or on a plate with the points marked with letters.

is connected to number one plug lead, it will light when that plug fires. By shining it at the timing marks on the rotating crankshaft pulley and engine block, the stroboscopic effect the lamp produces reveals the two marks in their relative positions.

Start by marking the pointer on the block and appropriate timing mark on the pulley as specified in your handbook.

Normally, you should connect the strobe light to the number one plug and its high tension lead. Note, however, that some engines are timed from a different cylinder, or with the vacuum advance tube disconnected. Check with your handbook to see either is the case. Run the engine at tickover speed or at the recommended handbook speed and aim the light at the marks – being careful to avoid the fan. If they do not coincide, switch off and loosen the distributor pinch-bolt. Restart the engine and twist the distributor to adjust its position until the marks coincide.

The strobe light can also be used to check the automatic advance. To check this, make sure the vacuum tube is connected, aim the light at the timing marks and blip the throttle. The marks should move apart briefly and then come together again. Disconnect the tube and gradually increase engine revolutions. If the centrifugal weights are operating, the marks will move apart steadily. If they remain together, the weights are not working. As these are situated inside the distributor, fixing them can be a tricky job and is best left to a competent mechanic.

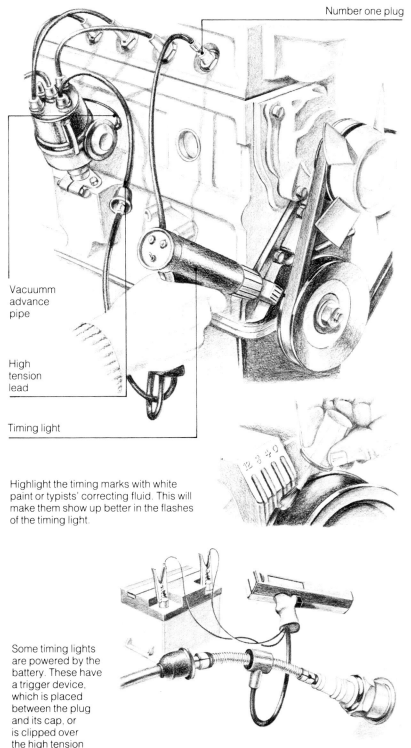

Number one plug

Vacuumm advance pipe

High tension lead

Timing light

Highlight the timing marks with white paint or typists' correcting fluid. This will make them show up better in the flashes of the timing light.

Some timing lights are powered by the battery. These have a trigger device, which is placed between the plug and its cap, or is clipped over the high tension lead.

Ignition coil

The coil is usually mounted on a bulkhead within the engine compartment. Its job is to boost the current supplied by the battery – normally 12 volts – to the high voltage required at the spark plugs.

The coil may fail suddenly, without prior warning. This is most likely to happen if the electrical connections to and from the coil become corroded, so inhibiting the flow of current.

Checking the coil

If you are faced with a starting problem, this will usually involve checking the coil to see if it is operating properly. To check that the coil is producing a spark, remove the coil's high tension lead from the distributor cap. It is held in place by a plastic collar that will either pull off, or unscrew.

Use insulated pliers to hold the brass connection on the lead about 13mm (½in) from a metal part of the engine – make sure that the part is well away from the carburettor fuel lines – and ask a helper to operate the ignition. A bright spark should jump between the lead and engine at regular intervals.

Alternatively, remove the high tension lead and the distributor cap. Check that the contact breaker points are closed – if not, you can close them manually by turning the crankshaft pulley with a spanner, or by pushing the car a short distance with top gear engaged. Switch on the ignition and use the insulated pliers to hold the exposed part of the high tension lead as before. Flick the contact breakers open with an insulated screwdriver. A bright spark should jump from the lead to the engine.

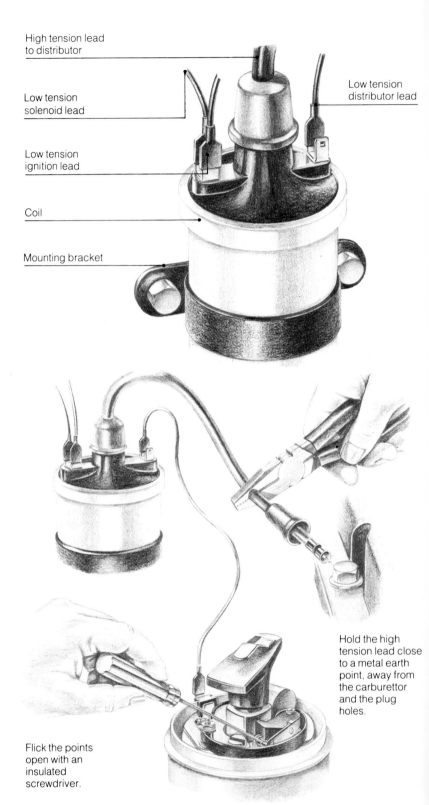

High tension lead to distributor

Low tension solenoid lead

Low tension ignition lead

Coil

Mounting bracket

Low tension distributor lead

Hold the high tension lead close to a metal earth point, away from the carburettor and the plug holes.

Flick the points open with an insulated screwdriver.

If the first test does not produce a spark, but a spark results from the second, check to see whether or not the contact breaker points are operating properly *(see p.124)*.

Checking coil connections

If no spark results in either case, the connections to the coil could be faulty. Remove both connections – these are held in position by spade connectors or small nuts and terminal posts – and make sure that the terminals and connectors are both clean. Gently crimp spade connectors with pliers before replacing them to ensure the connections will be tight. Check the coil's plastic top for cracks or signs of tracking – small burn marks.

Checking the feed circuit

The coil takes its power from an ignition feed. To check the circuit, you will need either a circuit tester, or a voltmeter. Connect either to the feed terminal and earth the other connection. Switch on the ignition. If the meter does not register, or if the tester's lamp fails to light, the feed circuit is faulty. Repairing this is a garage job.

If the circuit is functioning and the contact breaker points are in good condition *(see p.124)*, the coil is almost certainly faulty. If possible, have the coil checked over by a garage before buying a replacement.

If you do not have a voltmeter or circuit tester to hand, you can carry out the same check by substituting another car's coil for your own. This does not mean that you have to remove your your own coil, as the connections are simply transferred.

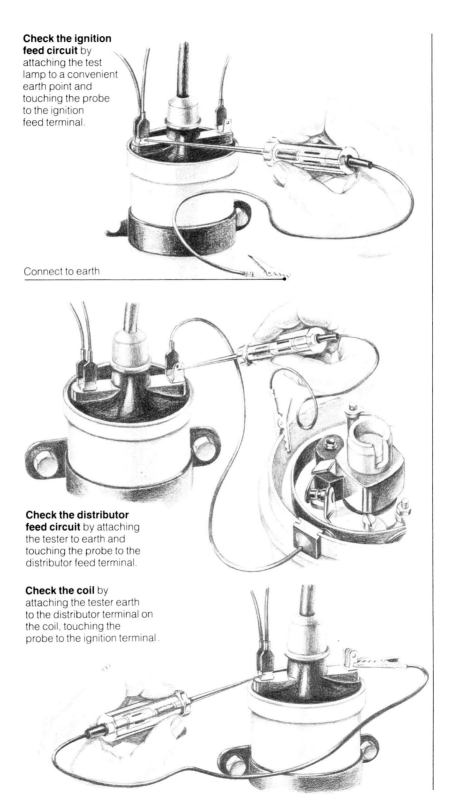

Check the ignition feed circuit by attaching the test lamp to a convenient earth point and touching the probe to the ignition feed terminal.

Connect to earth

Check the distributor feed circuit by attaching the tester to earth and touching the probe to the distributor feed terminal.

Check the coil by attaching the tester earth to the distributor terminal on the coil, touching the probe to the ignition terminal.

Starter motors

You will find that either of two types of starter motor are fitted to your car – the inertia type, or the pre-engaged type. An inertia starter has a separate solenoid, whereas the pre-engaged type has its solenoid mounted on it.

On both types, make sure the engine-to-chassis earth is undamaged and firmly connected. Poor earth contact can cause the starter to turn slowly and sometimes not at all.

Checking connections

You may find on occasion that, though the motor is not jammed and the connections are firm, it still refuses to turn. This means that electricity may not be reaching the motor. Check this with a circuit tester, or a voltmeter.

With the inertia type, connect the tester or meter to the main terminal at the starter and to a convenient earth. Ask a helper to turn on the ignition. If the test shows that power is not reaching the starter, the fault lies in the circuitry or with the solenoid.

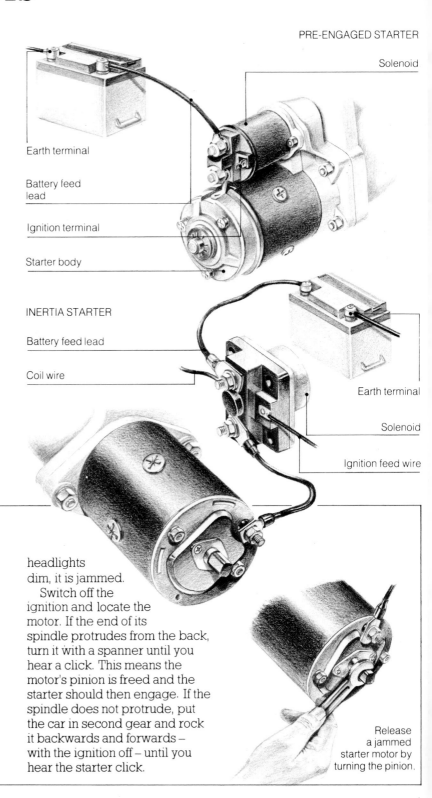

PRE-ENGAGED STARTER

Solenoid

Earth terminal

Battery feed lead

Ignition terminal

Starter body

INERTIA STARTER

Battery feed lead

Coil wire

Earth terminal

Solenoid

Ignition feed wire

Release a jammed starter motor by turning the pinion.

Freeing a jammed starter

One of the commonest of all starting problems occurs when the starter motor jams on engagement. The tell-tale sign of this is an audible loud 'clonk' from the starter as you operate the ignition, with the engine refusing to turn.

Provided you are certain that your battery is sufficiently charged to turn the motor, you can double-check whether or not the motor has jammed by switching on the headlights and then operating the starter. If it still does not turn, but the headlights dim, it is jammed.

Switch off the ignition and locate the motor. If the end of its spindle protrudes from the back, turn it with a spanner until you hear a click. This means the motor's pinion is freed and the starter should then engage. If the spindle does not protrude, put the car in second gear and rock it backwards and forwards – with the ignition off – until you hear the starter click.

With the pre-engaged type, connect the tester or meter to the terminal on the starter body and earth. Make the test as above. In either case, if the tester's bulb flashes, or the meter registers, the starter itself is at fault and must be overhauled – a specialist job – or replaced.

Checking the solenoid

A faulty solenoid will prevent the starter motor from operating. The starter will remain dead or the solenoid itself will make an audible 'click'. This will also occur if the battery is insufficiently charged and so does not have enough power to turn the starter.

The separate solenoid used with an inertia-type starter is usually secured in the engine bay. It can be traced by following the main live feed from the battery.

The main cable from the battery and the cable that runs to the starter motor are held in place by two large nuts. Disconnect the battery to avoid the risk of electrical sparks. Check both cables – and the smaller, ignition-feed wire –for security. Some cars are fitted with what is termed a ballast resistor circuit and there may be another small wire present. If in doubt, consult your handbook.

Check the ignition feed with a voltmeter, or circuit tester. Reconnect the battery. Remove the small wire and connect it to the meter or lamp, earthing the other connection. When the ignition is switched on, the meter should show a reading, or the tester's lamp should light. If not, the feed circuit is faulty, which is a job for a garage.

If the circuit is functioning, connect the meter or lamp to the small wire and its terminal. Switch on the ignition. If the meter does not register, or if the lamp fails to light, the solenoid's earth connection to the body is insufficient. Remove the connection – it is usually held by a couple of screws – and clean the mating parts of the solenoid and bodywork to shiny metal.

If current is reaching the solenoid and it is correctly earthed, you should now check its operation. Connect the tester or meter to the solenoid terminal running to the starter and the earth. Ask a helper to operate the starter switch. If the meter does not register, or if the lamp fails to light, the current is failing to flow through the solenoid, which must then be replaced. If current is flowing, the starter, or its connections, are at fault.

Follow the same procedure to check a pre-engaged starter. Remove the small wire and connect it to the test equipment, earthing the other connection. If the test shows that the current is flowing when the ignition key is turned, connect the test equipment between the wire and its terminal. If the current ceases to flow, there is an internal fault.

If the circuit is intact, connect the meter or tester to the lead from the solenoid to the starter and to earth. Turn the ignition switch. If the meter shows a reading, or if the lamp lights, the starter is faulty. If not, the solenoid is faulty and the unit itself or the complete assembly must be replaced by a garage.

Removing and checking the starter

Before removing the starter, disconnect both battery terminals. You may find it necessary to work from underneath the car, in which case it must be supported firmly on axle stands, or on wheel ramps.

Remove the power and ignition leads. Then, tackle the retaining bolts – you may need a socket spanner and extension bar to reach them. If there are shims (spacing washers) between the starter and bellhousing, note their positions, as, if they are not repositioned correctly on reassembly, the motor could jam.

With the inertia type, the bendix gear should be washed in paraffin, so that it is free to move up and down the shaft. Do not lubricate it. Examine the teeth. If they are damaged or worn unevenly, the motor must be overhauled, or replaced. Check the gear wheel on a pre-engaged starter for similar signs of uneven wear.

When refitting the motor, make sure it is pushed firmly and squarely home – with any shims fitting correctly – and screw in one of the retaining bolts finger-tight. Replace the other bolt or bolts and tighten progressively. Reconnect the wires and the battery terminals.

Undo the two or three bolts holding the starter motor to the engine block and make a note of any spacing washers that may be fitted. Withdraw the starter.

Engine lubrication

Checking the oil

You should always check the oil level once a week – more frequently if the engine is using an excessive amount – and always before a long journey. Ensure the car is on level ground. If the engine is warm, wait a few minutes to allow the oil to drain into the sump and take a reading with the dipstick, usually located in a tube on the side of the engine.

Remove the dipstick and wipe it clean with a non-fluffy cloth. Push it home and withdraw it again. The stick will be marked 'max' and 'min', or have two marks to indicate the upper and lower permitted oil levels. The oil should reach the upper mark. If not, replace the dipstick and add a small amount of the recommended grade of oil through the hole in the rocker or cam cover. Give this time to drain into the sump and check the dipstick again. Take care not to over-fill the sump, as this could cause excessive oil pressure and an oil seal or gasket could blow as a result.

Changing the oil

Regular oil changes are essential. They should usually be carried out every 6,000 miles (9,600km), or six months – whichever is the sooner. Run the engine for a few minutes to ensure that the oil is hot and flows easily. Depending on the engine lay-out, jack up and support the front or rear of the car to give you working space underneath it. Clean the sump's drain plug and the surrounding area with non-fluffy cloth. Then, place a container large enough to hold the sump's contents under the plug and unscrew the plug. If the plug has a hexagonal

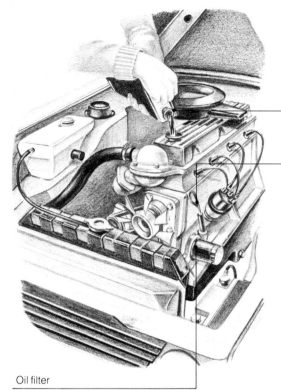

The oil is usually topped up through a hole in the rocker or camshaft cover. Be careful not to spill any on hot engine components.

Dipstick

The dipstick will be marked with two lines showing the maximum and minimum oil levels. The oil should always reach the upper mark.

Oil filter

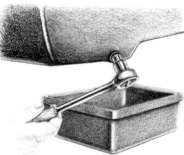

Position a container, big enough to hold all the engine oil, under the sump and undo the sump drain plug. Be careful when the oil comes out as it will be hot.

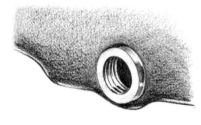

head, you can use a socket or ring spanner; otherwise a special sump-plug spanner will be needed.

Allow the oil to drain – take care, because it will be hot – clean the plug, check the sealing washer or gasket, if fitted, and replace the plug.

Clean the drain plug and thread in the sump with a non-fluffy cloth. Check the condition of the sealing washer, if fitted, and replace it if it is broken or distorted.

Replacing oil filters

The oil filter should be replaced at the same time as the oil is changed. If your car is fitted with a disposable 'cartridge' filter, the easiest way to remove it is to unscrew it with a strap or chain wrench.

After removing the filter, clean its mating flange and thread on the engine. Smear the new filter's rubber sealing ring with clean engine oil to prevent it distorting. Then screw it home just sufficiently to make the join oil-tight – never more, or the sealing ring will be damaged.

If your car is fitted with a replaceable paper element in a steel canister, undo the central bolt, and remove the canister and its sealing ring from the groove in the engine's mounting flange. Fit a new sealing ring as before. Remove the old element and clean the canister with paraffin. Fit the new element and refit the canister.

Refilling the sump

Before refilling, check the total capacity of the sump and filter in the car handbook. Also check in the handbook that the grade of oil you buy is correct for your car and whether a different grade is needed for summer and winter.

When refilling, do not add too much oil at once. Check the level at regular intervals. Remove the high-tension lead from the coil – so the engine cannot start – and turn the car over on the ignition switch to allow the oil to circulate. Replace the lead, start the engine and let it tick over until the oil pressure light goes out. Switch off, check for leaks and, after a few minutes, re-check the oil level.

Unscrew the filter in an anti-clockwise direction with a strap or chain wrench.

If you do not have a strap or chain wrench, you can remove the filter by piercing it with a screwdriver and use this as a lever to unscrew it.

Before refitting the filter, smear a little oil on to the sealing ring to prevent it distorting.

Remove a cannister-type filter by undoing the retaining bolt at the base of the cannister.

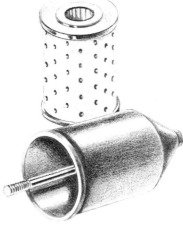

Remove the sealing ring, element, and spring and washer and clean all traces of oil sludge from the cannister. Replace the spring and washer in the correct order and insert the new filter. Fit a new sealing ring and smear it with a little oil before refitting the whole assembly.

Changing gaskets

Replacing a gasket

A leaking gasket must be replaced as quickly as possible to avoid the risk of major damage. Once the appropriate components have been removed, both faces must be thoroughly cleaned of all traces of old gasket. Use a sharpened piece of wood or a broad-bladed screwdriver for this, but take great care not to damage the metal, particularly when dealing with aluminium. Wipe down each face and look for signs of damage. If possible, check both of them with a straight-edge to make sure that they are not distorted.

It is a good idea to use gasket cement when refitting a gasket, as this minimizes the risk of the leak recurring. However, there is an exception to this rule. Cork gaskets rarely need a sealing compound – unless one is specified by the manufacturer – and a smear of grease on one of the sealing faces is usually sufficient to hold them in place while fitting them. With other types, smear one of the mating faces with gasket cement – there are many trade brands to choose from – and stick the gasket in place. Similarly smear the other side of the gasket with the cement and refit the component, checking carefully to see that the gasket has not moved. If you are dealing with components that may have to be removed frequently, seal the joint with a non-setting compound.

Tighten the retaining nuts or bolts to the correct torque, using a torque wrench. If this tool is unavailable, take care not to over-tighten the nuts or bolts. If you do, you may strip the threads.

Start the engine and check the gasket. If it still leaks, lightly nip up the nuts or bolts. If this does not solve the problem, the gasket must be replaced with a new one, or one of the mating faces has distorted.

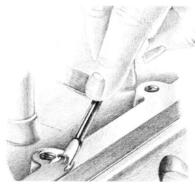

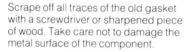

Scrape off all traces of the old gasket with a screwdriver or sharpened piece of wood. Take care not to damage the metal surface of the component.

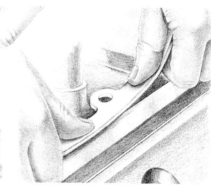

Position the new gasket and check that it is the right size and the right way round. Hold it in place with a smear of grease, or gasket cement.

Making a temporary gasket

Certain gaskets – such as the cylinder head and manifold gaskets – must always be replaced with the standard part. In an emergency, however, it is possible to make your own gaskets for use elsewhere. Thick card – a cereal packet, for instance – is ideal, but remember that the repair is only temporary and a new proprietary gasket must be fitted as soon as possible.

If the old gasket cannot be used as a template, trace round the component, including all the bolt holes. Cut out the profile you

have traced, paying particular attention to the inner shape of the gasket.

When fitting the card, always use a gasket compound to ensure a good seal.

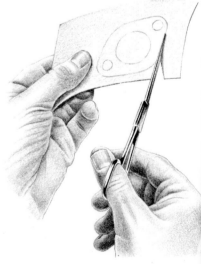

Electrical checks

Checking electrical circuits

An electrical component can stop working for either of two reasons. The component itself may be at fault, or there is a break in the electrical circuit. Start by eliminating the possibility of circuit failure, as this is far cheaper than buying a replacement – especially if this proves unnecessary. The first step is to make sure the relevant fuse is intact *(see p.138)*.

Circuits can be tested with either a voltmeter or circuit tester. A voltmeter shows a reading if the circuit is working; a circuit tester's bulb will light.

Testing a switch

Make your first check on the component's switch. Turn it on – plus the ignition, if the component is ignition-controlled. Connect the crocodile clip of the circuit tester to earth and touch the live battery terminal with the probe. Check the colours of the wires against the handbook's wiring diagram to find out which is live.

If the bulb fails to light, there is a fault in the wiring from the battery to the switch. If the bulb lights, leave the ignition and the switch on, and touch the probe on the other terminal. If the bulb then fails to light, the switch is faulty. If it does, it shows that current is passing through the switch, so there may be a fault in the wiring to the component.

Leave everything switched on and connect the crocodile clip to earth. Touch the live feed terminal with the probe. If the bulb does not light, there is a break in the circuit between the switch and the component. If the bulb does light, the feed circuit is intact and either the component is faulty or it is not

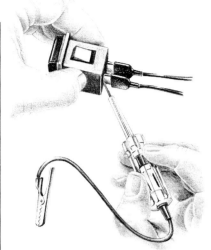

Test electrical circuits with a test screwdriver or voltmeter. Touch one probe to the component and attach the clip or other probe to earth.

The best way to check if a component is working is to connect it directly to the car battery. If there is an earth terminal on the component, make sure this is attached to the earth terminal of the battery.

properly earthed. Both can be checked using the tester.

Transfer the clip to the battery's live terminal and touch the component's earth terminal with the probe. If the bulb lights, the component is at fault. If the bulb does not light, there is a break in the earth circuit. If the component is earthed to the bodywork, make the test by touching a metal part of the component's body.

To check the component itself, connect a length of wire to the battery's live terminal and the live terminal of the component. Then connect up the battery's earth terminal and that of the component. If the component still does not work, it is faulty. If it works, there is a break in its circuit.

Checking relays

Some components – such as heated rear windows – are controlled by an electrical relay.

A relay has one thick cable coming from the live battery terminal and a second thick wire leading from the relay to the

component. A thin wire runs from the control switch to the relay and another thin wire runs from the relay to earth. The earth is usually the bodywork.

Connect the crocodile clip of the tester to earth and touch the live feed terminal of the relay with the probe. If the bulb does not light, there is a fault in the battery-to-relay circuit. If it does light, turn on the ignition and the controlling switch inside the car. Transfer the probe to the small terminal on the relay that is fed from the switch. If the probe's bulb does not light, current is not arriving at the relay, which shows that there is a fault in the switch or circuit leading to the relay.

If the bulb lights, touch the other thin wire with the probe. If there is no current, the relay is at fault. If the bulb lights, test the thick terminal that feeds the component. No current flowing here means that the relay is faulty. If the bulb lights, there is either a break in the wiring from relay to component, or the component itself is faulty.

Fuses

Checking and changing fuses

The electrical system in your car is protected by a bank of fuses. Any of these will blow if the circuit they control is overloaded. Without this protection, the overload could damage a component, or even cause an electrical fire.

The fuses are housed in a fuse box, normally located under the dashboard or on the bulkhead in the engine compartment. Refer to your handbook for the specific location. Each fuse is held by spring clips, which act as electrical contacts, and often protect a number of components in the same circuit. Your handbook should tell you which these are, but, if in any doubt as to which fuse to check, you should check them all.

The two most common fuses are the clear-glass type and the porcelain fuse, though a third – rectangular-shaped, with two push-in connectors – is now on the market. Whenever you fit a new fuse, check that the replacement is of the same type as the others and that it is of the correct rating – refer to your handbook to check this, or examine the blown fuse. This is important, as otherwise the circuit could be damaged.

If any fuse continually blows, this indicates a major electrical fault in the system. Repairing this is a job for a garage.

Line fuses

Some electrical components, such as radio/tape players, are additionally protected by what is termed a line fuse. This is usually fitted under the dashboard and consists of a plastic case with a wire at each end and the fuse inside it. The case is opened by twisting the

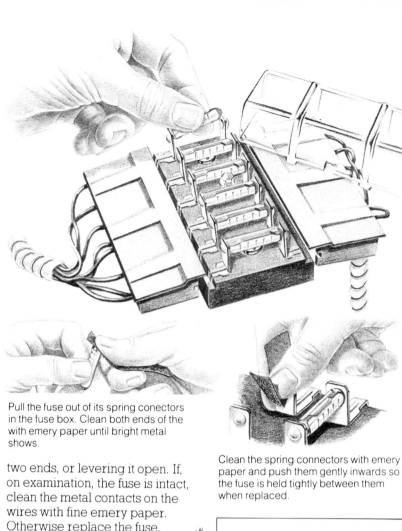

Pull the fuse out of its spring conectors in the fuse box. Clean both ends of the with emery paper until bright metal shows.

Clean the spring connectors with emery paper and push them gently inwards so the fuse is held tightly between them when replaced.

two ends, or levering it open. If, on examination, the fuse is intact, clean the metal contacts on the wires with fine emery paper. Otherwise replace the fuse.

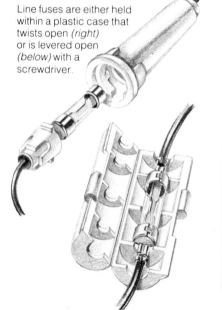

Line fuses are either held within a plastic case that twists open *(right)* or is levered open *(below)* with a screwdriver.

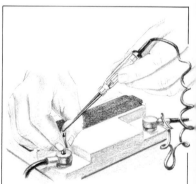

If you are not sure whether a fuse is blown or broken, you can test it with a circuit test screwdriver. Attach the earth wire of the screwdriver to the earth terminal of the battery. Hold one end of the fuse against the battery live terminal and touch the other end with the screwdriver blade. If the bulb in the handle of the screwdriver lights, the fuse is intact.

Bulbs

Checking and changing bulbs

The law states clearly that all of the lights on your car must work at all times. Not only is this a legal requirement – it is positively dangerous to drive a car if any light is not working. Check all your lights – especially direction indicators – once a week.

Checking rear lights

Normally, you can gain access to rear lights by removing the lens, though, on some cars, the bulb and holder must be withdrawn from inside the boot. In either case, the bulb is removed by twisting and pulling it. If the bulb is tight, use a piece of rag to grip it in case the glass breaks. A broken bulb can be removed by twisting it with a cork.

Hold the bulb to the light and check the filament to see if it is broken. If it appears intact, it can be tested fully with the car battery. If you are checking a bulb with a double filament, such as a combined stop and tail light, test each pole in turn.

If the bulb works in isolation, but will not light when replaced in its holder, a bad connection may be to blame. Make sure the

Check to see if current is reaching the bulb holder with a circuit test screwdriver.

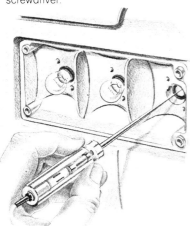

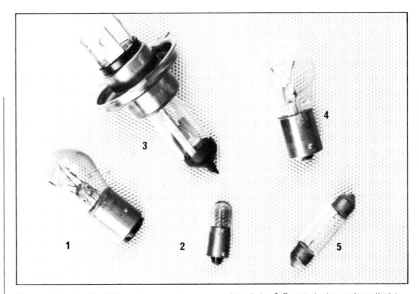

Cars are fitted with different types of bulbs for various uses. **1** Brake/ tail light with twin filaments. **2** Side light, number plate light. **3** Quartz halogen headlight bulb. **4** Indicator light. **5** Festoon, interior light.

lights are switched off and clean the inside of the holder by scraping it gently with a screwdriver.

You will need a voltmeter or circuit tester to check whether current is reaching the connection or not. Switch on the lights and connect the meter or bulb to the electrical contact and to an exposed metal part of the car to earth it. If the current flows, there is a poor earth connection. Deal with this by removing the complete light cluster and cleaning all mating metal faces. If the current is not flowing, repairing the fault should be left to a garage.

Checking headlamps

Though some headlamps have sealed-beam units (see p.141), the bulbs of others can be removed independently for testing. Pull off the connector from the back of the bulb – check that it is not fitted with a rubber shroud, which must be removed first.

The bulb is held in position with spring clips, or a collar. Remove the latter by twisting it and pulling it away cleanly. Check the filaments for damage.

If you are not sure whether or not the bulb is faulty, remove the bulb from the other headlamp and test it in the holder. If this second bulb fails to light, there is a wiring fault.

If current is reaching the connections, the earth connection is faulty. This is often a wire attached to the car's body by a cross-headed screw. Undo it and clean the mating surfaces back to bright metal.

If your car is fitted with halogen headlights – these are easily identifiable by the matt-black tips of the bulbs – never touch any part of the glass when removing or fitting a new bulb, or it will fail prematurely. Instead, handle it by the base.

Points to remember

Whenever you replace a bulb, make certain the replacement is the type recommended by the manufacturer. A bulb of the wrong rating may overload a circuit, while a wrongly-shaped bulb may not fit into the light unit. You could also be breaking the law by fitting a bulb of the wrong wattage, because there is a legal limit on how bright certain lights can be.

Checking indicator units

The law requires indicators to flash between 60 and 120 times a minute. To achieve this, either of two types of control unit is fitted – one operated by a bi-metallic strip, which makes and breaks the circuit, and the other transistorized. Only the bi-metallic type can be tested.

Locating and checking

It is easy to find a bi-metallic unit because of the characteristic click it makes when working. Transistorized units, on the other hand, are silent. The location of the unit depends on the design of the car. Some units are screwed behind or under the dashboard, and secured there with a spring clip. Others hang by their wires under the dashboard or are pushed home directly on to the fuse box.

Before checking the unit itself, make sure the rest of the components are not faulty. If one bulb stops working, it is probably the bulb itself, or the connection in the bulb-holder, that is at fault *(see p.139)*. If this is the case, the flashing will be much faster or slower than normal, depending on the type of unit. If all the flashers fail completely, a blown fuse could be the culprit. Confirm this by checking whether other components on the same fuse stop working as well *(see p.137)*.

The simplest way of establishing whether or not an indicator unit is faulty is to fit a replacement, but this involves what may prove unnecessary expense. It is just as simple – if more time-consuming – to check the unit with a circuit tester, or a voltmeter. Connect either to the terminal marked 'B' on the unit and to earth. Turn on the ignition. If the tester's lamp does

not light, or if the meter does not register, this shows that no current is flowing and you should look for a break in the wiring between unit and fuse box and in the fuse box itself.

If the current is flowing, switch off the ignition and connect the tester to the terminal marked 'L' and to earth. Switch on the ignition. If no current now flows, the flasher unit is faulty and must be replaced. If current flows, the unit is working and the fault is in the switch or wiring.

Testing the switch

Modern multi-function switches are complicated, but, though testing them thoroughly usually requires specialist knowledge, you can make a few basic checks. Remove the plastic shrouds surrounding the steering column – they are usually held in place by cross-headed screws.

With the switch exposed, move the stalk up and down to determine the position of the moving contacts. Check these carefully, as bent, dirty or broken contacts will stop the indicators from working. If they are dirty, clean the contacts with a piece of fine emery paper and, if they are bent, use a small screwdriver to bend them back into shape. If the contacts are broken, however, the switch must be replaced.

Check the switch for other obvious faults, such as a broken connection. Further testing is best left to a garage.

Fitting a new unit

If you have to replace the unit, take a careful note of the wiring before removing the connections from the old unit. It is best to label the wires or

make a sketch – fitting them incorrectly could damage the new unit. When buying a new unit, make sure it is suitable for use in your car. If necessary, compare it with the old unit, checking the type number, which is usually stamped on the cover.

Remember, if your car is used for towing *(see p.182)*, that a heavy duty unit must be fitted.

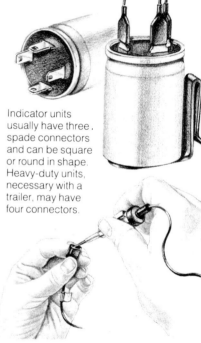

Indicator units usually have three spade connectors and can be square or round in shape. Heavy-duty units, necessary with a trailer, may have four connectors.

Test the indicator feed wires by turning on the indicator switch and touching the spade connector with a circuit test screwdriver or voltmeter.

Test to see whether the indicator unit is working by touching the spade connectors in turn with a circuit test screwdriver or voltmeter.

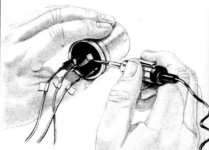

Sealed beam headlamps

Removing the unit

How you remove a sealed-beam unit depends on the type of car. The unit itself is held in place by a large metal retaining ring, secured by three small cross-headed screws on its outer edge. If these are fitted tightly, they can be easily damaged during removal, so use a screwdriver that is a good fit. Do not disturb the adjuster screws, or the headlamp alignment will be upset.

Testing the unit

Normally, either the dipped or the main beam stops working. If they both fail and the circuit is controlled by a fuse, this has probably blown (see p.138).

The simplest way to test the unit is to wire it between the two battery terminals. If the lamp fails to work on either of the terminals, it must be replaced. The unit should also be changed if the reflector has blackened or has started to peel through age.

If the unit is working, there is a fault in the wiring. Check the wiring (see p.137), trying both main and dipped beam terminals. If the unit glows dimly, there is probably a poor earth connection. Find the earth lead – this is usually located near the back of the headlight and fixed to the body with a self-tapping screw. Remove the lead and clean the mating faces with fine emery paper.

Replacing the unit

To replace the unit, first push home the connector block at the back. Make sure that the new unit is correctly located.

The glass has small pips, which fit into slots. Check the writing on the front of the unit to ensure you are not fitting it upside down and then replace the securing ring by either screwing or pressing it into position. If you feel resistance while doing this, the unit may have moved in its housing. If it has, it must be repositioned, as otherwise it could shatter. Before replacing the chrome surround or grille, check that both dipped and main beams are working properly.

Sealed beam unit

Retaining screw

Electrical connector box

The sealed beam unit is a one-piece glass envelope, containing two light filaments, one for the main beam, one for the dipped beam. In effect, it is a very large bulb. An electrical socket plugs into the back of the unit, where three spade connectors, one for each of the filaments and an earth, are moulded into the glass. The socket usually has the side-light bulb attached which fits within the unit when the socket is in position.

Remove the bezel that surrounds the headlamp unit. It is usually held in place with a single screw.

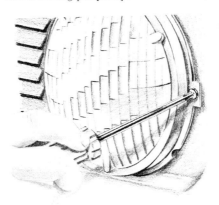

Slacken off the headlamp retaining screws, being careful not to confuse them with the adjusting screws. Push against the headlamp and rotate it so the retaining screws are opposite the holes in the retaining plates. Remove the headlamp.

With the headlamp clear of its housing, gently pull off the electrical connector block. Do not pull directly on the wires as this may break the connections within the block.

Clutch checks

In most modern cars, the clutch is operated by a cable, which should be checked during each major service. If the cable is too tight, there will be insufficient free play in the pedal and the clutch will soon start to slip – if there is too much free play, you will find it difficult to engage the gears.

With a rear-wheel-drive car, you must inspect the cable from underneath the body. The cable is attached to an actuating lever, usually with a threaded section and locknuts, a clevis bolt and split-pin, or by a nipple slotted into the arm. The lever itself may be covered by a rubber gaiter – this can be pulled off easily.

Release the end of the cable and inspect the inner cable for signs of fraying. If even a single strand is frayed, the cable must be replaced. If the clutch feels stiff when you operate it, check the cable for kinks along its entire length.

With most front-wheel-drive cars, the cable is under the bonnet and so easily removable.

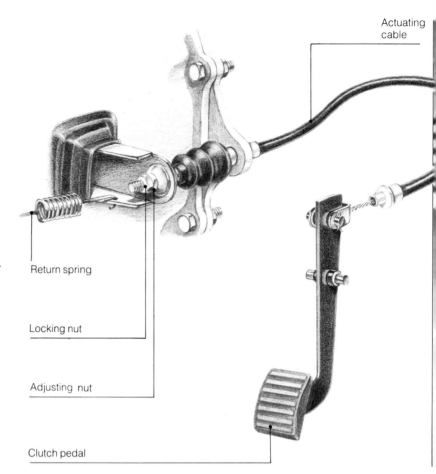

Actuating cable

Return spring

Locking nut

Adjusting nut

Clutch pedal

Hydraulic clutches

Hydraulic clutches are usually self-adjusting and therefore need little maintenance. However, the hydraulic fluid level in the master cylinder must be checked regularly.

Checking and repairing hydraulic clutches is usually a garage job. However, a few hydraulic clutch systems can be adjusted in much the same way as a cable clutch. Check in your handbook to see if this is possible.

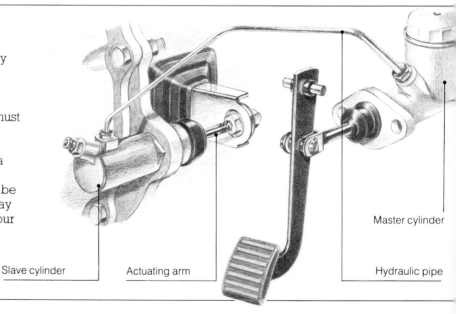

Slave cylinder

Actuating arm

Master cylinder

Hydraulic pipe

Adjusting the cable

The permissible amount of movement at the actuating lever, which, in turn, gives the correct amount of play at the clutch pedal, varies from car to car, but is specified in each car's handbook.

To check the movement, hold a ruler against the actuating lever and push it firmly towards the bell housing until you meet firm resistance. Measure the distance it travels. Adjustment is made by tightening or loosening the locknuts, or by screwing up or unscrewing a threaded sleeve on the outer cable at the bell housing. Then, adjust the cable at the gearbox, again checking the free play at the pedal.

With some cars, you must locate the sleeve containing the cable. This is normally found in the engine bay and is carved with a series of grooves, a circlip being fitted over one of them. To adjust the cable, remove the circlip and move the cable in or

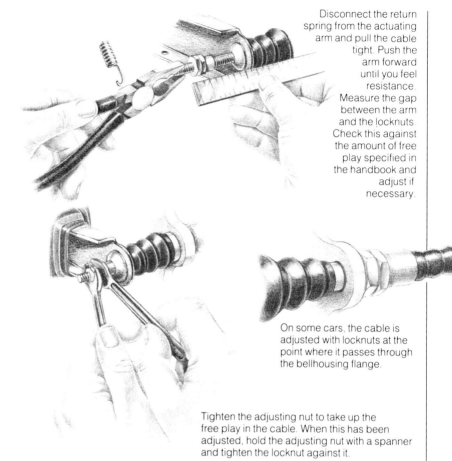

Disconnect the return spring from the actuating arm and pull the cable tight. Push the arm forward until you feel resistance. Measure the gap between the arm and the locknuts. Check this against the amount of free play specified in the handbook and adjust if necessary.

On some cars, the cable is adjusted with locknuts at the point where it passes through the bellhousing flange.

Tighten the adjusting nut to take up the free play in the cable. When this has been adjusted, hold the adjusting nut with a spanner and tighten the locknut against it.

Check the level of the hydraulic fluid in the master cylinder and top up if necessary. Wrap a piece of cloth around the cylinder to stop fluid getting on the paintwork.

out as required. After making the adjustment, replace the circlip in the appropriate groove.

Replacing a clutch cable

Disconnect the cable at the gearbox end. If the inner cable is threaded and has locknuts, these must be unscrewed. With the threaded-sleeve type, screw in the sleeve until there is sufficient slack to allow the cable to be released from the actuating arm. As stated, it will be held in place by a clevis bolt and split pin, or by a large nipple slotted into the arm.

Pull the outer cable from the bellhousing and then disconnect the inner cable from the clutch pedal. This is usually secured with a clevis bolt, passing through the pedal, and a split pin; or a large nipple fitting into a slot to hold it in place.

Withdraw the cable through the bulkhead into the engine bay, unscrewing, if necessary, a threaded collar, which screws into the bulkhead. Note carefully the order in which the various washers and spacers are fitted.

Making sure that the new cable matches the old, reverse the order of the instructions given above to refit the cable. Once it is refitted, adjust it as before.

Driving

In the years after drivers have passed their driving tests, many bad habits can be picked up, yet driving skills are never retested by any official. Every day, however, your skill as a driver is tested unofficially, by the varying road and traffic conditions that you meet.

If you consider driving to be a chore, your driving style – and your safety on the road – may reflect this attitude. But, if you enjoy driving and take an interest in all its aspects, your care and understanding will pay dividends, giving you efficient, economic and safe motoring.

Defensive driving
Many experts believe the best approach to driving is the defensive one. This does not mean that you should only take your car on to the road on sunny, traffic-free days. It does mean, however, that you should constantly assess the conditions around you and avoid getting yourself into a situation that could lead to trouble.

It is probably best to treat all other road users as totally unpredictable, though many of them will be just as careful and courteous as you. Many accidents have been caused by misunderstandings. For example, nearly every driver uses the headlights to signal to other drivers. But, does a flash signal a warning or is it a come on sign? How often have you followed a car with its indicator flashing and but making no apparent move to turn? Is the driver of the car in front looking for a side turning, or has he forgotten to cancel the indicator? Many instances like this occur every day and you should be on your guard against them.

Driving for economy and safety
In order to drive safely and economically, you must be relaxed, comfortable and alert when you are at the wheel. Your car, too, should be in prime mechanical condition.

A safe driver carries out every driving manoeuvre smoothly, thinks well in advance and never abuses his or her car. Do you match up to these guidelines? If you frequently find yourself braking heavily, for instance, or forcing other road-users to take sudden avoiding action – no matter how slight – then you are not driving at your best.

If you treat your car and other motorists with respect, you will make financial savings as well. You will not only reduce your petrol consumption, but help the components of your car to last longer.

The importance of servicing
Maximum economy and safety do not stem from good drivings habits alone. Regular, thorough servicing is equally essential. Even if you are not mechanically proficient, you should be aware of what your garage should be doing at the very least. Skimping servicing is not only a totally false economy – the long-term savings you will make more than compensate for garage charges – but extremely dangerous from the point of view of safety.

Your engine should be in a good state of tune – that is, with the plugs and contact breaker points correctly gapped, the ignition timing set correctly and the air-cleaner regularly changed. Your brakes need regular adjustment as well. Binding brakes not only waste fuel – they can be dangerous.

Faulty or badly adjusted wheel bearings also cause excessive drag, so increasing fuel consumption.

Reducing drag
Keep your tyres inflated at the pressures specified in your owner's handbook. Under-inflated tyres wear out prematurely and also increase fuel consumption through the extra resistance they create. However, you should never over-inflate tyres to reduce drag – if you do, roadholding will be affected and the tread will soon wear out. If you like, you can fit special economy tyres, which are purpose-designed to provide the lowest possible rolling resistance.

To reduce the drag on the engine, you can fit an electric fan. Such fans enable the engine to reach its normal operating temperature – and therefore the point of its peak efficiency – quickly. As a further measure, fit an air-dam – often referred to as a spoiler – to the front of your car. This reduces the amount of turbulent air that flows under the car, so reducing the drag.

Fuel economy
Many cars are now fitted with an economy warning light on the dashboard. This glows if you use excessive throttle. Alternatively, you can fit a vacuum gauge to supply the same information.

Such devices help you to improve your driving technique. Over-rapid acceleration when pulling away from the kerb, for instance, does not merely increase fuel consumption. It places unnecessary strain on the transmission and causes the tyres to wear prematurely. Reserve first gear purely for starting off and change up through the gearbox as quickly as possible, aiming to reach top gear or overdrive as soon as you can.

Heavy braking wastes fuel, too. What you should do is to reduce your speed earlier, so that you only have to brake lightly. This means you must anticipate what the road conditions ahead of you are likely to be and what other drivers are likely to do.

How you load the car also affects fuel economy. When loading a roof rack, for instance, make sure all the luggage is firmly strapped down and packed as compactly as possible to reduce air resistance to a minimum.

Using a tachometer

Every engine has a maximum power output – usually referred to as brake horsepower – and maximum torque – normally expressed in pounds/feet. Maximum power is produced when the engine is turning at its fastest, whereas maximum torque – think of this as slogging power – occurs much earlier. If your car is fitted with a tachometer, you can use these facts to substantial advantage.

Say, for example, that your engine produces maximum torque at 3,000 rpm. By keeping the engine revolutions down to around this figure, you will achieve the best possible combination of performance and economy. If you increase the revs, you will improve performance, but at the expense of economy; if you reduce them, the opposite applies.

Measuring miles per gallon

If you follow the advice given here, the amount of fuel you use should decrease significantly. The simplest way of checking this is to fill the fuel tank and make a note of what the mileage is on the odometer. Alternatively, if a trip meter is fitted, set this to zero.

When the tank is nearly empty, fill up again, noting how much fuel it will take. Divide the distance you have driven by the amount of fuel you have added to get the miles-per-gallon figure.

Fitting a mini-computer to the dashboard is a more accurate way of finding out the same information. As well as telling you your overall fuel consumption at the end of a journey, the computer will also indicate average fuel consumption while you are driving. This provides an immediate guide as to how much fuel you are using.

Comfort and safety

If you drive with consideration and keep your car well-maintained, you will save money and contribute greatly to road safety. As far as this second point is concerned, however, it is equally important that your car is comfortable and enjoyable to drive.

Perfect driving vision is extremely important. This means keeping the windows and windscreen clean, checking that the windscreen wipers and washers are working properly and that the headlamp lenses are not obscured by road grime. Do not cover the windscreen or rear window with stickers or badges.

This is especially important for night driving, when a clear view, forward and backward, is vital. Unfortunately, temperatures are lower at night. This means that the windscreen is more likely to become misted up, and the diffusion of the headlamp beams of an oncoming car can make the road ahead almost impossible to see.

Your seat should be comfortable and supportive. If it is not, fit specially-padded seat covers or a new seat. Always wear a seat belt and insist that your passengers wear theirs as well – it is now illegal to travel in the front of a car without wearing a seat belt. Even in the back of the car, never allow children or young babies to travel, if not firmly belted. If necessary, fit a special baby seat (see p.153). These can be bought in kit form. Many cars incorporate fixing lugs for baby seat webbing so there is no need to drill holes.

Long journeys can become boring for both driver and passengers. Buy a book of games to keep children happy and, as soon as you feel tired, stop and rest. If possible, keep a window partly open, or set the heater to cold to provide some fresh air. You should not drive with the heater full on and all the windows closed, as this may make you extremely drowsy.

If you are towing a caravan or trailer, the car must be equipped with a proper towbar – fitting this is usually a job for a garage – and the caravan or trailer must be securely hitched to it. The lights on the back of the caravan or trailer must work in conjunction with the car's lights.

Towing demands its own skills, so you should rehearse these before setting off (see p.156). The golden safety rule is never to allow passengers into a caravan.

Driving in safety/1

Driving in the city and country

Driving in towns and cities makes especial demands on both car and driver. This is because, although average speeds are generally low, traffic conditions and driving situations are constantly changing. You face many potential hazards and frustrations – all of which take an inevitable toll on clutch, gearbox and brakes, which are in almost constant use.

Driving hints

By showing a little care and forethought, you will not only be able to drive more safely, but also more economically – even in city conditions. When you start the car, for instance, move off straight away to warm the engine. Push in the choke as quickly as you can, although not soon enough to make the engine falter. Use first gear purely to move off and always drive in the highest gear possible.

Remember that excessive use of the throttle is one of the main causes of excessive fuel consumption. It is pointless accelerating hard for a short stretch when you know a road junction lies ahead. It is far better to accelerate gently and to decelerate so that only moderate braking is needed.

Always approach traffic lights and pedestrian crossings with the belief that the lights will change or somebody might rush out on to the crossing. Keep checking in your rear-view mirror in case you have to brake suddenly. Your aim should be to give drivers behind you advance warning of your intention to stop by gently reducing your own speed and making a slowing-down hand signal. Never overtake on a pedestrian crossing.

Give cyclists and motorcyclists the widest possible berth. Similarly, if you are passing a line of parked cars, remember that doors can be suddenly opened. Again, allow sufficient overtaking margin.

Potential hazards

Look out for advance warning of all potential hazards. If you are driving behind a bus, for instance, and notice passengers gathering by its doors, it should be obvious that the bus may suddenly stop to let them off. If you are passing a school at the beginning or end of the school day, watch out for youngsters dashing out into the road or parents suddenly pulling away from the kerb. Also be ready for the school crossing attendant to halt traffic.

When pulling out from a side turning, the usual procedure is to look right, left and right again to check that the road is clear before driving off. However, it pays to take a further final look to the left in case an oncoming car is being overtaken by another on your side of the road.

Driving discipline

While sitting in traffic, do not rest your foot on the clutch pedal. This habit will eventually lead to premature clutch failure. Always apply the handbrake and put the car in neutral if you are stopped for more than a few seconds.

Traffic jams waste petrol. Plan and get to know alternate routes around traffic black spots. The alternate route may well be longer, but will involve less stopping and starting. As a result, not only will your fuel consumption figures be improved, but the drive will also be more enjoyable.

Country driving

Though driving in the country is generally far more pleasant than driving in a town or city, it has its own range of hazards, some of which you rarely find in urban surroundings. It is equally important to keep your eye – and mind – on the road, as the speeds at which you drive will generally be higher.

Follow the same basic rules governing the use of throttle and gears as you would in a town. On a steep hill, it is often better to use a lower gear with moderate throttle, than to force the car to labour up the hill in top gear with your accelerator flat on the floorboards.

If you see a bend in the distance – or one is indicated by road signs – decelerate in plenty of time. This will probably enable you to negotiate the bend without braking. Never approach a bend too fast, especially if the road is totally unfamiliar. If possible, never brake while in a bend, since that is the moment when tyres offer the least traction. In such circumstances, hard braking can lead to an uncontrollable skid.

Country hazards

The road surface provides its own clues as to what lies ahead. Mud on the road, for instance, means that you should slow down because the surface will be slippery. It could indicate a slow-moving tractor around the corner as well. Newly-laid grit, or tarmac, could mean there is a gritting lorry or a road-works crew ahead. Be prepared for either eventuality. If you drive through a ford, always test brakes immediately afterwards – the water can make them fade.

Rural roads team with concealed farm and cottage entrances and vehicles from either are all too likely to pull out in front of you without warning. Look for obvious breaks in fencing and hedges and slow down when you see them.

Horses pose particular problems, as they can easily panic at the sound of an engine. If you see horse dung on the road, reduce speed and prepare to stop. When overtaking a horseback rider, do it slowly, giving animal and rider as wide a berth as possible. Never rev your engine or change gear noisily– this will frighten the horse. Also be on the lookout for other animals – such as cows and deer – which may wander onto the road.

In windy weather, watch out for fallen trees or branches. Either can easily block a narrow country lane.

Passing discipline

On narrow country roads and lanes, it is quite frequently impossible for two cars to pass each other. If so, small lay-bys are provided at regular intervals. These are passing places – not parking places. Make a note of each as you drive by. If you meet another car, you will then know how far back you must reverse to let it pass.

If you see a car in the distance and it is obvious that one of you must give way, pull into a lay-by if there is one handy – before you meet the car. This will only delay you for a short time and save you the bother of reversing.

Always observe speed limits when driving through villages.

Remember that the inhabitants may not be used to dense traffic passing through the main street, particularly if it is travelling fast.

As a survival measure, it is always worth filling your tank when you see a village service station. Fuel pumps can be few and far between.

Driving in adverse conditions

When driving in adverse weather conditions, try to relax. If you are tense, you may become insensitive to the steering, and fail to notice if the wheels loose their grip on the road surface. Also, do not drive beyond your capabilities, and do not let yourself become harrassed by any impatient drivers behind you. If a car's closeness bothers you, slow down and pull over to allow it to pass.

Rain

Accidents are far more likely to happen in the wet than in the dry. Rain means reduced visibility, accompanied by the risk of skidding and not being able to stop effectively on the wet road surface. Driving in the wet thus demands the closest possible concentration, with careful use of brakes, steering and the accelerator. You should also allow for more room when manoeuvring in case of any possible emergency.

One major problem can be caused by the film of water rain leaves on the road. Normally, the tread pattern of the car's tyre copes with this by squeezing water from beneath the tyre as the car moves forward. However, if the car is moving at speed, the tyre tread cannot cope with the water – on a motorway, for instance, a tyre

has to deal with over a gallon of water a second. Consequently the tyre loses contact with the road.

This problem is called aquaplaning. If your tyres are worn, the car will begin to aquaplane all the sooner, as the worn tread is even less able to cope with the water.

If your car starts to aquaplane, you will feel a lightness in the steering. If this happens, slow down gently by decelerating, not by applying the brakes, until the steering feels normal again. Beware especially of wet roads when rain has fallen after a long dry spell. The water combines with oil and rubber already on the road to produce an extremely slippery and dangerous surface.

If rain falls on to a dry windscreen, use your windscreen washers to lubricate the wiper blades on their first sweeps – this will prevent the glass becoming smeared and affecting your vision, and will also protect the blades from excessive wear. If the rain is falling so heavily that the wipers cannot cope with clearing the windscreen, slow down and stop until the rain slackens – usually this will cost you only a few minutes. As rain also causes car windows to mist up quickly, make sure that your heater is switched on to the 'demist' position.

Beware of flooded roads. If you drive into flood water at speed, you can easily lose control of the car. Do not attempt to drive through floods if you are not sure of the water depth. The chances are that the engine will stall and you could find yourself stranded. If you know that the flood is only shallow, and decide

Driving in safety/2

to drive through it, then drive slowly in low gear, slipping the clutch and revving the engine to stop it from stalling. Immediately after passing through the water, apply the brakes gently while the car is on the move. This will dry them out. Make sure that they are working normally before you begin travelling at speed again.

Fog

Fog is potentially the most dangerous weather condition a motorist can face, especially on motorways. No amount of driving skill can compensate for bad visibility, so always drive within the limits of your vision.

Make sure that your windscreen is clear. Use your windscreen wipers and washers regularly to prevent moisture building up on the glass, which may easily go unnoticed. Make sure that all your lights are working correctly, including your front and rear fog lamps, and keep to well-lit roads where you can. If your car is not fitted with fog lamps, use dipped headlights – not full beam, as this may reflect back from the fog and dazzle you. Try to travel, when possible, in convoy fashion, following the lights of the car in front, but taking care not to get too close.

Another useful guide is the nearside kerb, if visible. However, you should beware of vehicles that may be parked at the side of the road without lights. Sometimes sound can be helpful, so open the window a little.

Snow and ice

Many drivers are are relatively inexperienced in coping with with snow and ice. The one golden rule to follow when driving in such conditions is to always drive gently – harsh acceleration or braking may cause the car to skid, or if you are skidding, will only make the situation worse.

In extreme winter conditions, it is best to drive in the highest gear with the lowest possible revs. This will give the wheels maximum grip without making them spin. If the road is icy and you find it impossible to even start, trying driving the car backwards and forwards a few times and then try to pull away in high gear. Some sacking or a rough mat placed under the driving wheels will help, so it is worth considering carrying such items – or a set of chains – in the boot during the winter. A small shovel may also be useful.

When climbing a snow-covered hill, try to keep going without stopping at all, keeping the car in as high a gear as possible. If it is clear that cars in front of you are not reaching the top, you should consider taking an alternative route.

Even after the snow and ice has disappeared, still take care. Slush can be treacherous, especially if a subsequent cold snap freezes it, while black ice – patches of ice concealed by road dirt – can be extremely difficult to spot.

Skidding

Skidding occurs when the wheels slide instead of turning. It usually results when you drive too fast for the road conditions. Apart from the obvious perils of snow, ice and rain, mud and fallen leaves on the road are common skidding hazards.

It is an instinctive reaction to brake sharply when you see a hazard ahead of you. In adverse weather conditions, this can cause skidding. If you have to brake when the weather is bad, you should pump the brake pedal so that the wheels can still keep turning, rather than brake harshly. If you do skid, try to steer the car into the direction of the skid, without using the brakes at all; if the back end of the car moves to the right, steer to the right, and vice versa. In some circumstances, steering away from the direction of the skid to make the car spin, may be used to advantage – when there is a hazard in the road ahead, for instance.

You should never experiment with skidding on the roads, as this can be dangerous. If you want to experiment, you should locate a skidpan. The AA or the RAC will be able to give you the address of your nearest skidpan centre.

Motorway driving

Motorways are the safest roads in the world, with less accidents per mile than any other type of road. However, because the traffic on them generally travels at high speed, accidents, when they occur, tend to be more serious. The faster you go, the less margin there is for error.

Consequently, motorway driving demands total concentration from all drivers. Bear in mind that at 70mph (112kph) you are travelling at over 100 feet per second. One sneeze, and you may have covered 100 yards without being able to see clearly.

Accidents on motorways are usually caused by driving too fast, especially in adverse weather conditions *(see p. 147)*, by lack of concentration, and by

Controlling a car that has lost grip on the road is something most drivers have to do only rarely, and, for that reason, the situation takes a lot of people by surprise.

The main thing to remember is, *don't panic*. Hasty actions taken without thinking can often get you into deeper trouble and heavy braking or jerky steering will not help the car regain grip.

Braking control

When road conditions reduce the grip the tyres have on the road – during heavy rain or in snow and ice, for example – the chances of accidents occuring increase greatly. You may be called on to brake heavily to avoid an emergency and this, in turn, can produce its own emergency as a result.

The front brakes of a car are always more powerful than rear ones, as braking throws most of the car's weight to the front. If the road conditions are bad, there is a good chance of the front wheels locking under heavy braking – that is, the wheels stop rotating while the car is still moving forward. If this happens, you will lose all directional control; no matter which way you turn the steering wheel, the car will travel the way in which it is pointing.

If you feel the front wheels lose their grip, try pumping the brakes on and off. This will slow the car a little, but, at the same time, still allow the wheels to turn, so that you can maintain directional control. If the car is slowed down sufficiently, you should then be able to steer out of trouble.

If the front wheels lock and pumping the brakes fails, there is an emergency procedure you can follow. With your foot still on the brake pedal, and the front wheels still locked, turn the steering wheel to full lock in the direction you want to go. Even though the car may not appear to slow down, its speed will fall sufficiently to ensure that the car will turn in the direction you are steering when you release the brakes.

Always remember, however, that these are difficult manoeuvres to accomplish safely and should only be attempted in a real emergency. Do not try them out on public roads; if you want to practise them, you should seek instruction on a skid-pan from a qualified instructor.

CAR CONTROL IN ADVERSE CONDITIONS

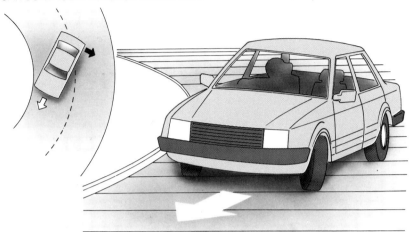

Rear wheel skid If the rear wheels lose their grip on the road and the front wheels do not, the back of the car will swing out, away from the corner. If this goes uncorrected, the car will spin around. To correct the skid, lift your foot off the accelerator and de-clutch immediately. Do not touch the brakes. Steer in the opposite direction to the way the car is pointing. When you feel the rear wheels gripping, steer back into the corner but be prepared to apply corrective steering if the rear wheels lose their grip again.

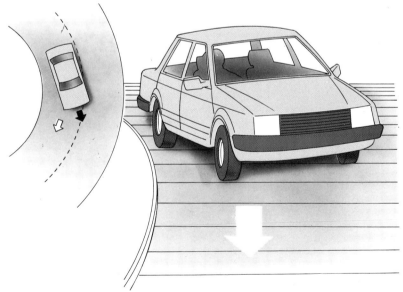

Front wheel skid If the front wheels lose their grip when cornering, the car will tend to go straight on. Lift your foot off the accelerator and de-clutch immediately. Do not touch the brakes, as this will cause the front wheels to lock. To enable the front wheels to regain their grip, turn the steering wheel to point the wheels in the direction the car is travelling. When you feel the front wheels gripping again, steer back into the corner.

Driving in safety/3

driving too close to vehicles in front of you. Cocooned in a warm car, you will often find it difficult to judge your speed. It is all too easy to forget that you are travelling at a speed that may be dangerous if your concentration lapses, while, since all the traffic is travelling at a similar speed, you may actually forget how fast you are going.

When travelling at speed, it is important you work out the safe stopping distance for the amount of road ahead. Allow for rain, snow, ice or fog (see p.147) when calculating stopping distances, allowing at least double, if not treble, the normal stopping distance.

Watch out!

You should be constantly aware of the vehicles travelling in front, behind, and alongside you. Make frequent use of your mirrors – both rear and wing – and always doublecheck behind you before changing lanes. Remember that there may be vehicles hidden from view in the blind spot – the area to the rear half of the car on either side, the view of which is obscured in both rear or door mirrors.

Entrance and exit

When you drive on to any slip road leading on to a motorway, start by gradually adjusting your speed to suit the speed of the traffic in the nearside lane. When you see a gap in the traffic, increase your speed, check your mirrors, signal your intention of joining the motorway, and pull into the nearside lane. Give yourself time to become accustomed to the speed of other vehicles before moving into the middle lane.

When you decide to leave the motorway, watch for the one mile indication point for your chosen exit. Make your way over to the nearside lane, and then watch for the half mile warning sign, and the countdown signs at three hundred, two hundred, and one hundred yards before the actual exit. When you reach this, move smoothly into the slip road, signalling your intentions to the traffic behind you and gradually reducing speed. Check your speedometer to make sure that you are driving within the speed limit – driving constantly at a high speed on the motorway can impair your judgement.

If you miss your exit, you must drive on to the next exit. You cannot stop, turn or cross the central reservation under any circumstances.

Lane discipline

Most modern motorways have three lanes plus a hard shoulder, although some older ones have two lane stretches. The left hand, or nearside, lane is used by slow-moving traffic, usually large trucks. However, if it is clear, you should use it, provided that you do not have to pull in and out of the lane constantly to pass other vehicles. If the left hand lane is busy, use the middle lane and stay there unless you are overtaking, in which case you use the third, or fast, lane.

The third lane should be used only for overtaking – as soon as you have done this, pull back into the middle lane, making sure that you do so gradually, leaving plenty of room between your car and the vehicle you have just overtaken. Large commercial vehicles, and those pulling trailers are not allowed in the third lane.

Whenever you are driving in the centre lane, always drive in the middle, leaving plenty of room for traffic to pass either side of you. This is extremely important on windy days, when a sudden gust of wind can force a car over in the direction in which the wind is blowing. Only change lanes one at a time and, before doing so, give plenty of warning of your intentions, signalling them clearly and well in advance.

Try to avoid driving three abreast, as this leaves you little rooom for evasive action should another driver make an error, or another vehicle lose control.

Night driving

When you drive on a motorway at night, you should take even more care to adjust your driving habits to the conditions. If it is raining, for instance, you should reduce your speed, while, if it is misty, watch out for rolling banks of fog. These can be lethal if you drive into one unexpectedly.

Whenever possible, try to drive on dipped headlights, as sidelights provide insufficient illumination, even if the motorway itself is lit by street lamps. You should not drive with your headlights on full beam unless the road ahead of you is clear. Driving on full beam can blind both on-coming traffic and cars in front of you. If you are doing much motorway driving, it will pay you to fit an anti-dazzle driving mirror.

Emergency action

The hard shoulder is for emergencies only; whenever it is illegal to park on it in any other circumstance. If possible,

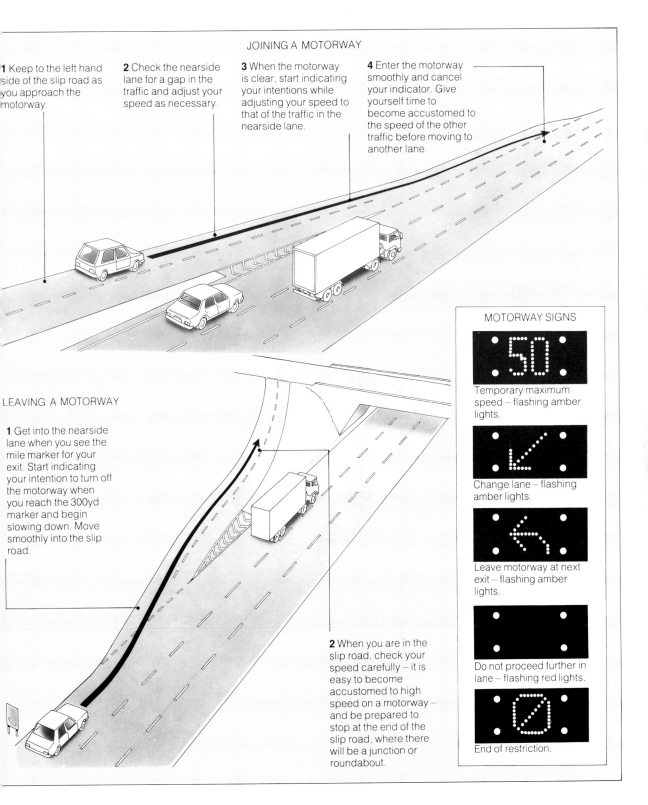

JOINING A MOTORWAY

1 Keep to the left hand side of the slip road as you approach the motorway.

2 Check the nearside lane for a gap in the traffic and adjust your speed as necessary.

3 When the motorway is clear, start indicating your intentions while adjusting your speed to that of the traffic in the nearside lane.

4 Enter the motorway smoothly and cancel your indicator. Give yourself time to become accustomed to the speed of the other traffic before moving to another lane.

LEAVING A MOTORWAY

1 Get into the nearside lane when you see the mile marker for your exit. Start indicating your intention to turn off the motorway when you reach the 300yd marker and begin slowing down. Move smoothly into the slip road.

2 When you are in the slip road, check your speed carefully – it is easy to become accustomed to high speed on a motorway – and be prepared to stop at the end of the slip road, where there will be a junction or roundabout.

MOTORWAY SIGNS

Temporary maximum speed – flashing amber lights.

Change lane – flashing amber lights.

Leave motorway at next exit – flashing amber lights.

Do not proceed further in lane – flashing red lights.

End of restriction.

Driving in safety/4

you should always try to reach the next service area if there is something wrong with your car. If you do have to stop, switch on your hazard warning lights (if fitted) and, if you have one, place a red warning triangle a reasonable distance behind the car.

Leave the car by the door facing *away* from the motorway unless you can see that the road is clear for some distance behind you. The slipstream from passing vehicles can snatch the driver's door open. If you can, ask your passengers to stay in their seats until help arrives – a motorway is no place for standing or wandering around. If it is essential to get your passengers out of the car, do this calmly and make sure that they stand out of harm's way.

Getting help
You will find emergency telelphones spaced along the hard shoulder. Look at the distance markers along the motorway to establish where the closest telephone is to you, as these indicate the direction to walk to reach the nearest one. The telephone will put you in touch with the regional police control room, which will identify where you are and send help as quickly as possible.

Occasionally, you may find that a telephone is out of action. If so, there is no reason to panic. The police will be aware of the fault and will be patrolling the affected stretch of motorway as a result. Return to your car and wait for a patrol to locate you.

The dangers of fatigue
We all suffer from lapses of concentration at some time or other, but if such a lapse occurs

while you are driving, the consequences can be disastrous. Driving is a skilful operation that demands your full attention at all times; if you are tired, your reactions will become slower than normal and your judgement will be impaired.

Medical studies have shown that a tired driver has to work harder than other drivers to maintain concentration, while driving performance is less satisfactory. This is especially the case at the end of a long journey, when coordination also becomes affected.

Signs of fatigue are often similar to those of drunkenness – the driver may actually feel slightly drunk as well as drowsy. You should learn to recognize these potential danger signs, as there is far more chance of you being involved in an accident when you are tired than at other times.

How to avoid fatigue
By following certain rules, you avoid, or at the least minimize the problem of tiredness at the wheel. The first rule is to have a good night's rest before making a journey. If you are travelling far, plan ahead, giving yourself enough time to make regular stops. Allow at least ten minutes rest for each hour of driving, and try to get out of the car so that you can stretch your legs and breathe in fresh air.

Never travel a long distance without eating something beforehand or en route, though it is better to eat small regular snacks rather than one large meal. This will maintain your blood sugar level, while guarding against fatigue. In no circumstances should you drink

and drive. Remember, although you may have drunk under the legal limit, even a small amount of alcohol will impair your judgement, and may make you feel sleepy. Drugs may also dull your senses and affect your driving ability. If you are given a prescription by your doctor, check that it will not cause drowsiness.

Fresh air is very important. Even in cold weather with the heater on, it is essential to keep the car well ventilated. Modern cars are equipped with fresh air ventilation systems, which you should use at all times, positioning the ducts to avoid draughts. But, if you are aware that you are tired, directing the current of fresh air towards your face will help to revive you. If your car is not fitted with such a system, wind the window down a little instead.

Rattles and vibrations
Although you may be unaware of their effect, rattles, noises and vibrations can all contribute to tiredness. If you notice a rattle or vibration of any kind from your car, try to solve the problem yourself, or tell the garage about it before work begins on your car at its next service. If your car is generally noisy, you may be able to quieten it with a soundproofing kit. Such kits are available for most makes of car. The key element is the various forms of soundproofing material they contain, which must be positioned strategically around the car – in the boot, on the floor, under the bonnet and across the bulkhead.

Tension
It is important that you feel relaxed when you are behind

the wheel, without becoming lethargic. Tension is a common cause of tiredness, especially after a long day. Allow for any traffic problems and give yourself plenty of time to reach your destination – it is better to arrive early and relaxed than late and tired.

One of the most important ways to avoid tension is to make sure that your driving position is comfortable; it is surprising how may people fail to observe this fundamental rule

Difficult or frustrating traffic conditions, or something on your mind, will also make you feel tense. Although you cannot do anything about the traffic and may not be able to solve the problem immediately, simply being aware of the fact that both may combine to make you irritable and aggressive will help you combat the mounting tension.

Boredom
Being bored can also contribute to fatigue. Whenever possible, travel with a passenger. This will relieve the tedium of long journeys. You can also lessen the demands made on your powers of concentration by sharing the burden of the driving – but check first that your insurance allows you to do this.

A car radio can also play a useful role in helping to keep your mind on your driving. However, if you are tired, you will find that the spoken word will hold your attention more effectively; beware of the lulling effect of relaxing music in a warm, cosy car.

Seating basics
A comfortable driver is a

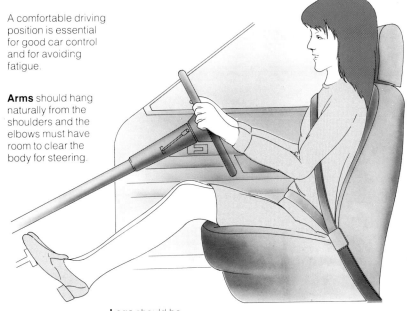

A comfortable driving position is essential for good car control and for avoiding fatigue.

Arms should hang naturally from the shoulders and the elbows must have room to clear the body for steering.

Feet should not have to bend back to work the pedals and heels should remain in contact with the floor.

Legs should be slightly bent, while there should be a slight gap between the underside of the thighs and the front few inches of the seat.

Head and back The head should tilt forward slightly, while the upper part of the back should recline at an angle of about 20°. The small of the back should be hollowed slightly, with the seat reclined by 5°.

relaxed driver and the more comfortable your driving position, the more relaxed you will be, especially on a long journey. If you are travelling with children in the car, you will feel more relaxed if they are safe and comfortable, too.

As far as adults are concerned, the most important priority is to sit correctly. Sitting incorrectly, though seemingly comfortable at first, can lead to discomfort later, with the development of unnoticed fatigue and consequent lack of concentration.

You should adjust your seat to give the best possible view of the road ahead, with all the car's controls within easy reach. Your aim should be to drive with maximum efficiency, yet in maximum comfort.

Even on the most modern cars, however, not all seats are perfect. If yours are not, consider what minor adjustments you can make to them, or whether or not to fit a better, upgraded seat. If you decide on this, there are many types from which to choose. Another alternative is to purchase a seat taken from a model similar to your own car, but higher in the range. A breaker's yard can be a good starting point in such cases.

Your driving position
When determining your driving position, there are certain basic rules that you should follow. If you observe them, they will become established as a habit, no matter what type of car you may be driving. They will

Driving in safety/5

enable you to assess the comfort of a car very quickly as well.

When you place your hands on the steering wheel, think of the wheel as a clock and put your hands in the 'ten to two' position. They should fall below shoulder height. Make sure that your arms are not excessively bent or too straight – either can be tiring. Elbows should clear the body easily when manoeuvering.

The angle between foot and ankle should never be less than 90° – 100° is thought to be the most comfortable. Your heels should be in contact with the floor when operating any of the pedals. Obviously, your shoes should be suitable for driving as well.

Knees should be bent at an angle of between 15° and 60°, while legs should never be straight, even when operating pedal controls. The backs of the knees should not be in contact with the seat. Although the seat should support the thighs, there should be a slight gap between the first few inches of the seat cushion and the underside of the thigh.

The upper part of your back should recline at about 20° from the vertical. If you recline further than this, your head will be too far forward, which leads to discomfort after a time. The shoulders should be well-supported, although their movement should not be restricted.

A good driving seat will give you plenty of support in the small of the back – sitting with a rounded back for a prolonged period can lead to strained ligaments in the lumbar region. The backrest should slope at an angle of around 5° from vertical.

Your eyes should be able to read dashboard instruments and use rear-view and wing mirrors effortlessly. When you drive, it is important that your gaze should be level. Hold your head high and tuck in your chin. If the head is positioned correctly, the neck will fall naturally into the right position – leaning forward about 15° from the vertical.

The effect of seat belts

Seat belts can affect driving comfort adversely if the angle of the belt across the shoulder is incorrect. You should take steps to deal with this problem if it occurs, since it is now compulsory for drivers and front-seat passengers to wear seat belts while the car is on the move.

If the belt anchorage point is too high, for instance, you can fit a small extension bracket that will lower the anchorage point to suit your needs. If your car is fitted with old-fashioned static seat belts, you may find these uncomfortable, especially when reaching for the glove box, or a dashboard control. Here, you should consider updating your car by fitting one of the many inertia seat-belt kits that are now widely available.

Child passengers

It is best for children to travel in the back of the car and to wear rear seat belts – this is now compulsory in many European countries. As such belts are not as yet a legal requirement in Britain, however, a child is better off travelling belted in the front seat, rather than unbelted in the back.

Generally, children are far happier belted, especially when they see that adults are wearing

A booster cushion enables a child to wear an adult seat belt in the front or back of the car. The booster raises the child so that the seat belt is positioned correctly over the shoulder.

seat belts as well. With very young children, you should consider fitting a child seat or cushion – either will lift the child above the conventional seat, so enabling him or her to look out of the window easily. This makes a journey far less boring for the child – and car sickness more unlikely.

As a general rule, babies aged six months or under should travel in carry-cots – the cot being restrained on the back seat – children up to the age of four should travel in child seats and older children should be harnessed in a seat belt, with the aid of a booster cushion. This is particularly useful when children are travelling in a car without child seats, since it can be used in conjunction with an adult seat belt.

The cushion is designed to stop a child sliding under the restraining belt. Tests by Britain's Motor Industry Research Association show that using a normal soft cushion with a seat belt is of little benefit.

Rear seat belts are now standard fittings in many cars. If your car is not equipped with them, you can fit a d-i-y kit, but check first to see if there are anchorage points for the new belts on the chassis.

You can fit special belts to hold a carry cot securely on the back seat *(above)*, or, for a slightly older child, a combined unit of belts and travelling seat *(below)*. This will not only hold the child securely, but provide a comfortable place in which to play.

With the advent of the booster cushion, it is now more sensible to fit a generation belt in the rear of the car. This can be used by adults and children alike, with or without a cushion.

Fitting rear seat belts

There are many types of child restraint on the market, but you should always choose one marked as meeting official safety standards. Regardless of the type of car you own, there will be a way of fitting rear seat belts, baby seats, or carry-cot restraints, though, naturally enough, this will be easier in some cases than in others. If you are not sure whether your car has existing fitting points, ask your local car dealer, who will explain where they can be found – normally under the rear seat and below the rear parcel shelf.

If your car is fitted with rear-seat anchorage points, fitting a belt is a relatively easy job. Remember, too, that the points can be utilized for a baby seat, or harness. If not, the instructions

with the seat or belts will tell you where to drill holes and how to fix the anchorage plates. If you want to fix more than one harness, you can still use one fixing point – longer bolts are available for this purpose.

On hatchbacks and estate cars, longer straps are needed. You can get these from the seat or belt manufacturer. If you are changing a seat over from a saloon to a hatchback, separate extension belt kits are available, together with transfer kits, which are useful when changing cars. All help to keep costs down.

If the rear of an estate car or hatchback is frequently fully loaded, you may find that anchoring long straps to the floor can create a storage problem. The solution here, although an expensive one, is to fit a special seat belt that stretches across the car behind the rear seat. The belt is anchored to the normal pillar mounting points, with the seat, or harness straps, being attached to the bar instead of to the floor.

Towing/1

Towing is an art in itself. Quite apart from acquiring the necessary skills, you must also take all the necessary steps to comply with the law and to avoid creating a hazard for yourself and other road-users.

If you are equipping your car for permanent towing, a certain amount of modification will be required. This can either be carried out professionally or on a do-it-yourself basis. Find out what will be involved first and then decide whether or not you can tackle the job.

Towbars

If you intend to tow a caravan, your car must be fitted with a towbar. Either have one installed by a garage, complete with all the necessary wiring to link your rear lights with those of the caravan, or buy a kit and tackle the job at home, if you feel competent to do so. Such kits are specifically designed to suit most makes of car.

The towing bracket is attached to a sturdy angle-iron frame, which in turn is secured to the chassis. In both cases, you must drill large holes with a heavy-duty drill to take the large bolts that are required.

The towing ball's normal height from the ground is 175mm (7in). If a lightweight caravan with small wheels is to be towed, a special drop-plate can be used to lower the towing ball to the appropriate position. The bar itself needs no maintenance other than regular greasing. When not in use, it should be protected by a plastic or alloy cover.

By law, all lights on a caravan or trailer must be linked to the lights on your car, so that the two operate simultaneously. This

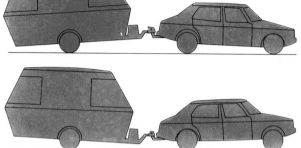

BALANCING THE LOAD

Too much weight at the back of the caravan will raise the back of the car, reducing the grip on the road of the back wheels.

Too much weight at the front of the caravan will lift the front of the car, reducing the grip of the front wheels and making steering difficult.

means that a special electrical socket must be fitted. With older cars, a single seven-pin socket is adequate; with newer models – especially those fitted with rear fog lamps – you will need an extra seven-pin socket to service all the caravan's internal accessories, such as a refrigerator or television.

Depending on its chosen position, fitting the socket usually involves further drilling into the bodywork. Examine the kit's wiring diagram carefully before you start and, if in doubt when connecting up to the car's electrical circuit, check the wiring diagram in your manual as well. This will tell you which wires control the lights and indicators.

All connections must be strong and totally sealed against the effects of weather. You will also need a heavy-duty flasher unit to cope with the caravan's indicators as well as the car's.

When fitting towbars and sockets, make sure that you buy standard parts. A 50cm (20in) towing ball is the conventional size. Failure to do this may well mean that the car cannot be used to tow a caravan other than your own and this will affect the

car's resale value. The wiring, too, should conform to international regulations.

Caravans

The size of caravan you can tow is ultimately dictated by the size of your car. If you aim to tow the caravan at speeds up to 50mph (80kph), its maximum gross weight must be no more than the kerb (unladen) weight of the car. This will be specified in the manufacturer's handbook. If the caravan's weight is greater than this, you are restricted to a speed of no more than 40mph (64kph).

Generally speaking, a car needs at least a 1500-cc engine to tow a caravan easily. A car with a smaller engine might appear to do the job, but the strain towing this extra weight will impose, will show in decreased performance and increased fuel consumption.

Your car may need extra accessories as well. Depending on the caravan's width, you may have to fit extended overtaking mirrors. Special roof-mounted rear-view mirrors are available, too – they act like a periscope, allowing you to keep an eye on the caravan and the road behind

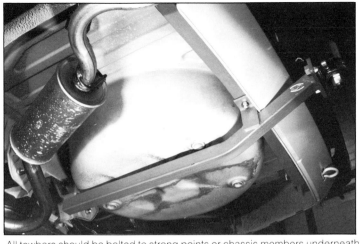

All towbars should be bolted to strong points or chassis members underneath the back of the car.

Trailer brake

Handle for raising dolley wheel

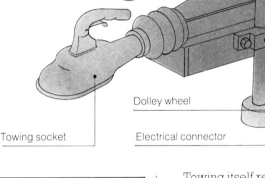

Dolley wheel

Electrical connector

Towing socket

Towing ball

Electrical socket

it. With automatic transmission, the gearbox will be under extra strain, so an oil-cooler may be necessary. Check in the handbook to see whether or not this is the case.

Your car's rear suspension may also have to be strengthened to cope with the extra load. Confirm whether or not this is the case by a trial road test. Load the car and caravan with the amount of luggage and number of passengers you normally intend to carry. If the car's handling suffers or the back end sags – possibly causing the wheels to foul the arches – then strengthening is

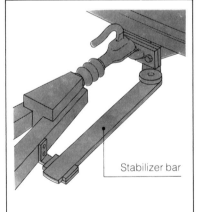

Stabilizer bar

By fitting a stabilizer between the trailer and the towbar, the lateral movement, or swing, of the trailer will be reduced.

necessary. There are various ways in which this can be done. You can fit stiffer shock absorbers, spring assisters, or an extra leaf spring on each side of the car.

Towing itself requires practice, as you must familiarize yourself with the caravan's extra weight and length. Remember that the caravan extends the wheelbase, so, when cornering, allow a little more space to avoid hitting the kerb with the wheels. If the caravan has a long over-hang, the tail will swing round sharply when turning a tight corner and could hit passing cars, so take extra care.

When reversing, a caravan behaves in the completely opposite way to a car on its own. Before you do so, check behind for pedestrians or obstructions and, if possible, get someone to guide you. Start reversing in a straight line and gradually apply the opposite steering lock to the direction you wish to take. Move slowly and turn the wheel gradually – too much lock and the caravan will jacknife and damage the car.

Towing/2

While towing, make sure everything inside the caravan is securely packed and that the load is evenly spread. Never let anybody travel in it while you are on the move.

Trailers

A towbar must be fitted to tow a trailer but you will only need one seven-pin plug for the necessary extra lights.

A trailer fitted with its own independent suspension is a far better buy than a solid axle one. You will need a tarpaulin cover for the trailer box – it should be possible to strap this down – though a locking lid provides even better security. Make sure that the contents of the trailer are packed securely and evenly, so that their weight is distributed correctly.

Manoeuvring a trailer is easier than a caravan, but the same rules apply for cornering and reversing. Because most trailers are lightweight – even when fully-loaded – take extra care on bumpy roads. Their affect on handling can be dramatic.

Just as with a caravan, you may need to strengthen your car's rear suspension, depending on the size of the trailer and the load being carried in it. Confirm this by test-loading the trailer and trial-towing it, checking the handling and the effect on the suspension.

Towing cars

Obviously, the cheapest way of getting a totally immobilized car home is to ask a friend to tow it. This, however, is not always as simple as it seems – it is all too easy to have an accident, or to damage the cars.

Purpose-made tow ropes can be bought – they are usually

REVERSING A CARAVAN OR TRAILER

Turn the wheel so the back of the car swings away from the curb. The back of the caravan or trailer will swing into the corner.

As the caravan or trailer enters the corner, start to steer the car the other way to follow the trailer around the corner.

made from tough nylon compound – but it is possible to use strong webbing or a thick conventional rope. Whichever you choose – or, more likely, whichever is available – it is important to attach it in the right place. This varies from car to car and from the car doing the towing to the one that is being towed.

With the former, the rope should be attached to a strong part of the suspension, or, on rear-wheel-drive cars, round the back axle. Look for a towing hook – such hooks are welded to a strong body member on many modern cars. Do not attach the rope to the exhaust or bumper. With the latter, attach the rope to a cross-member or strong suspension component. On front-wheel-drive cars, take care not to wrap it round a drive shaft and, in all cases, avoid utilizing

any component that could affect the steering. Do not attach it to the bumper. With both cars, however, you might find that the bumper is bolted to the chassis with sturdy angle-iron brackets. These are normally strong enough to take the strain. The rope should be attached to the offside of both cars to avoid dragging the car you are towing across the kerb on left-hand corners.

Once the rope is attached, take up the slack gently. Make sure that it is not fouling the bodywork or a steering component. Remember to put the ignition key in place, so the steering lock cannot be activated.

There should be a gap of at least 10 to 12 feet (3m) between the two cars with the rope taut and a brightly-coloured piece of rag should be tied in the middle as a visual warning of its presence. A clear 'On Tow' sign must be attached to the rear of the car that is being towed.

Plan the route home to avoid the greatest possible number of hills, road junctions and traffic lights – even if this it means travelling a few extra miles. Both drivers should be sure of the route in advance. The car doing the towing should have its headlights switched on, while the car being towed must have its rear lights working.

When starting off, the driver in the front car should allow the car to creep forward until any slack in the rope has been taken up fully. Only then should he or she gradually move off, if necessary slipping the clutch until the car behind starts to move. Change gear gently to avoid the rope slackening and then tightening suddenly as you speed up again. Drive as slowly as possible. Though the legal maximum speed limit is 40mph (64kph), you should drive at this speed only if it proves absolutely necessary. The driver of the car being towed should gently apply its brakes now and then to maintain the towrope's tension. If an excess of slack builds up, the car could run over the rope.

When pulling out of a road junction, the driver in front must remember that progress will be slow and there is another car involved to consider. Do not try to pull out sharply. Instead, wait for a large gap in the traffic. Take care that the road is clear of pedestrians as well – not just for the obvious reasons, but because the rope will be slack when both cars are stationary. If any pedestrian fails to notice the rope and walks between the cars, he or she may be injured

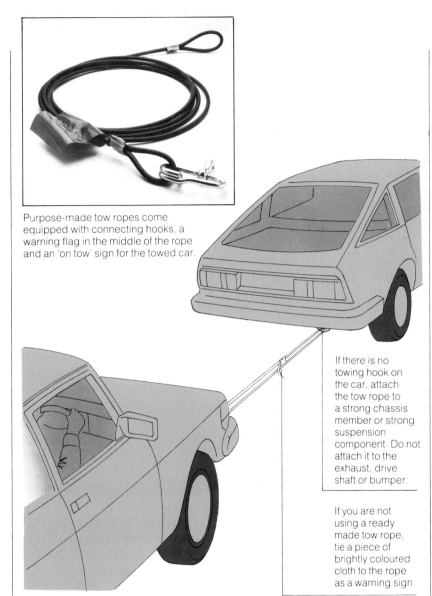

Purpose-made tow ropes come equipped with connecting hooks, a warning flag in the middle of the rope and an 'on tow' sign for the towed car.

If there is no towing hook on the car, attach the tow rope to a strong chassis member or strong suspension component. Do not attach it to the exhaust, drive shaft or bumper.

If you are not using a ready made tow rope, tie a piece of brightly coloured cloth to the rope as a warning sign.

as you move off and the rope suddenly tightens.

If you are towing an car with automatic transmission, you face an additional problem. Many automatic gearboxes rely on the engine's revolutions to operate their internal lubricating pumps and thus could be ruined by towing. With automatic rear-wheel-drive cars, the propshaft must be disconnected. With a front-wheel-drive car, the

problem is even more difficult to overcome, short of disconnecting the driveshafts. If in doubt, consult your handbook.

Towing is sometimes used to start a car. All of the previous rules apply, but the two drivers should also agree a signal – such as sounding the horn – to let the other know that the engine has started. Tow at low speeds in case the car behind suddenly springs forward when it starts.

The keys to survival

The word 'survival' may sound somewhat over-dramatic in the context of owning and running a car, but, in fact, this is far from the case. The pitfalls of car ownership can be many and, if you are not careful, extremely expensive.

The simplest way of maintaining your car is to entrust it to a garage for servicing and repair – but this is also the most expensive. If you have not bargained for them, garage bills can drastically increase the cost of running a car, so it is important to choose the right garage, making sure that you get a thorough job carried out at reasonable cost.

Recommendations from friends and acquaintances can be of tremendous value here. What you should remember, however, is that, though the recommended garage may be equipped to deal with your friend's car, this does not necessarily mean that it will be suited to yours. This can be the case with franchised garages, as many of these specialize in one particular make of car.

Obviously, a franchised garage dealing with your make of car will possess the specialised equipment needed to deal with any job that is required. But, although such garages will service and repair other models, it is fair to assume that they may not possess the specialised tools necessary to carry out certain repairs. This means that the work they do may take longer and that you will pay more as a consequence.

Checking the facilities
Garages and their facilities vary enormously, so, before deciding to entrust your car to any garage, make sure that you inspect the workshop closely. First impressions here can be extremely valuable – a clean, tidy and busy workshop is a good sign. Being able to talk to the mechanic working on your car can be helpful as well – explaining a problem to a receptionist who lacks mechanical knowledge can be impossible.

Larger garages normally have reception engineers, who are capable of road testing and diagnosing particular problems that you may find difficult to describe. Remember, it costs nothing to ask advice from any garage. If the staff are unhelpful, this may be an indication of the general attitude, which may sour the relationship in the future.

The relationship that you develop should stand you in good stead over the years. A regular customer is more likely to obtain prompt assistance when in difficulties than a passing motorist.

Both the AA and the RAC publish lists of recommended garages, together with a guide to their facilities.

Checking cost and time
Always ask for an estimate when booking the car in for a service or repair – if there is any doubt, ask what the maximum is likely to be. Make sure that you leave a telephone number, so that you can be contacted quickly should the need arise. If an unexpected problem is discovered, the garage will then have no excuse for going ahead and spending your money without prior consultation.

Expensive estimates should always be confirmed in writing. This particularly applies to estimates for bodywork repairs, when you should always insist on a formal written estimate before authorizing work to start. The estimate should include labour charges and the cost of the parts that will be needed.

Always check with the garage to ascertain how long they are likely to need the car. Every wise motorist builds in a few extra hours – or even a day – to account for problems. A part that is needed may be out of stock, for example.

Checking the work
Not every garage is out to deceive you – most are reliable and will do a good job. But, if you are a first-time customer, it will pay you to check just how good a garage is. By checking just a few points, you can satisfy yourself at the least that the garage has tackled the jobs you are paying it to do.

When you take your car in for a service, you should make a list of the work that should be carried out in advance and a list of components, such as the oil filter, that should be replaced. You will find a check list of what needs doing when in the service book supplied with each new car; if you do not possess a service book, then it is worthwhile obtaining one from a franchised dealer, or the manufacturer.

A visual check should quickly tell you whether or not specified parts have been replaced and routine maintenance has been carried out. As well as checking for a new oil filter – look at the filter assembly – check that the engine oil has been changed as well. This should be done as part of each major service. Check the oil on the dipstick to ensure that it is clean.

If the garage has to remove the wheels to check the brakes, then you can easily mark the wheel nuts beforehand to check if they have actually been removed. A piece of chalk will do the job nicely. It pays, however, to be subtle and not over-obvious. A garage or, more likely, a mechanic with an inkling of what you are doing may play you at your own game.

Doing it yourself

Many people tackle car maintenance for the first time out of necessity and end up enjoying it so much that it becomes a major hobby. Such people may even end up looking after a neighbour's car as well!

If you decide to do-it-yourself, remember that it does not necessarily pay to rush out and buy a whole range of expensive tools that may not be used regularly. This section of this book details all the tools that you are likely to need at first and then suggests the tools you can consider adding to your basic kit at a later date, depending on how advanced you become.

A point worth bearing in mind is the cost of good tools. Certainly, better tools cost more, but, at the same time, are a worthwhile investment in the long term. Also do not necessarily purchase tools specifically designed to suit your particular car. You will be keeping the tools for a lot longer, so take the long-term view with each purchase. Whatever tools you buy, looking after them carefully pays dividends. They should be stored in a tool box or cupboard and kept clean and dry. If they are to be stored without being used for some

time, then smear the metal parts with oil or grease.

Using tools effectively

Possessing the right tools is essential, but knowing how to use them effectively is equally important. Turning a spanner or screwdriver, for instance, sounds quite simple -- and so it is, with a little experience. But, by following a few golden rules, you can avoid the risk of a nasty accident occuring.

The process of popping a spanner on to a nut and turning it sounds so obvious as not to need further explanation. But do you know whether you should push or pull? First of all, make sure that you have a spanner that fits securely. Ideally, you should use a ring spanner, as the use of this tool lessens the risk of the spanner slipping off, especially if the bolt or nut is tightly fixed. Whenever possible, use two hands – one to steady the spanner on the nut and the other to apply the force required to move it. Pay attention to your stance, too. The more secure your body is, the less likely you will be to slip.

Given the choice, always try and pull the spanner towards you. This gives you more control over the action. If, because of the position of the nut or bolt, you have to push the spanner away from your body, make certain that you use the palm of your hand in the open position as this protects your knuckles if your hand slips. If you are working in a confined space, use your hand muscles to move the spanner, rather than arm movement. This can be achieved easily by hooking another finger around a nearby object and using pressure between this and the

spanner to move it. Again, this method gives you maximum control.

When using a screwdriver, try and use the thickest and widest blade that will fit the screw. If the blade is a loose fit, you may damage it and the screwhead when you turn the screwdriver. It is also worth cleaning the screw slot before using a screwdriver, as dirt or paint will stop the screwdriver entering the slot properly. If you remove a screw with a damaged head, always replace it with a new one.

Finding the parts

Modern cars are generally much simpler to service than their predecessors, although, when it comes to repairs, it is likely that parts will have to be replaced completely, rather than mended. This is well worth bearing in mind if you decide to carry out at least some routine maintenance yourself – the process may not be as difficult as you imagine. Also, many spare parts' manufacturers supply detailed fitting instructions to suit d-i-y enthusiasts.

Breakdowns

Preventative maintenance means just that. Hopefully, by looking after your car on a regular basis, you will spot problems long before they occur. But, if the unexpected does happen, you should be prepared to deal with it. Coping with many minor breakdowns is a simple matter of carrying some of the tools you use for home maintenance in the boot of the car. These will not take up an excessive amount of room and, if you do break down, you will be certainly glad that you did so.

Dealing with a garage/1

How to choose a garage

In common with every other motorist, you want your garage to provide competent workmanship and prompt service at reasonable prices. Above all, you want it to be honest, so that you never end up paying for repairs that were either never made, or proved unnecessary.

You probably chose the garage at which you have your car serviced for one of two reasons. Either you bought your car there, or it is conveniently located close to your home or office. Obviously, with a new car, it is best to get the dealer who sold you the car to service it, or to go to a main dealer with a franchise for that particular make. If, however, you have bought a second-hand car privately, or from a dealer who does not offer a repair and maintenance service, it is up to you to find a garage that will carry out the regular servicing that all cars need to the standards you should demand.

Finding your garage

When you start the search for a good garage, one possible way of finding one is through the recommendation of friends, who have had good service from a particular garage over a period of time. Otherwise the choice is wide, ranging from small 'one man' concerns to franchised main dealers.

Many motorists favour the small business, since they believe that this will cost them less and, because such garages are usually minimally manned, their cars will receive 'personal' attention. Both points can be true – small garages have lower overheads than large ones, so

there is less to be passed on to the customer, while, if there is only one mechanic, he will be the person actually working on your car. However, there are drawbacks as well and here the type of repair or service you need should be taken into consideration.

As all garages pay roughly the same for spare parts, you will probably pay less for a standard service – where the cost of the parts is smaller than the labour charges involved – at a small garage than at a large one. However, when more complicated or large-scale work is involved, the small garage loses out. Even though the hourly rate such a garage charges for labour may be lower than that of a main dealer, the small concern may not possess the specialized tools such a job demands, or be familiar with what the work entails. As a result, the work takes longer and the price is correspondingly higher. There may also be a delay while parts that are not kept in stock are ordered, thus increasing the time your car is off the road. This must be taken into consideration, especially as you will probably be spending money on alternate forms of transport.

The importance of inspection

If you are considering having a service or a repair carried out at a small garage, visit the premises to have a look around. The state of the workshop will provide a general guide to the quality of work. It should be reasonably clean and tidy, warm and light. Everybody works better in a pleasant environment. By the same token, the environment usually reflects

the work force's attitude.

Explain the nature of the fault to the mechanic. If he is competent, he should be able to make a reasonably accurate assessment of how long the job will take and the rough cost it will involve. Obviously, unless the job is a known quantity, such as a clutch change or the fitting of a new water pump, he will not be able to make a completely accurate estimate, but he should at least be in a position to provide an upper price limit.

If you are unhappy about either the proposed cost of the job, or how long it is estimated to take, telephone some more garages and ask for a comparative quotation. Make sure that at least one of these garages is a main dealer. If all the quotations are appreciably higher than the original, the first garage may not have taken into consideration all the factors involved in the job. Once again, bear in mind the type of work to be done when choosing garages to supply such quotations.

Your car and your garage

If you own a high-performance car, or a foreign model, you would be well advised to entrust the work to either a main dealer or a garage that specializes in that particular make. Some of the jobs involved will demand special tools and equipment that not only save time – and therefore money – but also ensure that adjustments and repairs are carried out correctly. If, for example, your car is fitted with electronic ignition, this can be serviced only with the proper tools. Without the right equipment, the job is not only impossible, but the ignition system can also be damaged. Remember as well that a mechanic dealing with the same type of car every day will have a comprehensive knowledge of its inherent faults and troublesome areas and therefore is able to pin-point any fault more quickly.

Specialist garages

Just as there are specialists who deal with one type of car, so there are garages who deal with particular jobs. Fitting an exhaust, for instance, though not technically difficult, can be time-consuming. Here, you will find that you will save time and money by taking your car to an exhaust centre. Such centres do nothing else but fit exhausts and possess exactly the right tools and equipment to ensure a quick replacement. They also buy exhaust systems in bulk and, therefore, more cheaply.

Other garages specialize in clutch changes and electronic tuning. Because they are geared to this kind of work, the cost of the job – and the time it takes – will invariably be attractive.

It may be worth splitting the work to be done between two garages to get the best of both worlds. Sometimes, however, it will work out cheaper to have a component replaced, rather than get a specialist to repair it. Having a fault cured in an automatic gearbox, for instance, is a highly-skilled job and requires specialist training. It is more straightforward to have the gearbox replaced – this is a fairly easy job, which should be well within the capabilities of any competent mechanic.

Body repairs

When choosing a garage for body repairs, the choice is once again between the specialist and the general garage. In this case, the specialist is a better bet, provided that the repair is fairly minor and the bulk of the job involves painting.

Before making your choice, examine the state of the workshop. Its general cleanliness is again vitally important – the quality of the finish depends on it. If possible, ask to see an example of the standard of work produced by the garage of your choice. If it handles insurance claims on a regular basis with a reputable company, then it is almost certain that its standards are high.

A main dealer, however, will probably be better equipped to handle major crash damage. The dealer will find it quicker to obtain replacement panels and is more likely to have a better knowledge of what the complete repair entails.

When comparing the cost of body repairs, ask for the estimate to be split into two parts – the first giving the cost of removing and refitting any parts and the second giving the cost of any new panels or parts. You will then be able to make a reasonable assessment of the total price for the job.

A fair deal

Check whether or not the garage you use is a member of the Motor Agents' Association. Many garages – particularly the larger ones – belong to this trade organization.

Membership does not necessarily guarantee that jobs will be carried out more efficiently, or cost less, than at non-member garages. However, if you have been over-charged or been the victim of shoddy workmanship, there is a much greater chance that your complaints will be satisfied if your garage belongs to the association.

What to tell your garage

It is all too easy to criticize a garage for carrying out work unnecessarily , or for taking too long over a particular job. Remember that, if this occurs, the responsibility is sometimes shared. You may not have given the garage sufficient information or, just as bad, you may told the mechanic only half the story. If, say, you are taking your car in for its regular service, but if you know – or even think – that there are additional faults the service will not tackle, make a list of them and their symptoms and make sure that the mechanic is aware of it.

Any mechanic needs to know not only the symptoms of a fault and the circumstances in which they occur, but also how much you are prepared to spend and how long you can do without your car. Most importantly, you must tell him the exact make, model and age of the vehicle; quite frequently, he needs to know the engine capacity and sometimes the chassis number as well. This is because, during a long production run, the components fitted to the car – especially those in the electrical and ignition systems – can vary, so different spare parts or servicing techniques may well be required.

Briefing a mechanic

If you supply all these details in advance, the chances of incurring extra expense, or of the job taking longer than

Dealing with a garage/2

expected, will be significantly reduced. However, you should never jump to conclusions and tell the mechanic actually what to do. You can help by simply describing the problem as best you can and how and when it is apparent, rather than embarking on self-diagnosis of the problem.

There could be several reasons for your car overheating, for instance. Indeed, there may be as many as two or three faults, all of which are contributing to the general symptoms. You need not have identified any, or all, of these, but you might have spotted droplets of water in the exhaust and jumped to the conclusion that the head gasket is damaged. This is a fairly expensive job. If, acting on your hunch, you tell the mechanic to replace the head gasket, he cannot be blamed for doing so, even if this proves unnecessary. The droplets could just as simply be condensation and the overheating caused by something completely different, such as a jammed thermostat. So you could well end up paying for unnecessary work and then face another bill before the real fault is corrected.

The best way to help the mechanic to establish the real cause of the problem is for you to describe how and when the overheating occurs as accurately as possible. The car might overheat immediately after starting, for instance, or only in heavy traffic or after a fast motorway run. There may be other symptoms, such as loss of coolant or an ineffective heater. Each symptom helps the mechanic make a diagnosis and, therefore, carry out the repair that much quicker.

Sounds peculiar
A fault that shows up only as a noise can be more difficult to track down, but, once again, you can give the mechanic valuable clues by describing the circumstances under which it occurs. A noise that increases and decreases parallel with engine speed, for instance, points to a problem inside the engine bay, but a noise that varies according to road speed could mean problems in the drive, or in the wheel bearings. The problem can be pin-pointed further if it occurs only during certain driving manoeuvres, such as turning or reversing.

If you give the mechanic all such information before he carries out any repair, he will be able to road-test it on completing work to check it in the conditions under which the fault originally occurred.

Diagnosing breakdowns
If your engine has failed, will not re-start and you have had to call out a mechanic, or be towed to a garage as a consequence, describe exactly what happened at the moment of the breakdown. If you heard a knocking, banging or some other mechanical noise, then it was almost certain to have come from a failing component; an accurate description might help the mechanic identify the cause immediately. If the engine suddenly cuts out without prior warning, the ignition is probably to blame. A methodical series of checks will soon enable the mechanic to isolate the fault.

An engine that falters, picks up, dies and then repeats this cycle several times before stopping is usually suffering from a fuel problem. There may have been other symptoms leading up to the breakdown, such as poor starting, or increased fuel consumption. These could, for example, point to a badly blocked air filter element, or a malfunctioning choke.

In the garage
Provided that the problem is not a major one, book the car in for attention at a time when it is least needed once you have given the garage exact details. By planning this carefully, you will experience minimum inconvenience, if, for any · reason, the work takes longer than expected.

Tell the mechanic exactly how much you want to spend and leave a telephone number where you can be contacted – business, home or both – so that he can get in touch with you quickly should he come across an unexpected problem. You will be in a position to give him the go-ahead or to tell him to stop work. In the second case, he will still charge you for the exploratory work he has done to pin-point the problem, but at least you will know what needs to be done and how much it will cost. This advice can be particularly relevant when a car is undergoing a routine service. As there is a fixed list of checks and adjustments that must be carried out – consult your handbook for details – your garage should be able to give an accurate estimate of the time the service will take and how much it should cost, provided that nothing extra crops up.

Apart from the routine tasks, however, a service is a vital piece of preventive maintenance. A good mechanic will know if a component is worn or likely to fail in the near future. If you have not left sufficient instructions, or a telephone number, he will not know whether to carry out the extra work he considers to be necessary. If he does not, the car will be unfinished when you go to collect it.

As an example, a mechanic can easily estimate the useful life left in brake pads by the amount of friction material left on them. He may consider, for instance, that your pads have a remaining life of half the distance to the next routine service. So, although the car is still perfectly roadworthy, the pads should still be changed.

Whatever work you are having carried out, give the mechanic details of previous recent repairs, if possible. If the work has been carried out incorrectly or a non-standard part has been fitted, he will find this prior knowledge helpful.

How to check your garage's work

If you are an average motorist, the inevitable garage bill can often come as something of a shock when you examine the figures on their own without any knowledge of what lies behind them. Any reputable garage should itemize not only the new parts that have been fitted during a repair or service – together with their prices – but also the exact nature of the work that has been carried out. This is often scribbled down in a kind of mechanics' shorthand. As this can be difficult to decipher, ask the mechanic to go through the bill with you if you are in any doubt about any of its contents.

Actually seeing for yourself the results of the garage's work can be difficult, unless it involves a component that did not work and now obviously does. It will be self-evident whether or not a failed exhaust, for instance, has been replaced. But, because a thorough inspection of many of the components of your car would involve stripping them down at least partially, you must take a certain amount of what the garage tells you on trust when you are told that the work you wanted done has been carried out and parts have been replaced accordingly. The only way to be absolutely sure that a complete new clutch has been fitted, for example, is to separate the engine from the gearbox.

Precautions and checks

In most cases, there are a number of precautions and checks you can carry out to ensure that you are getting what you paid for. This may sound slightly underhand, but it is not. It is simply a matter of establishing that a job has been carried out properly, not only for your own peace of mind, but also to ascertain whether or not the garage is one you can trust in the future. Because modern cars are extremely complex and the span of potential repairs so great as a consequence, the precautions and checks listed are split into sections covering the most common jobs.

Major service

You must have your car serviced at the routine intervals specified in the manufacturer's handbook – this is vital for the sake of both safety and reliability. The handbook usually has a chart of what needs to be done at each service interval.

Any routine service will involve at least 20 jobs, and checking whether most of these have been done adequately will take you only a few minutes. It is easy to tell whether or not a new oil filter has been fitted. Locate the filter on the side of the engine block and see if it looks new and clean. The oil, too, should have been changed. Remove the dipstick and check that the oil is clean and at the correct level.

In addition to the oil level, check all other fluid levels – that of the hydraulic fluid in the brake master cylinder, the electrolyte in the battery, the coolant in the radiator and the water in the windscreen-washer bottle. All of them should have been checked and topped up.

Check that the spark plugs have been replaced – if they have, the metal sections will be bright and shiny and the ceramic parts clean. A new set of contact breaker points should have been fitted as well, so remove the distributor cap to make sure that this is the case. The contact points of the old set would be pitted, so it is easy to see the difference. As a secondary check, you could dab white paint on the old set before the service.

Any major service requires the valve clearances to be adjusted. This involves removing the rocker cover – or cam cover on OHC engines – which should be fitted with a new gasket. You can tell whether this has been done by looking along the bottom of the cover. The clean cork edge of the new gasket should be clearly visible.

Take off the air filter cover (see p.116) to check that a new element has been fitted. The old

Dealing with a garage/3

one would have areas of grey dirt on it.

The fan belt should have been set at the correct tension and the radiator hoses checked for wear. If a hose has been replaced, it will appear shinier than the others.

Work on brakes and wheel bearings involves the garage removing the road wheels. Before the service, mark the nuts and studs with a dab of paint, so you will know whether this has been done or not.

If the garage claims that new parts have been fitted and your checks lead you to suspect that this is not the case, ask to see the old ones.

Engine
Because it is difficult, if not totally impossible, to check work in detail, you should ask to see the old components, if in doubt, and, if the garage is a small one, receipts for new ones. Before the car goes into the garage, dab paint on the various nuts and bolts that are likely to be disturbed or removed. Major work – such as a rebore or having new big-end bearings fitted – means a major strip down. Again make sure that a new oil filter has been fitted and that the oil is fresh.

Transmission
A visual check will make it obvious that a new gearbox has been fitted. Ask to see the old unit and receipts. However, checking a new clutch is not so simple. All three components – the pressure plate, friction plate and release bearing – must be replaced. Ask to see all three, and receipts. If you are in doubt about whether or not they come from your car, take them to a main dealer to establish that they are from your model.

Brakes
You can make a thorough check to see if work has been done on the brakes by removing the front wheels. This involves jacking up the car, supporting it on axle stands or wheel ramps, and inspecting the components. You can tell almost at a glance whether or not new pads have been fitted on the front wheels, though inspecting the rear shoes involves removing the drums. Similarly, you can tell if new wheel cylinders or hydraulic pipes have been fitted by their new, shiny appearance.

Steering and suspension
Check both steering and suspension at the same time as you check the brakes. New items will be clean. Ask to see the old components if you are in doubt about replacements. Be particularly careful if a garage says that a new steering rack has been fitted. It is possible to take up wear by adjusting the old rack, rather than replacing it.

Bodywork
It is quite acceptable for accident damage to be repaired with body filler, unless you have specified that new panels should be fitted. If a garage charges you for new panels, check them with a magnet. Hold the magnet slightly above the surface of the body and run it across the suspect area. It will not stick to body filler.

Tips and hints
When checking to satisfy yourself that any work has, in fact, been done, it is always worth asking to see the old components. Tell the garage in advance that you want to see them, so that they cannot claim to have thrown them away.

If possible, visit the garage at least once while the work is being carried out. This will give you some idea of the extent of the job, while the garage will also be aware that you are vigilant. Any reputable garage should welcome it when a customer calls in to see how the job is going.

After any major service or repair, the garage should test drive the car before handing it over to you. If you take it out on the road and find any obvious driving faults – excess play in the clutch, binding brakes or unbalanced wheels, for instance – it is a clear sign that something has been skimped or work has been carried out inefficiently. Take the car back to the garage at once, and complain.

Finally, if you are still in doubt as to whether or not your car has been properly serviced or repaired, have another garage check over the car independently. The second garage will charge you a small exploratory fee. You need not say you are questioning the work of a different garage. Just say that the car has been suffering from a particular problem and you would like to know the reason for it and what it will take to put it right.

If the garage finds the work has not been carried out as stated on your original bill, ask them for a written report on the car's condition and approach the original garage with a view to having the faults put right. If they refuse on unreasonable grounds, it is worth approaching the manufacturer – if the garage

FOR CARRYING OUT MAJOR (12,000 MILE/20,000 KM) SERVICE	PARTS NEEDED
Check operation of all interior and exterior lights	REPLACE BULBS IF NECESSARY
Check condition and inflation of tyres – including spare	
Check operation of doors and locks – lubricate if necessary	
Check operation of bonnet safety catch	
Check wheelnuts for tightness	
Check and top up coolant levels if necessary	
Check hydraulic fuel levels – top up if necessary	
Check tension of fan belt – adjust if necessary	
Check battery terminals – clean and grease if necessary	
Check valve clearances	
Change spark plugs	
Change contact breaker points	REPLACE WITH NEW SET OF SPARK PLUGS
Check condition of H.T. Leads	REPLACE WITH NEW SET OF CONTACT BREAKERS
Clean and lubricate distributor	
Adjust ignition timing	
Check slow idle speed – adjust if necessary	
Check all hoses for deterioration	
Check and adjust throttle leakage	
Check engine oil and filter	REPLACE IF NECESSARY
Check rear axle oil level – top up if necessary	REPLACE OIL AND FILTER
Check brake pads and linings for wear	
Check brake pipes and unions for leaks and wear	
Check clutch pedal free play	
Check steering and suspension linkages for wear	
Check for exhaust leaks	
Road test	
TOTAL LABOUR TIME	3½ – 4 hours

concerned is a recognized main dealer – or one of the motoring organizations, or The Motor Agents' Association, for legal advice.

Depending on the type of car you have, most or all of these jobs should be carried out by your garage during a major (12,000 mile/20,000km) service.

Tools and equipment/1

Building up your tool kit

Every basic tool kit should contain the minimum number of tools required for simple repairs. Once you have built this up, you can go on to add the extra equipment that will enable you to tackle more advanced jobs successfully, so making your motoring life easier.

These pages are therefore divided into two sections. The first of these deals with the basic tools you will need and the second covers the equipment you may well want to add to your tool kit as you become more proficient and confident.

Choosing tools

Whenever you choose a tool, always buy one made by a reputable manufacturer, even if it is more expensive than less well-known alternatives. Cheap tools are a false economy, as they tend to wear out quickly or break. If you need a specialist tool, such as a torque wrench, for one-time use, hire one from a tool-hire specialist. Treat such tools carefully though, because, if they are returned damaged, you will lose your deposit.

Your basic kit

Spanners come in two types – open-ended and ring – the best being forged from chrome vanadium. When you make your selection, remember that, although most cars are now fitted with metric nuts and bolts, a few older cars still use imperial sizes, or AF (across flats), measured in fractions of an inch. Choose the spanners to suit your car.

Both open-ended and ring spanners are best bought in sets purpose-planned to cope with most of the nut and bolt sizes you

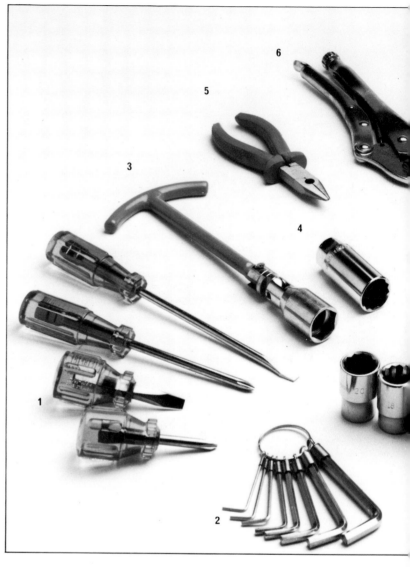

are likely to encounter. Ideally, you should have a set of both types of spanner. Before buying a plug spanner, check the size of your plugs – they can be 10mm, 12mm, 14mm, or 18mm.

A comprehensive socket set considerably increases the range of jobs you can tackle. A good set should consist of at least 12 sockets, a ratchet drive, an extension bar, a tommy bar for extra leverage and possibly a knuckle joint and plug spanner.

The 12mm (½-in) drive sets are good for all-purpose work. For finer jobs, you may want to add a smaller drive set.

You may need a special spanner to fit the sump plug and gearbox filler plug. Universal spanners are available in up to ten different head sizes.

A 300mm- (12in-) long adjustable spanner is a handy tool to have on hand. Before you buy one, make sure that there is no free play in the jaws and that

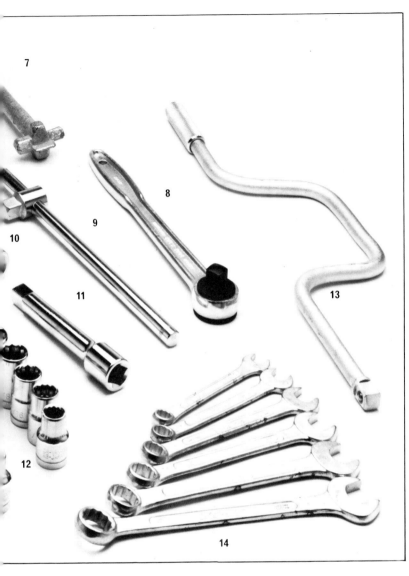

The basic toolkit

These tools will equip you to tackle most of the basic maintenance and repair jobs you may need to carry out. **1** Screwdrivers – long and short crosshead and flat bladed. **2** Allen keys. **3** Spark plug spanner. **4** Spark plug socket to fit ratchet drive. **5** Pliers – thin-nosed or heavy-duty pliers are needed according to the job. **6** Self-locking grips. **7** Universal sump plug spanner. **8** Ratchet drive. **9** Tommy bar with drive peg. **10** Knuckle joint for ratchet drive. **11** Extension bar. **12** Set of sockets for ratchet drive (metric or AF). **13** Brace to fit sockets. **14** Set of combination open ended and ring spanners (metric or AF).

ball-pein hammer, plus a small punch and chisel, should also be included.

If you intend to do a lot of work on your car, it is well worth investing in a bottle jack, since this is far superior to the jack the manufacturer supplies with the car. A trolley jack is even better, but more expensive. You can buy wheel ramps to support the car, but, if you are working with a wheel removed, a set of axle stands will be required as well. A creeper – sometimes called a crawler – makes working under the car more comfortable.

Additional equipment

A battery charger can be an extremely good buy. Choose the best model you can afford, preferably one with a charging rate dial. A wandering lead light is also useful – both mains-operated lights and ones that will run from the car's battery are available.

When tackling more complex jobs, you will probably use a torque wrench more frequently than any other specialist tool. Where necessary, the wrench is used to tighten nuts and bolts to a fixed leverage to prevent them

they close squarely when screwed up. Self-locking wrenches (mole grips) can be locked in place to leave both your hands free. They come in many jaw shapes, but the commonest – and most convenient – are the ones with serrated jaws.

Combination pliers have serrated jaws with a flat section for gripping metal, a round section for gripping bars and rods and cutting edges for snipping soft metal and wire. A pair of long-nose pliers is ideal for working in confined spaces.

You will need a good set of screwdrivers, with both flat and cross-headed blades. Buy a short- and long-bladed version of each. An electrician's screwdriver, with its small, slim blade, is also useful.

A set of metric or imperial feeler gauges – vital for setting the contact breaker points gap – is absolutely essential, while a

Tools and equipment/2

becoming damaged or slackening off. Cheaper wrenches have a dial and pointer which indicates when the correct torque has been reached, but more expensive types have a pre-set scale. The wrench makes an audible click when the desired torque has been reached.

If you are checking and setting the ignition timing (see *p.128*), two items of equipment are essential – a stroboscopic light and a dwell meter. A light with an xenon tube is considerably more expensive, but much more powerful than the cheaper alternatives. Dwell meters measure the angle of dwell before the points open and are far more accurate than a feeler gauge.

A voltmeter is extremely useful when checking circuits. Alternatively, you can buy a multimeter. This performs a variety of functions, including those of a dwell meter, voltmeter and tachometer.

The most useful power tool you can buy is an electric drill with a set of good-quality twist drills, preferably with tungsten tips and a sanding disc for bodywork repairs. A two-speed drill provides more flexibility than a single-speed version.

Remember that the suggestions for more advanced equipment given here are intended only as a rough guide. As you gradually progress to more complex maintenance and repairs, you will discover that you need additional tools specifically for your car. These should be added to your tool kit as and when required.

Using your tools

Whenever you use a tool,

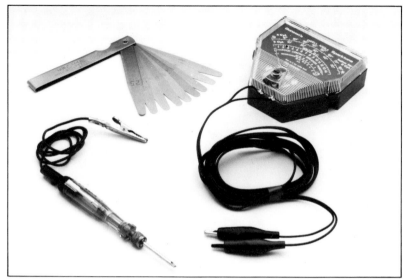

Specialized tools are required for carrying out electrical tests and setting the ignition timing. A set of feeler blades in metric or imperial sizes is needed for setting the contact breaker points gap. A multi-function meter is very handy for testing the voltage of a circuit and usually has the facility to check the dwell angle when setting the contact breaker points gap. The circuit test screwdriver, which contains a bulb that lights when an electrical circuit is made, is a cheap and efficient tool for checking circuits and can be used to set the static ignition timing.

remember that it is designed for a specific purpose. Thus, it is important to choose and use the piece of equipment that suits the particular job.

This advice applies to spanners and screwdrivers in particular. If the wrong size of spanner is used, it will probably slip and the nut or bolt will be rounded off as a consequence. Whenever possible, use a ring spanner – this will grip the hexagonal bolt-head or nut all the way round and so cannot easily slip. Though open-ended spanners are often more convenient to use, they grip only on two flats of the hexagon and so can slip off. If you encounter a bolt with an extremely tight thread – and there is sufficient room – use a ring spanner to loosen it, but finish unscrewing with an open-ended spanner to speed up the job.

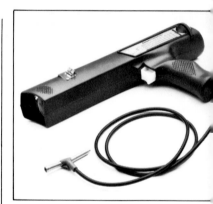

Stroboscopic timing lights vary in price and sophistication. The more expensive lights produce a brighter flash and can be adjusted with the engine speed.

Sockets give the ultimate in grip. They also save time when a ratchet wrench is used. You will find an extension bar helpful in dealing with recessed nuts or bolts. A knuckle joint allows you to reach awkwardly placed nuts, while a tommy bar provides you with extra leverage.

Torque wrenches invariably use 13mm (½in) drive sockets. With the dial and pointer type, tighten the nut or bolt until the wrench distorts and the needle points to the correct torque setting. With the more expensive variety, set the micrometer-type scale to the desired torque and tighten the wrench until it clicks.

When using a spark plug spanner, make sure that it fits squarely on the plug before turning it. Otherwise you will break the plug's porcelain.

Adjustable spanners should be used only if you do not possess the size of open-ended spanner you need for a particular job, or if extra leverage is required. Ensure that the jaws are tightened to a snug fit over the nut.

Self-locking wrenches are ideal for gripping round or irregular-shaped components that cannot be held with a spanner. The knurled nut on the end of the handle is adjusted so that the jaws bite hard on the component concerned. They can then be locked into position, leaving both your hands free.

A screwdriver blade must fit the screw head, as otherwise it may slip and damage the screw. Always angle a screwdriver away from your and, in case you slip, never hold a component in one hand and use the screwdriver with the other. Screwdrivers should never be used as substitutes for chisels or punches.

To use a feeler gauge, slide the appropriate blade between the two components being set. After making any necessary adjustment, you should feel a slight, but even, resistance as the blade is withdrawn. Keep each blade lubricated with a light film of oil, but clean this off thoroughly if contact breakers are being set. Re-lubricate the blade after use.

A small punch is ideal for driving out stubborn pins and even bolts – if they are to be discarded – and should always be used to mark a hole before drilling. Chisels have a variety of uses, including the splitting of nuts and for chopping the heads off stubborn bolts.

A bottle or trolley jack should only be used on solid ground, such as concrete, and never on soft tarmac or earth. Position the head under a strong part of the chassis and place chocks behind two wheels at the opposite end to the one you are jacking up. Never work underneath a car unless it is supported either with wheel ramps or axle stands. The stands should also be positioned underneath a strong metal section.

Electrical tools

Before using a battery charger, remove the battery filler caps and top up the cells with distilled water. Then, connect the charger's crocodile clips to the positive and negative terminals respectively – the charger's leads are normally colour coded to ensure you get them the right way round. Plug in the charger and switch on. Once the battery has been fully charged – this will be indicated by the charger's dial– switch off at the mains and remove the crocodile clips. When doing this – or any other battery maintenance – never smoke, as the battery gives off explosive gases.

Stroboscopic timing lights are used to align the timing marks on the crankshaft pulley and timing case (see p.150). The simplest kind has two leads, one of which is connected to the high-tension lead running from the distributor to what is termed number one spark plug and the other to the plug itself. Route the light's cables so they are well away from moving components, such as the fan.

Dwell meters are connected between the coil terminal marked CB or - and earth. The dial tells you the exact angle of dwell between each opening of the contact breakers (see p.126).

Voltmeters are used for checking low-tension circuits. If you suspect that current is failing to reach a particular component, for instance, you should connect the meter between the component's feed wire and earth. A reading should appear on the scale. The circuit can be checked further with an ammeter (for amps) and an ohmeter (for resistance) according to the manufacturer's instructions.

Tool maintenance

If you look after your tools properly, they will last for an extremely long time – in some cases, practically for ever. Always wipe a tool clean after you have used it and never put it away if it is damp or wet, as, if you do, the tool may well rust. Only use a tool for the job that it was designed to carry out. Using the wrong size of spanner or socket, for instance, means that the edges of a nut or bolt will not just be rounded off, but the tool itself may be damaged. Maintain your equipment and you will find working on your car that much easier in the future.

The survival kit

If your car breaks down, a well-equipped tool kit and a few essential spare parts in your boot can make all the difference between finding yourself stranded by the roadside and getting home safely.

Every new car is supplied with a basic manufacturer's tool kit, a jack and, most importantly, a spare wheel. You should check the inflation pressure and general condition of the spare wheel regularly – remember it is now illegal to drive with a tyre whose tread is bald at any point.

Carry a foot-pump in case of emergencies and a universal wheel brace, which will suit the wheel locking nuts of any car. As an alternative to a foot-pump, you can buy a puncture-repair aerosol, which inflates a punctured tyre and seals the puncture. Follow the manufacturer's instructions extremely carefully when you use it, especially those covering the speed and permanency of the repair.

Carry a filled petrol can and filler funnel, checking that the can you buy meets the necessary safety standards. Use a can, preferably a plastic one, to hold water. You should have at least a gallon of this to hand. Also carry a couple of cans of engine oil. An aerosol water-dispersant is a good buy, as this will help you to get your car started if the ignition system becomes wet or damp – this is a common hazard, especially first thing in the morning.

Always keep a set of jump leads handy in case your battery runs flat, a tow-rope and an 'on tow' sign. To ensure safety in the dark, carry a reflective warning triangle to alert other drivers to the fact that you have broken down – such a triangle is now a legal requirement in Europe – together with a powerful torch or a portable light-fitting with a long flex that can be connected to the car battery.

A pair of overalls, or an old blanket to protect your clothes if you have to get under the car, are both good ideas.

Tools

Most manufacturers supply only the most basic of tool kits, while a second-hand car may not come with any tools at all. At the very least, you should carry the right tools to enable you to tackle essential emergency repairs, such as replacing a radiator hose, a fan belt, spark plugs, light bulbs, contact breaker points and throttle cable.

The minimum realistic requirement is a set of open-ended spanners and a plug spanner, preferably complemented with a set of ring spanners. An adjustable spanner, a set of self-locking grips and a pair of pliers are also useful. Make sure you have a screwdriver to suit any potential problem. This means carrying flat-bladed and cross-headed types in both long and short versions.

Spare parts

You should always carry a spare fan belt, a set of contact breaker points, spare light bulbs, fuses – check in the manufacturer's manual to see which ratings of fuse you will need – and two or three spark plugs. If you are making a long journey, or going abroad, an emergency windscreen can be a good idea – this can be fitted in minutes.

Carry a spare top and bottom radiator hose and a length of heater hose, together with the necessary hose clips. If you find yourself without a spare heater hose, however, it is still possible to get yourself out of trouble by by-passing the circuit. Simply remove one of the existing hoses from the heater and re-connect it at the point where the other hose joins the engine.

Tips and hints

Keep a few spare lengths of electrical wire handy. These can be used to repair a broken circuit, but the join must then be protected with insulation tape. Such tape can be used to temporarily seal a burst radiator hose as well. However, you should never try to repair a fractured fuel line with tape. A petrol leak can be dealt with safely only by fitting a spare length of fuel hose, clipped securely into place.

If your car is overheating, you can almost certainly continue to drive it if you remove the thermostat (see p.32) to increase the coolant flow. Remember, though, that, after you have removed the thermostat, you will have to fit a new gasket to avoid a coolant leak. If you are without a spare gasket, a piece of cardboard cut to fit the part can serve as a temporary substitute.

A length of string, or piano wire, can be used to support the exhaust if one of the supporting brackets fractures. An old wire coat hanger can be used for the same purpose.

Finally, always keep some loose change in the car. You may need this for a telephone if all your attempts to get the car running fail!

Your survival kit

Most drivers would never contemplate a car journey without carrying a few basic necessities in the boot. A spare wheel is vital, as well as the tools necessary to change a wheel. However, by carrying a few extra items, many of the normal causes of a breakdown can be rectified with a minimum of trouble and expense.
1 Reflective warning triangle – this is mandatory in Europe. **2** Jack. **3** Fire extinguisher – this is best carried inside the car. **4** Plastic water can – this should hold about a gallon of water. **5** Petrol can. **6** Puncture repair aerosol – this seals small punctures and reinflates the tyre. **7** Water dispersant spray – this will help get the car started if the ignition system is damp. **8** Emergency replacement windscreen. **9** Jump leads. **10** Universal wheel brace – will fit most cars. **11** Foot pump. **12** Fanbelt. **13** Water hoses to fit the top and bottom radiator connections. **14** Jubilee clips. **15** Insulating tape – can be used as a temporary seal on a split water hose as well as to join electrical connections. **16** Contact breaker points. **17** Fuses and bulbs – make sure they are of the correct rating and fitting.

Improving your investment

Apart from a house, a car is probably the most expensive single investment you will ever make, so, having decided on it, it obviously makes good economic sense to keep your purchase in tip-top condition. Taking care of your car not only minimizes the chances of mechanical failure, but also helps to keep up its re-sale value.

You can do more than this, however. If you are prepared to spend a little time and money on the task, you can improve on your investment as well. By paying just that little bit more attention to the state of the bodywork and by adding desirable accessories, you should ensure that your car retains a higher than normal second-hand value. You will also create an individual form of transport that will enhance your pride of ownership.

Protecting bodywork
When considering how best to maintain your car's bodywork, remember every good mechanic's axiom – prevention is better than cure. This means protecting the body against rust, which is every motorist's arch enemy. You can use a do-it-yourself rust prevention kit – this will take a couple of hours work – or get the job done professionally. In the latter case, make sure that you get a written guarantee.

Regular, thorough washing and polishing is vital to preserve paintwork. Wash the car once a week, whether it appears to be dirty or not. Although its paint may look clean, it will inevitably have accumulated a film of dirt. Eventually, this will discolour the paintwork. Use a good quality shampoo designed for the job

and never washing-up detergents. These will remove the protective silicones and therefore expose the paint to weather damage. Polish the car about every three months. Thorough polishing also greatly reduces the chance of the paintwork fading.

Dealing with damage
If, despite precautions, rust damage occurs, it should be treated as quickly as possible to stop the corrosion from spreading. Make a thorough job of this, fitting a new panel to replace the damaged one if necessary. Rust in one panel can easily spread to another, so the long-term savings will be worthwhile. Minor dents should be knocked out and filled just as promptly. Otherwise the bare metal that is inevitably exposed will soon start to rust. Deal with minor scratches and stone chips as they occur as well – even the most minor damages can eventually lead to substantial corrosion, if left untreated.

Provided that you are not dealing with large areas of rust damage, you can spray the damage with an aerosol and achieve reasonably professional results. If you lack the confidence to apply the final finishing coats, you can still prepare and treat the damaged area yourself and leave the final finishing to a garage. The savings will be considerable.

The personal touch
Like many motorists, you may feel that your car lacks that personal sense of identity to make it stand out from others on the road. You can change this by investing in a body kit – a number of these are available –

which will enable you to personalize the appearance of your car. One of the most popular additions is a glass-fibre or rubber front spoiler (otherwise known as an air dam), which fits beneath the bumper. Such spoilers are relatively easy to fit. Apart from enhancing the car's looks and providing added protection against flying stones, a front spoiler can also marginally improve fuel consumption and car performance through its superior aerodynamics.

Rear spoilers – you can buy them to suit hatchbacks and saloons – are equally popular. They not only look impressive, but also improve stability at speed. In either case, you can leave the spoilers in their natural colour – this is usually black – or spray them to match the bodywork.

Fitting a smart set of alloy wheels will also improve your car's looks dramatically. There are literally hundreds of types to choose from, but, before you make your final decision, check that the wheels you pick are not wide enough to foul the bodywork when you fit them. Also remember that wider-than-standard wheels will mean buying a new set of tyres.

Auxiliary lights are both attractive and practical. You can fit a set of driving lamps to increase penetration power, while fog lamps can improve visibility dramatically in poor driving conditions. Auxiliary lamps can be bought in either round or rectangular designs, so pick the design that suits the existing lights on your car.

Though not an obvious visual improvement, a stainless steel exhaust system can be a worthwhile investment. Such systems last for many years and thus are an obvious added attraction for any potential buyer when you come to sell the car. However, they are considerably more expensive than conventional systems.

Interior accessories

Equally as many accessories are available to enhance the interior of your car. You can buy such extras purely for cosmetic reasons, for their practical advantages, because they make driving more enjoyable, or as a combination of all three.

A good sound system, for instance, not only looks visually attractive, but helps you to feel more relaxed and comfortable, particularly on a long journey. Boredom can lead to a lack of concentration, which is dangerous at best and potentially fatal at worst.

Dashboard extras

Extra instrumentation is always worth considering, especially on mass-market cars. You can mount extra gauges in the dashboard, or in separate consoles above or below it.

The three extra instruments the average driver finds the most useful are an oil pressure gauge, water temperature gauge (a special gauge is more accurate than the one normally fitted) and a battery condition indicator. The first two can warn you of a potential problem long before it develops into a serious fault. The battery condition indicator will tell you whether or not the charging circuit is working correctly and also give you an accurate guide to the state of the battery.

A tachometer – often called a rev counter – is not a vital extra, but is nevertheless useful. By using it correctly, you will keep the engine within its safe revolution limits and also make the most of what is termed engine torque, or pulling power. This enables you to combine maximum performance with maximum economy.

Other improvements

Every driver spends long hours in the driving seat, so it is well worth making sure that you maximize your comfort. Except for more expensive cars, seats are designed as a compromise between supportiveness and comfort. By fitting rally-type seats, you will provide far more of both – though such seats are expensive, the choice is so wide that you are bound to find one that suits you almost perfectly.

Seat covers are far less expensive, but almost as effective. These are designed to give improved lateral and lumbar support, as well as to enhance the appearance of the interior of the car. They also protect the seats underneath them from dirt and damage.

Other useful and practical accessories include electric washers, rear screen washers and wipers, heated rear window kits, intermittent windscreen wiper conversions, electric windows and electric radio aerials. One particularly luxurious extra is a sunshine roof. The most basic type is a simple fixed plastic window, followed by the tilting roof. The most costly can be fully retracted, or are completely removeable. Whatever type you choose, however, it is best to have it fitted professionally, since a botched amateur job will have expensive consequences.

Pre-plan your improvements

Regardless of what you decide to do to your car and how much you intend to spend, plan each improvement in advance. It is generally far better to take a subtle approach, concentrating on what is actually useful, than falling head over heels for flamboyance. If you fit wider-than-standard wheels and extended wheel arches, for instance, you may find it more difficult to sell the car, since, rightly or wrongly, potential buyers may assume that it has been hard driven.

If you want to change the appearance of your car, but cannot decide exactly how to go about it, look at a similar model that the manufacturer has produced in 'up market' form. This will give you a good idea as to how effective body kits, different wheels, spoilers and interior improvements will be in transforming appearance.

Protecting your investment

Whatever improvements you have made, you car will now be far more attractive – to thieves, as well as to you. Therefore, an efficient anti-theft device is the essential finishing touch.

There are many different security devices on the market and they vary in price according to what they do. The cheapest type locks the steering wheel or handbrake lever, but, if you are prepared to pay more, you can fit a system that will immobilize the car completely. The most sophisticated – and expensive – devices kill the ignition and sound a piercing alarm, and sometimes flash the headlights, if any part of the car is disturbed.

Repairing rust damage/1

In the majority of cars, corrosion starts from inside – where panels have been exposed to water. Front wings and rear wheel arches are particularly prone to rusting because they hold mud, which contains moisture.

A panel will rot through quickly once rust has taken a hold, but you will find that it is possible to repair even quite extensive damage on a do-it-yourself basis. However, you should never try to mend a key structural feature, such as an underbody box section or a door sill, yourself. This could well be dangerous and, in any case, is illegal. Such repairs must be left to a body shop and a professional welder.

Dealing with panels

When dealing with a rusty panel, thoroughness should be your watchword. If you skimp the job, the corrosion will quickly return. Remove all traces of rust from the outside first, using an electric drill and coarse sanding disc to grind the damaged area until you are left with shiny metal. Wear goggles to protect your eyes. You will find that the extent of the damage is usually far greater than you expected, because the rust has spread beneath the surface of the paint.

When all of the rust has been ground away, you will be left with a hole with jagged edges. Trim off as much weak metal as you can with a pair of pliers.

Then, dish in the edges with a hammer, so that they are below the surface of the surrounding bodywork. This will allow body filler to be added later and, when the edges of the metal begin to rust again – this is unfortunately inevitable – the corrosion will take far longer to reach the surface.

Treat the exposed metal with a rust converter. There are several types available in either liquid or jelly form. Some are brushed on and then washed off, while others are left to dry on the metal after their application. All are devised to convert the rust into an inert film and prevent future outbreaks of rusting for a considerable period. Some contain a mild

Filling a hole with wire mesh

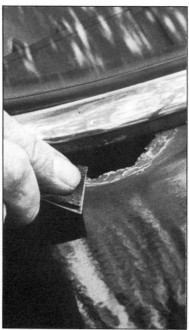

1 Rub down the area to be repaired with coarse glass paper to remove any rust and flaking paint. Continue until bare metal shows all around it. Make sure that no metal protrudes above the surface of the surrounding bodywork.

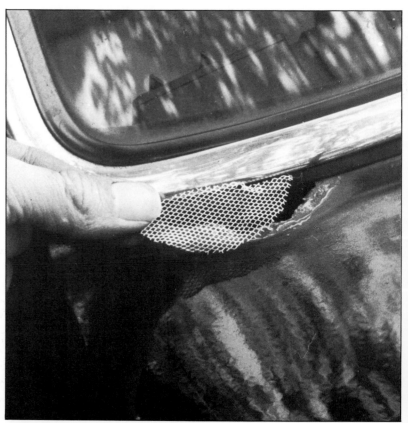

2 Cut a piece of wire mesh a little larger than the hole to suit its general shape.

acid, so take care not to get them on your skin or in your eyes.

If you can get behind the panel, clean the damaged area with a wire brush and apply another coat of rust converter. If this is impossible, work in as much converter as you can from the outside.

The next step is to bridge the hole with a firm base for the body filler. With small holes, a piece of aluminium tape can be stuck on to the inside of the panel to serve this purpose. If the hole is larger, a more substantial patch will be required. Use either an aluminium or zinc mesh – these are available from accessory shops and are purpose-made for the job. They are easy to cut cut

and shape and will not rust.

The larger the hole, the greater the strength of the repair should be. Glass-fibre matting and resin is the best way of achieving this. You can buy kits containing several sheets of matting, resin and hardener. Because the job is a messy one, it is advisable to wear gloves – the resin is extremely hard to remove. If you can get behind the panel, coat the underside of the repaired area with underbody sealant as well.

Repairing difficult panels

If rust has attacked a section of bodywork with double curves – such as a rear wheel arch – it is both difficult and time-consuming to make the damage

good. Rather than doing this, fit the part-panel designed for the job. Many body shops stock such panels. They include wheel arches, rear quarter panels (beneath the rear bumper on each side of the car) and door sill covers (these should be fitted only if the sill is not a load-bearing part of the structure).

However, fitting these panels and tackling the damage may be beyond your scope. If you have any doubts about making the repair to a satisfactory standard, it is better to have it done by a qualified mechanic.

Obviously, prevention is far better than cure. If your car is in good condition with little or no sign of rust, it should be rust-proofed *(see p.28)*.

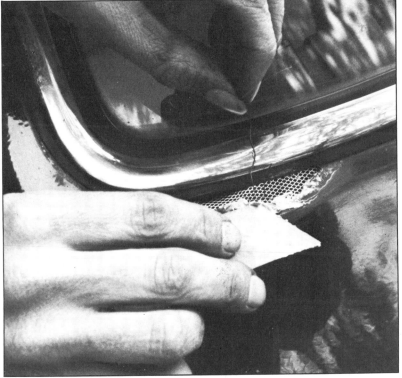

3 Loop a piece of wire through the mesh so you can hold it in place. Position the mesh in the hole and tack its edges to the surrounding bodywork with small amounts of filler. Keep hold of the wire until the filler has hardened enough to support the mesh. Then withdraw the wire.

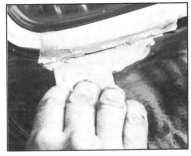

4 Apply filler to the mesh. Build it up so that the hole is completely covered and the filler stands slightly proud above the surrounding surface. If, as in this case, there is any trim or rubber sealing along an edge of the hole, protect it with a strip of masking tape.

5 Rub the filler down with coarse glass paper to remove any rough edges and finally smooth it out with fine grade wet-and-dry paper. It can now be primed and painted.

Repairing rust damage/2

Filling a hole with glass fibre

1 Before filling, the hole and its surrounding area must be sanded down to remove any rusted metal and flaking paint. It is quickest to use an electric drill with a coarse sanding disc. Clean the area until bare, shiny metal is revealed, but be careful not to damage any good paintwork around it.

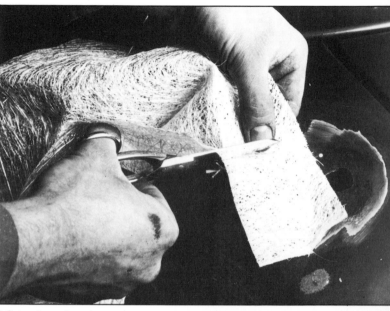

2 Cut a piece of matting about 25mm (1in) larger all round than the hole you intend to fill

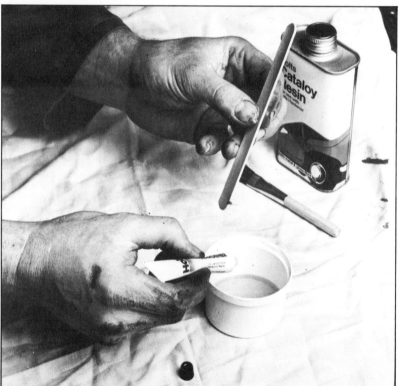

3 Mix up the resin with its hardener, following the manufacturer's instructions on the amounts of each to use. Be careful not to spill any on the paintwork.

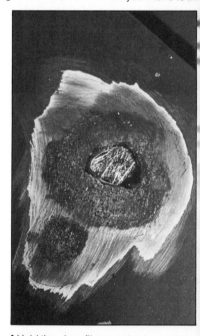

4 Hold the glass fibre matting in position and stipple the resin into it around the edges of the hole. Make sure the matting is dished inwards to accept the body filler you will use later. Once the resin has cured, apply another layer of matting for extra strength. Do not worry if the matting stands proud of the hole, as it can be sanded down later.

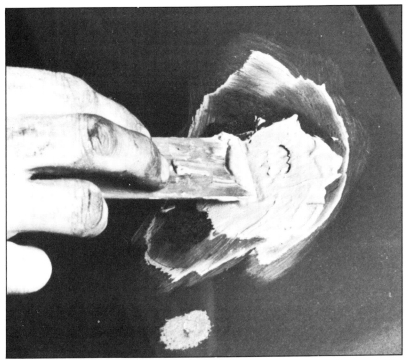

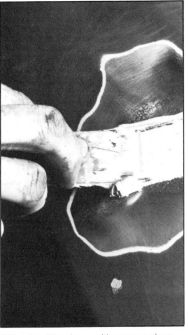

5 When the glass fibre has fully hardened, the hole can be filled with body filler. Mix up enough filler to cover both the hole and some of the surrounding area and apply it thickly with a spatula. Make sure the surface of the filler is above the surrounding bodywork.

6 Rub the filler down with coarse glass paper until it is blended into the contour of the repaired area. If there are any dents or pits left, apply another, thin layer of filler. Rub it down with fine wet-and-dry paper.

7 Fill any scratches in the filler with knifing stopper. Give the repaired area a final rub down with fine wet-and-dry paper, smoothing the filler level with the surrounding paintwork. It can now be painted.

Filling dents/1

Filling dents

Badly buckled or dented panels must be replaced and this is a job for a garage. However, small dents can be repaired at home and, with a little patience, good results can be achieved.

Tapping out dents

If you can get behind the dented panel, the job is made slightly easier, as you can gently tap out the damaged area with a hammer. Do not try to fully restore the contours of the damaged area, however, or the metal could be irreparably stretched out of shape. Instead, knock out the worst of the dent and leave the metal slightly dished inwards.

The process will almost certainly remove underbody sealant from the rear of the panel, which could lead to corrosion. Give the area a fresh coat of sealant, if necessary.

If you cannot tap the dent out from behind, it can be pulled out. Drill a small hole into the deepest part of the dent and screw a self-tapping screw part of the way home. Grip the head of the screw with a pair of pliers or mole grips and pull out the dent.

If this, too, proves difficult, the dent can be levered out. Hook the claw of a hammer under the screw head, then, using a block of wood as a fulcrum under the hammer head, lever out the dent.

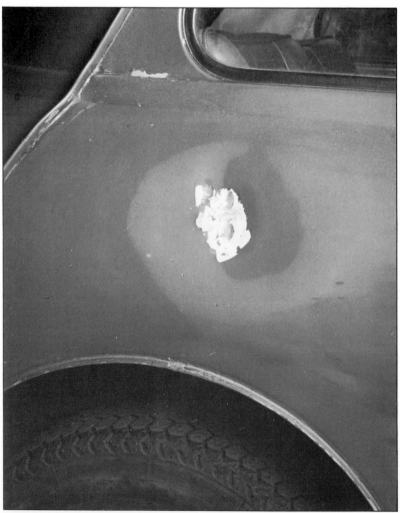

1 A dent like this is probably the most common and the most unsightly. As the the dent cannot be reached from behind and pushed out and is too deep just to be filled with body filler, it must be pulled out.

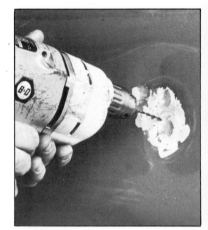

2 Drill a small hole at the deepest point of the dent.

3 Screw a self-tapping screw into the hole, leaving about a quarter of its length exposed.

4 Hook the claw end of a hammer under the head of the screw. Place a piece of wood under the hammer head and, using the wood as a fulcrum, lever the screw, and the dent, towards you. You may have to repeat the operation with screws placed at different points of the dent to pull it out fully.

5 When the dent is as flat as you can make it, check that none of the metal protrudes above the surface of the surrounding bodywork. If it does, tap it down with a hammer.

Keying the surface

The outside of the damaged area must now be keyed – that is, given a rough surface – to accept body filler. Use either 80-grit abrasive paper or a drill and coarse sanding disc to scuff the area thoroughly. As well as providing a good base to which body filler can adhere, this removes flaking paint as well.

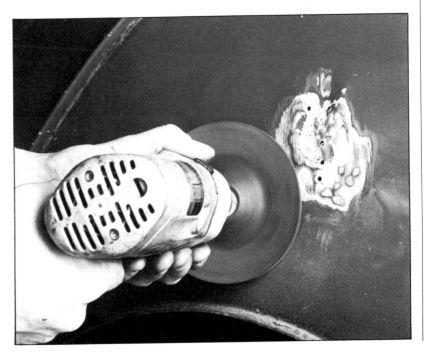

6 Before filler can be added, the surface must be roughened to give the filler a key. Use a coarse sanding disc on an electric drill. Sand the area of the dent and an area about 25mm (1in) around it down to bright metal.

Filling dents/2

Which filler?

The type of filler you should use depends on the nature of the repair. Standard fillers are reasonably strong, but will crack if subjected to flexing. To overcome this, elasticated fillers are available which will withstand a certain amount of this. When repairing a solid area, you should use a standard filler, but when dealing with a panel subject to flexing – a door panel, for instance – use the elasticated type.

Fillers are available in kits containing paste and a small tube of hardener. They must be mixed in according to the manufacturer's instructions. If insufficient hardener is added, the mix may not cure, but, if you add too much, the mix will probably cure too quickly and crack.

Applying the filler

Use a flat clean board to mix the paste and hardener – a piece of plywood is ideal. A small wallpaper scraper makes a good spatula for mixing. Keep mixing the paste and hardener until colour and consistency are constant. Cleanliness is vital, because dirt will scratch the filler when it is applied.

Body filler kits also contain a plastic spreader with which the filler is applied. Spread it on to the damaged area, using a fairly firm pressure and a slightly curved spreading action. This ensures maximum adhesion and expels air bubbles.

Do not try to fill the dent in one go. Instead, gradually build up the area with thin coats of filler, allowing each to cure before applying the next. Applying too much filler at once or not allowing each layer to cure could cause it to crack later.

Keep adding filler until it stands proud from the rest of the panel's contours.

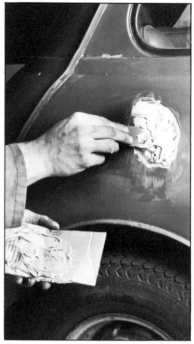

1 Mix the filler with its hardener on a piece of card and work it into the dent dent with a spatula. Do not try and fill the whole area at once but build the filler up in layers.

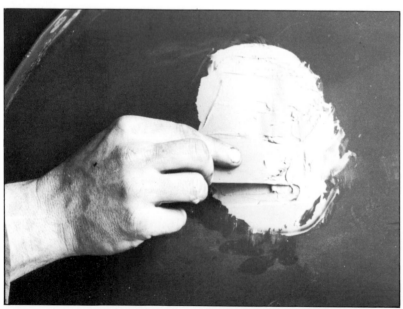

2 When the first layer of filler has hardened, apply more layers, building them up so that the whole area is covered and the filler stands slightly proud above the level of the surrounding bodywork.

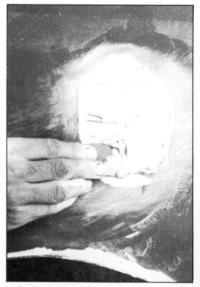

3 Rub the filler down until it roughly blends with the contours of the bodywork. If there are any dips or dents, apply small amounts of filler to make the surface of the repair level and even.

Rubbing down

Use an electric drill and a coarse sanding disc to rub down the filler initially. Carefully grind it back until all rough edges have been removed. Run your hand over the repaired area to feel for 'low' spots. These must be filled. Once the filler has been roughly smoothed to shape, the final contours are achieved with a rubbing block and 80-grit abrasive paper.

When dealing with tricky contours, you may find you have to rub the area down without the aid of a sanding block. Take care to apply an even finger pressure, as it is easy to rub a groove or dip in the filler accidentally.

Use the rubbing block in short, even strokes, working your way progressively across the repair so that it blends with the rest of the panel. You will need considerable patience when dealing with curved areas and, even at this stage, you might find that further filling and rubbing down is necessary.

Once you are satisfied with the shape, rub the area down with 400-grit wet-or-dry paper, used wet to prevent clogging. Ensure that you remove all of the scratches left by the coarser paper and also that you feather in the edges of the filler with the surrounding bodywork. Dip the paper in clean water frequently to flush off tiny particles of paint and filler.

For the final smoothing, use a rubbing block and 600-grit wet-or-dry paper, used wet. This removes the small scratches left by the 400-grit paper. Then, wash down the area with a sponge and clean, non-soapy water and thoroughly dry it with a chamois leather. All traces of

water must be removed or they will affect the paint finish later. The area must also be completely free of grease or other impurities. A clean, soft but non-fluffy piece of cloth with a small drop of white spirit works well – do not use cellulose thinners, which will remove good paintwork.

Inspect the filler closely for minor blemishes and imperfections. Deal with these by applying knife stopper. Use a small knife to spread a thin coat of stopper over the blemish, making sure it is firmly worked into place. Once the stopper has cured, rub it down with 600-grit wet-or-dry, used wet. The area is now ready for applying a priming coat of paint.

4 With the dent completely filled, the surface must be rubbed smooth. Start with coarse glass paper, either on a sanding disc or wrapped around a sanding block. Continue rubbing down with wet-and-dry paper.

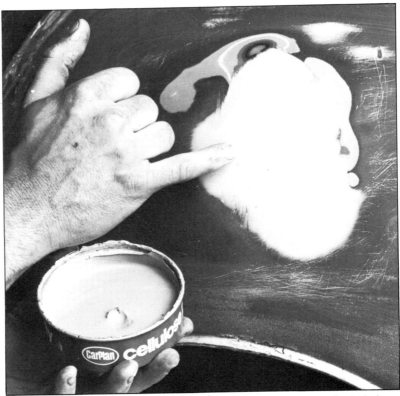

5 When the repaired area is smooth and blended into the surrounding bodywork, fill any scratches with knifing stopper.

Give the the whole area a final rub down with fine wet-and-dry paper.

Painting/1

Painting out chips and scratches

Minor chips and scratches not only look unsightly, so reducing the value of your car. They also can lead to rust, if left untreated. You should inspect the bodywork regularly, looking for any area where the paint surface has been broken. The leading edge of the bonnet and the front valance below the bumper and door sills are the places most prone to damage from flying stones.

Dealing with chips

It is easy to deal with tiny chips, where the paint surface has been broken but the primer is still intact. You will find a touch-up kit to match most colours – such kits come with a small brush for you to dab on the fresh paint. Once dry, the area can be compounded with a liquid cutting compound and then finished with a good quality polish *(see p.24)*.

Bare metal should be treated with a dab of rust converter. Several types are available – in either liquid or jelly form – and all of them work on the same principle, reacting with the rust to form an inert film. Depending on the type, you either wash the converter off after a recommended period, or leave it to dry and paint over it. After this, dab on primer and then follow up with touch-up paint.

Removing minor scratches

Minor scratches can often be removed by compounding and polishing. Use liquid cutting compound, covering the whole of the panel, followed by a good quality polish.

If the scratch is too deep to polish out, it must be rubbed down using 600-grit wet-or-dry paper. Use rust converter if corrosion has started, even if there is only a surface layer.

If the metal itself has been scratched, knife stopper (also known as cellulose putty) is the easiest way of dealing with the problem. Spread a thin coat over the scratch with a knife and rub down with 400-grit and then 600-grit wet-and-dry paper, using both papers wet.

Prime the area with either a brush or an aerosol. Mask off surrounding panels and trim to protect them from overspray. Spray the colour coats with the aerosol in even strokes, working from side to side. Release the nozzle at the end of each stroke and build up several coats.

Once the paint has hardened, compound the area with cutting compound, covering the whole of the panel. The final finish is achieved by polishing the complete panel.

1 Shake the can for at least two minutes to mix up the paint and spray a small amount into the cap.

2 Use a good quality, soft brush to paint over a scratch. Apply the paint fairly thickly and allow it to form a ridge above the surface. When the paint has fully hardened, rub it down with fine wet-and-dry paper until it is level with and blended into the surrounding paintwork. Polish the area with rubbing paste and liquid cutting compound to bring up the shine.

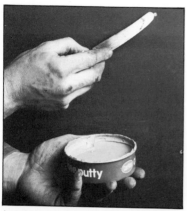

Any deep scratches or chips should be filled with knifing stopper and rubbed down to a smooth finish before painting.

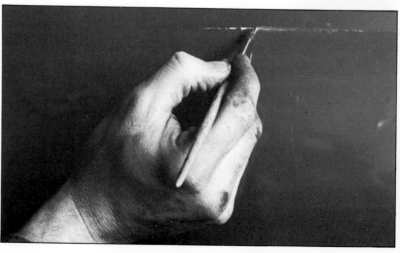

Effective spray painting

Spray painting is usually the most effective way of concealing a repair. However, you should remember that it is sometimes far better to spray complete panels rather than isolated areas. If you have repaired two dents, or dealt with an extensive scratch, for instance, it will involve you in far less work if you spray the whole panel, rather than spraying just part of it and then having to compound the new paint to blend it in with the existing surface.

Masking

You must mask off the area you intend to spray to avoid hitting other panels and trim with the inevitable overspray. If you are spraying a front wing, for instance, you will need to mask off the door, bonnet, headlight, part of the grille and bumper and the wheel. Use masking tape to hold your mask in place – this is available in various sizes, but 25mm- (1in-) thick tape is the easiest to use.

Stick a length of tape along a natural join, carefully following the contour of the panel. Do not run tape across a completely smooth area of the panel – if you do, the paint will form a ridge against the edge of the tape and this will make it difficult to blend the repair into the surrounding area.

Stick another length of tape along the edge of the masking paper, overlapping it by about 13mm (½in) and lay it over the tape on the panel. Cover the joins in the paper with more tape.

At least half of the bonnet must be masked in this fashion. Do the same for the door. The headlight, grille and part of the bumper can be masked off using tape and small pieces of paper, cut to size. A large piece of clean cloth is ideal for covering the wheel.

If a strip of side trim could be affected, mask it with tape. The tape must not cover any part of the panel which is being sprayed. If there is any overlap, trim the tape off with a craft knife.

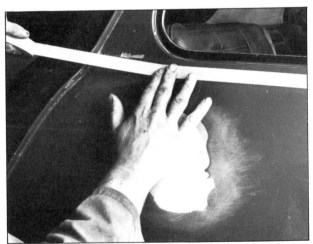

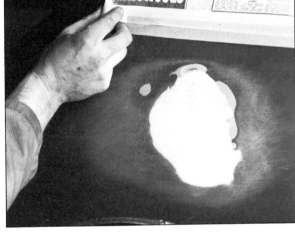

1 Lay masking tape along the outer edges of the area to be sprayed. Follow a natural crease in the bodywork where any 'edge' the spray may produce will not show.

2 Stick a length of masking tape along the edge of a piece of newspaper, with about half of the tape overlapping. Stick the newspaper to the tape that is already in position.

3 Tyres can be effectively masked by laying a large piece of clean cloth over them.

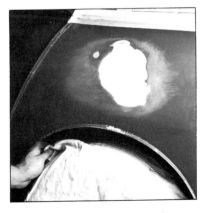

4 Mask any trim carefully. Make sure the tape is positioned exactiy along the edge of the trim and does not overlap onto the bodywork. If necessary, trim off any excess tape with a sharp knife.

Painting/2

Preparing a panel

Because the standard of finish you achieve depends on the level of preparation, be patient when preparing a panel for spraying. Even the smallest blemish will stand out noticeably when the colour coats have been applied.

Whatever the repair, you must rub down and prime the affected area first. Brush on the first coat of primer – it is better to use a brush at this stage than an aerosol – and, when the paint has hardened, smooth it down with a rubbing block and 400-grit wet-or-dry abrasive paper used wet. Then, spray on two or three more coats of primer and finally rub down the complete panel using a rubbing block and 600-grit wet-or-dry used wet. It is important that you do as thorough a job as possible, since all traces of road film and silicones (from polishes) must be removed. If any remain, they could react with the new paint and ruin the finish. Rubbing down is also necessary to key the old paint so that it will readily accept the new coats.

When you finish, the panel should have a matt finish all over it. To check that it has been rubbed down properly, smear it with water. The water should lie in an unbroken film.

Wash the panel down with clean, non-soapy water and thoroughly dry it with a chamois leather. Make sure there are no droplets of water hidden behind trim or door handles. Finally, to make sure that the panel is completely clean, rub it over with a non-fluffy cloth and a small drop of white spirit. Do not use a cellulose-based solvent, as this could remove the existing paint or the fresh primer.

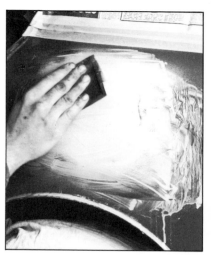

1 Apply the first coat of primer fairly thickly, with a brush. The primer will fill in any small scratches left in the filler. Give the primer time to harden fully – you can test it by tapping the surface with a fingernail – and then rub the whole surface down with fine grade wet and dry paper until it is perfectly smooth.

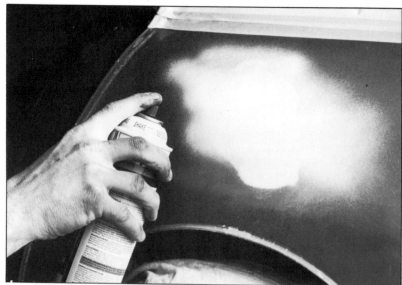

2 Spray on one or two more coats of primer. Make sure you shake the spray can for at least two minutes before spraying so the primer is properly mixed. Hold the spray can about 150mm (6in) from the surface and spray from side to side, stopping at the end of each stroke. If the primer runs, wait until it hardens and rub it down until the surface is smooth.

3 When the surface is covered completely with primer and the primer has hardened, give it a final rub down with fine grade wet-and-dry paper. Make sure that the sprayed area is blended into the surrounding paintwork and that there are no ridges or runs.

Spraying

The panel is now ready for spraying. Buy more aerosols than you need – it is far better to have some left over than to run out before the job has been completed. The actual spraying requires practice, so experiment first on an old piece of metal.

Shake the can thoroughly to mix the paint. Hold it about 150mm (6in) away from the panel, squeeze the nozzle and move it horizontally across. Release the nozzle at the end of the stroke and make a return stroke, so that the spray pattern half-overlaps. Gradually work your way down the panel in the same way, releasing the nozzle at the end of each stroke, until the whole panel has been covered.

By varying the speed at which you spray and the distance of the aerosol from the panel, you can create different finishes to suit your requirements. Take care, however, not to move the spray too slowly or hold it too close to the panel – if you do, the paint will be applied too thickly and either run or sag. On the other hand, if you move the spray too quickly or hold the aerosol too far from the panel, the paint will dry with a matt finish.

Once you have perfected your technique, start spraying the actual panel. Apply several coats of paint, allowing each one to dry and cure in turn. Do not attempt to complete the job in one go with a single thick coat.

Finishing off

Once the final coat has been applied and it has hardened, compound the panel with a liquid cutting compound and finish with a good quality polish.

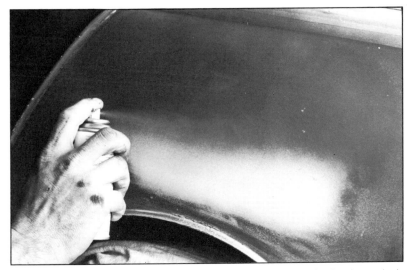

1 With the surface prepared, the top coat can be applied. Shake the spray can for at least two minutes before spraying to mix the paint fully. Spray about 150mm (6in) from the surface, using even strokes from side to side. If the paint runs, leave it to harden and rub down with fine wet-and-dry paper. You will probably have to spray several coats to provide the necessary depth of paint to cover the primer and blend in with the surrounding paintwork.

2 When the top coat has hardened, it is best to leave it overnight before polishing the surface. Use rubbing compound initially, applied with a damp cloth, to bring out the shine and complete the process with liquid cutting compound.

Achieving a shine with metallic paint can be difficult, and compounding sometimes makes the newly-painted surface matt as well. To deal with the problem, spray the surface with two coats of clear lacquer – such lacquers are available in aerosol form – to make the paint shine.

Remove the masking tape and paper. The new paintwork may stand out against the old. If so, compound and polish the surrounding panels to create a matching finish.

3 The sprayed area can be given a final shine and some added protection with a coat of wax.

Accessories

In-car entertainment

If you decide to fit a radio, cassette player, or combination unit to your car, where do you start? The range of available models is vast – there are several hundred to choose from on the market – while the prices for identical sets can vary significantly, because discounts vary from retailer to retailer. So, to make a final choice, you must weigh the quality of reproduction and level of sophistication you require with what you can afford.

Generally speaking, the more you are prepared to pay, the better hi-fi performance will be. To maximize this, however, it is vital to buy speakers that match the output and quality of the amplifier to ensure top-quality reproduction.

Car radios

The lower end of the car radio market is dominated by basic mono models. These produce a reasonable sound, but the cheapest operate only on medium and long wave – for a few pounds more, you can opt for FM reception. Many such models have push-button pre-selection.

An FM radio with five-button pre-selection is an ideal first-time buy for a car without a radio, or as a replacement for the basic radio fitted by the manufacturer. Again, for only a little more money, you could buy a stereo receiver.

Cassette players

Individually, cassette players are also reasonably inexpensive, but remember that, if you car is fitted only with a mono radio, you will need an extra pair of speakers to accommodate the player.

Check the power output per

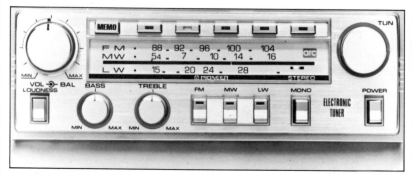

Radios vary in price according to their sophistication. You can replace the standard unit that comes with the car with one with FM reception. This frequency gives better quality reception in stereo.

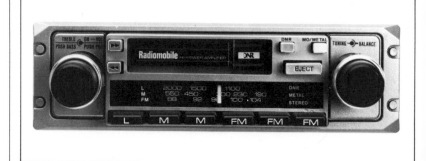

A combination unit of radio and tape player provides the best of both worlds in car entertainment. Such units vary in sophistication and price, but generally cost about a third more than a radio on its own.

channel as well. On cheaper units, this is usually between two and four watts per channel; though you may not need more than this, such a set will always be operating near its capacity. Thus, it is a good idea to assess the sound such sets produce at full output before buying one. While the sheer volume produced may be sufficient for your needs, the quality of reproduction could suffer because of distortion or speaker vibration.

Combination units

Though the choice of combination radio/tape player units at the cheaper end of the market is more limited, there are some budget buys. These provide the basics – a pre-selector radio, with medium wave, long wave and FM reception, and a tape player, usually with fast-forward wind. If, however, you are prepared to pay about half as much again, the choice is considerably wider, since the majority of available units offer an FM stereo radio combination. Some of these have an auto-reverse tape deck with programme search. This stops the tape at gaps between each track, allowing you to select individual items easily.

Check to see that the model you choose has the following features, all of which are worthwhile. The radio should have five or six buttons that can be pre-set to specific stations on FM, long wave and medium wave, and efficient noise suppression circuitry. On the tape deck, look for locking fast-forward and reverse winds, and an automatic tape stop and tape ejection. If you do not mind the lack of FM reception, you could choose one of the many two-waveband combination units available – they will probably compensate for the absence of FM by having slightly better-quality tape decks fitted to them.

Improving performance

Your sound system's performance can be improved significantly by the addition of a graphic equalizer or a power amplifier. Either of these will cost about the same as a reasonably-priced combination unit; they provide fine tuning of tonal balance and extra power.

Most manufacturers make these extra pieces of equipment to visually and electronically match their own radio/tape players. In any case, before buying an equalizer or amplifier, check with the manufacturer or your local stockist to make sure it is compatible with your existing equipment.

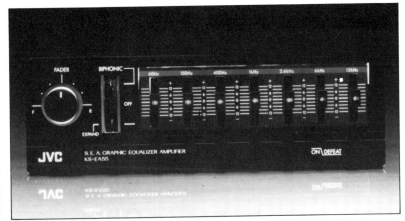

A graphic equalizer is a useful addition to a sound system, as it helps provide clearer reproduction and extra power.

Choose one that matches the existing system both electrically and visually.

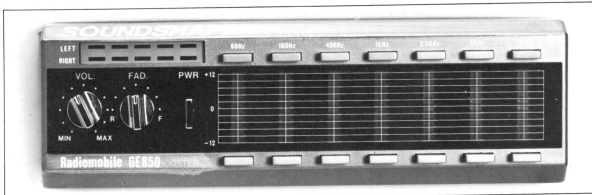

Accessories

If you are prepared to pay even more, you can choose from some extremely sophisticated equipment, much of which is capable of competing with a home hi-fi set. Many such sets do away with the pointer of the conventional tuning display in favour of light-emitting diodes, or other non-mechanical devices. Features such as automatic tape slack control, auto-reverse and noise suppression will almost certainly be included.

From stereo to quadraphonic

Most people find two car speakers sufficient, but it is worth noting that some sets have four outputs for quadraphonic sound. Though these are capable of delivering up to 20 watts per channel, it is doubtful whether the average motorist will ever use them to their full capacity. But, because they are never fully stressed, reproduction will be greatly improved.

Combination units

If you are prepared to spend a considerable sum of money, the level of sophistication and quality of combination units is almost limitless. All of the previously-mentioned features – such as auto-reverse, noise suppression, programme search – will be included – while you can expect at least five electronic memory station pre-sets.

Some sets have liquid crystal digital frequency displays and around a dozen station pre-sets. Micro-computer control is another feature that may appeal to you. The electronic tuning system can be programmed to up to 10 or more transmission frequencies of a single station. As the car travels from area to area, the set automatically tunes itself

Speakers can be mounted with the radio, or in the front doors, as well as on the shelf by the rear window. There are many makes of speaker that can be positioned in this way, including the directional variety. These can be rotated in any direction to give the best sound balance.

into the strongest signal among those it recognizes.

Locating the set

Before buying any set, decide where it is to be mounted. Make sure there is enough depth and width to accommodate it. If in doubt, measure the space available in the car and then measure the set.

Choosing speakers

As with radios, cassette players and combination units, the choice of speakers is wide.

There are three general guidelines to follow to help you decide which to buy – the performance (that is, how much power the speakers can handle), the design and the price.

Always buy speakers that are more than capable of handling the output of your set. For example, if your unit can produce 6 watts per channel, buy speakers that are rated to at least 8 watts. Buy an even more powerful set if you are planning to fit an amplifier at a later stage. By erring on the side of caution, the speakers will never be overstressed and so always give the best possible sound reproduction.

The choice of design is a partly a matter of personal preference and partly depends on where the speakers are to be mounted. You can pick from square, oblong, round or oval speakers, all of which come in a variety of finishes. These include chromium plate, satin and matt-black.

If the speakers are to be fitted in the door panels, for instance, you will need the flush-fitting type. You should also make sure that they are shallow enough to avoid touching the insides of the panels. Speakers can also be flush-mounted on the rear parcel shelf – although this does not give ideal sound distribution – or mounted on top of the shelf. In this case, you will need speakers that come complete with their own mounting pods. Measure the space available in your car to make sure there is enough room to fit them.

A cheap pair of speakers will cost very little but their wattage capability will be low. Always buy the best you can afford because the price will be

When fitting speakers in the doors, you will probably have to remove the window winding arm and door handle in order to take off the inner panel to cut the hole for the speaker.

reflected in the quality of sound they produce. At the upper end of the scale, you can pay as much for a set of speakers as a reasonable combination unit.

Choosing an aerial

The quality of radio reception is directly related to the quality of your car aerial. Buy the best you can afford. Aerials with a short mast can work well, but usually need some form of performance-boosting circuit built into them. If this is required, the instructions will tell you to connect a separate power source to the base. If no power is required, the aerial will almost certainly give poor reception.

The conventional telescopic-mast and roof-mounted aerials give good reception. Choose one with a good quality chrome finish or, better still, one with polished stainless steel sections. Whatever the material, look for a fairly tight fit between the sections.

The supply lead should be fairly thick and well sealed at the base. An FM-rated cable, with its extra thick insulation, is the best

buy. This works just as well with MW/LW sets as with FM ones, while its use means that you will not have to change the aerial if you fit a more sophisticated radio.

Look for a strong earthing clamp at the base. Ideally, the tubular body should be made of metal, rather than plastic. The aerial should be mounted as far away from the engine as possible – preferably on the rear wing – to give you the best reception, without interference. This means that an extension co-axial cable will be required to link aerial and radio.

Electrically-operated aerials are extremely convenient, but obviously far more expensive than conventional ones. If you plan to fit one, make sure there is

When fitting an electric aerial, bear in mind you will need a lot more space beneath the aerial for the motor and its wiring than for a standard aerial. You may find that fitting it in the boot is easiest, though this may entail adding to the wiring so that it can reach both radio and power source.

Accessories

enough clearance for the motor beneath the wing, or wherever you decide to fit it.

Fitting a sound system

Many car radio specialists will fit a complete sound system quite cheaply, particularly if they sold you the equipment. It will take a competent specialist less than a day to do the job. However, if you are a d-i-y enthusiast, you can tackle the job yourself almost as easily.

No special tools are required, while the position of the set will probably have already been decided for you in advance. Most modern cars come fitted either with their own basic radio, or with a fitting space – covered with a plastic blanking piece – in the fascia. You secure the set in place by tightening the nuts on the pillars of the control knobs and by fitting a steadying bracket – this comes with the set – which you attach to a convenient firm object behind the dashboard.

If no fitting space has been provided, you can easily mount the set under the dashboard, using your own brackets, or cut your own hole in the fascia to take the set. Remember, though, that if you cut the fascia, the set is in the car for good. You will find it more difficult to sell the car if if the fascia has been cut and the radio removed.

As an alternative, bolt-on centre consoles are available for many popular cars. Roof-mounted consoles are also available, but you may find it necessary to remove the headlining to connect up the wires.

Wiring up

Wiring up is fairly simple. With a combination radio and cassette player, for instance, there will be two pairs of wires to the speakers, an earth wire and a live wire, with an in-line fuse. The last should be connected to an ignition-controlled power source, or a permanent live feed – the fuse box is ideal. Some sets have an extra wire for an electrically-operated aerial. It automatically raises and retracts itself as the radio is switched on and off.

Fitting speakers

The easiest type of speakers to fit are those mounted on the rear parcel shelf. They are held in place with self-tapping screws. With the door-mounted type, the trim must be removed and carefully cut, while it is also important to check behind the trim to make sure that the speakers will not foul the window or winder mechanism. The speaker wires pass through a hole drilled in the leading edge of the door and then through the door pillar into the car. Grommets must be used to prevent chafing. When fitting a door mounted speaker, make sure that it is not obscured by the seat when the door is closed. If it is, reproduction will be muffled.

Another alternative is to mount speakers under the rear seat. Although the sound distribution will not be ideal, the position may prove to be the most convenient one. Neatly route all wires under carpets and beneath the seats and trim, making sure that the wires cannot be trodden or sat on and keeping them as short as possible. If there is excessive slack, tape the surplus wire beneath the dashboard so that it will be hidden, but take care not to foul the heater controls.

Fitting the aerial

As previously stated, the aerial should be mounted as far away from the engine as possible on the rear wing and an extension lead fitted to link it to the radio. However, an aerial mounted on the front wing still gives good reception.

Check beneath the wing for obstructions before deciding on the final position, and then lightly centre punch the metal. Alternatively, cover the area in masking tape to stop the drill slipping. Drill a hole, or cut one with a hole cutter, making the hole large enough for the aerial to just slide through it. The aerial must make a good earth contact with the body. Use the bracing bracket supplied to stop it from flexing.

Do not cut the co-axial lead if it is too long. Instead, coil it into gentle loops – not tight coils – to lose some of the length.

Dealing with interference

The two main causes of radio interference are the ignition system and the generator. Interference from the ignition causes crackling, while the generator will make the radio whine, the whine speeding up and slowing down in time with the engine.

If your car is not fitted with suppressors – look in the handbook to check this – deal with the problem by fitting the recommended suppressors to the ignition coil and generator. If you like, you can further suppress the ignition system by fitting specially-suppressed spark plug leads. If interference persists after this, turn on the set and run the engine with the aerial disconnected. If interference stops, then the aerial is at fault. It is probably making a poor earth connection with the body.

Suppressing a glass-fibre car is time consuming. At the very least, the inside of the bonnet must be covered with aluminium foil, which is then earthed to the chassis. If interference persists, dealing with it is a job for an expert.

Player and tape care

Whatever type of player you buy, it will need periodical servicing – usually about every two years – to ensure both the player and the tapes survive for their maximum working lives. Always buy reputable brand-name tapes. Buying cheap tapes is a false economy, as they may damage your player. The tapes should be kept in protective boxes, or in a cassette holder. Never allow them to be exposed to heat, sunlight or moisture, or store them near the magnetic fields that can be created by loudspeakers or tape motors.

As tapes are played, they leave deposits of dust or magnetic material inside the player. The inside of the player – particularly the tape heads – should be cleaned regularly to remove this. Use a kit from an audio store to do this, finishing the job by running a special cleaning tape through the machine. This gives the tape contact areas a final polish.

The most expensive tapes have a coating of chromium dioxide (CrO_2), a mixture called ferro-chrome or pure metal. They should not be used unless the tape heads of the player are hard enough to handle them. Check the player's specifications to see if this is the case.

Understanding the language

As in any specialist field, in-car entertainment has its own language, some of whose terms can be confusing for the layman, especially when it comes to considering specifications. To help you, here is a list of some of the more common terminology and what each means:

Agc – Automatic gain control. This optimizes the sound output levels from a wide range of station signal strengths.

Alc – Automatic loudness circuit. This amplifies the bass and treble to compensate for low volume.

Analogue tuning display – This replaces the conventional pointer on the tuning dial of a radio. It is usually a light-emitting diode read-out.

Anti-rolling system – This reduces the amount of tape wow and flutter and lessens the effects of car movement.

Asc – Automatic separation control. This reduces interference on FM stereo broadcasts when the station signal is weak and the set is switching between stereo and mono output as a consequence.

Auto-eject – The tape automatically stops and ejects at the end of each side.

Auto-reverse – The tape automatically stops at the end of a side, direction is reversed and the second side is played.

Autostop – The tape automatically stops at the end of a side and the player switches over to the radio.

Digital tuning – The tuned frequencies are displayed in digital form by light-emitting diodes or liquid crystal.

Digital-analogue tuning – This is a mechanically-tuned set with a digital display.

Dolby – A system incorporated in some tape decks to reduce tape hiss.

Frequency response – A measure of how effectively set or speakers transmit the full range of sound frequencies. The wider the frequency range response, the better.

Inter-station muting – This cuts out the background noise in between stations while the set is tuned.

Local/dx – A device on FM sets that seeks out the strongest signal. The system is usually only found on self-seek radios.

Pll synthesizer – A tuning system in which the selected digital station frequency is compared with a reference frequency generated by a quartz crystal circuit, like an electronic wrist-watch.

Scan - A type of self-seek system, which retunes the set. However, it does not lock on to the station. It gives you about five seconds to decide whether you want to listen to the programme before automatically seeking another station.

Self-seek – This automatically retunes the set to the next-strongest signal on the dial at the push of a button.

Soft-muting – This reduces the sound output automatically when signal strength falls to inaudible levels and only interference can be heard.

Total harmonic distortion – A measure of all the harmonies of a sound which an amplifier or other part of the set adds to or subtracts from the original audio signal.

Accessories

Personalizing your car

The shape and design of modern cars – apart from that of expensive, exotic models – is largely dictated by economic factors. All manufacturers aim to provide comfort and an attractive body shape, while keeping their production costs to a minimum.

By the time that the layout of the engine and its supporting mechanical systems, the seating arrangement and the body's aerodynamics have been established, it is a fact that all cars in the same class often look very much the same. This maxim holds true from one make to another, as every manufacturer is basically aiming at the same compromise. However, many motorists find this unsatisfactory. Anybody who enjoys motoring and takes pride in car ownership always likes their car to stand out just that little bit from the pack.

Bolt-on body kits

The easiest way of making your car into something more than a mass-produced model is to customize it. You can do this by buying one of the many aftermarket kits now on the market, which are designed to personalize a car without altering its basic structure.

The lengths to which you can go are limited only by the amount you want to spend and the extent to which you want your car to stand out from others. You can limit yourself to making a few simple, but subtle, changes or add a complete body kit to totally transform the car's appearance.

Simple styling

Before you add anything to the bodywork, make a sketch of the car (or use a photograph) and then pencil in the changes you are planning. This will give you a fair idea of the finished effect.

The most sophisticated body kits can completely transform a car's appearance. They include a front spoiler and headlight/radiator grill surround, wheel arches blended in with side body mouldings and often a rear spoiler. A kit like this will change the image of a mass-produced saloon into that of an individually- styled sports car.

Remember, it is often better to aim for subtlety, rather than total flamboyance.

Before going to the extreme of fitting new panels, for instance, consider making one or two minor cosmetic changes that are effective, but cheap. Take your radiator grille, for instance. The front grilles of most cars are made from matt-black plastic, which can be made to look much smarter if you spray them the colour of the car's bodywork. This will not take you long. Simply remove the grille and rub it down with wet-and-dry abrasive paper. Then spray it with the appropriate aerosol. Matt-black door mirrors can similarly be sprayed to match the bodywork.

The rubber inserts fitted to some bumpers also look extremely distinctive when colour-matched to the bodywork. Tell your paint supplier what you plan to do, so that you get the correct type of paint. This should be designed to adhere to rubber and resist cracking.

The total transformation

Recently, rather than developing a host of varieties, manufacturers are concentrating more and more on offering 'option packs' for one basic model, including boot-spoilers and side-trims. You can buy these packs from your main dealer. Their advantage is that you will know what they look like before fitting them.

If, however, you decide to go further than this, you can fit totally new panels. One of the most popular of these is a front air dam. This is often referred to as a 'spoiler' and fits beneath the front bumper. Most

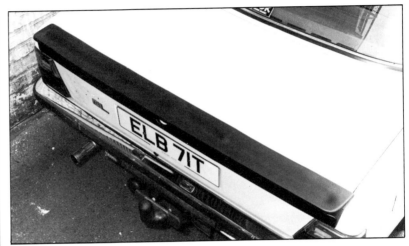

There are two types of rear spoiler that can be fitted – the 'lip' type *(above)* that fits along the back edge of the boot or the 'wing' type *(below)* that is bolted to the boot lid or wing panels. They smooth the air flow over the back of the car, reducing turbulence and thus drag.

Front spoilers reduce the amount of air flowing under the car. This reduces the lift the air gives to the front of the car and makes it more stable. However, when choosing a spoiler, make sure that it allows air to flow adequately around the engine sump. A good flow of air is needed to maintain the engine oil at its correct temperature and to stop overheating.

Accessories

manufacturers claim that a spoiler improves the car's aerodynamics. However, any improvement is probably marginal at best – the gain is mostly confined to appearance.

Spoilers are made from moulded glass-fibre, which has the advantage of being resistant to corrosion. They are held in place with self-tapping screws, or blind rivets and then reinforced on the inside with glass-fibre matting and resin.

The most basic type of spoiler consists of shaped sheets of glass-fibre, but, if you are prepared to pay more, you can buy spoilers complete with cut-outs to accept fog-lights. On some, further cut-outs means that the flow of cool air to the brakes is not blocked.

Fitting a spoiler
Fitting a spoiler requires patience and careful workmanship, but the job is well within the capabilities of a competent home handyman. The first step is to position the spoiler on the body and to mark this out with a felt-tip pen. You then drill the first two holes for the self-tapping screws – one hole at either end of the planned final position – and temporarily secure the spoiler. Only drill the rest of the holes when you are satisfied with the spoiler's position.

No spoiler will be a perfect fit, so you must blend it with the body. Use body filler to do this. As the colour of the filler will probably not match that of the bodywork, spray it to complete the job *(see p.186)*.

Rear spoilers
Rear spoilers can be fitted to booted cars and hatchbacks, the

If you fit wide 'sports' wheels that protrude beyond the edge of the bodywork, you must fit wheel arches to cover them. These are often available as part of an overall body kit and blend in well with a front spoiler.

majority of them being made from tough rubber. They are designed to improve the stability of the rear end of the car at high speed by forcing the tail downward. However, as with front spoilers, the improvement is more visual than practical, unless a large or very expensive spoiler is fitted. You may find, too, that the extra weight upsets the spring-loaded mechanism of the boot or tailgate, making it difficult to open. If so, you can adjust the mechanism to compensate for this on the majority of models.

To fit a rear spoiler, hold it in position and mark this on the bodywork with a felt-tip pen as before. Then, drill holes through the boot or hatchback and bolt the spoiler into place.

With a rear spoiler, you will not need to apply body filler to finish the job. However, it is a good idea to spray it to match

the bodywork colour before fitting it.

Wheel arches
Another way of giving your car that personal look is to fit flared wheel arches. Remember, though, that these will look out of place unless you are prepared to fit wider wheels and tyres as well to take up the extra width.

As an alternative, you can fit flared side panels that are designed to blend into your wings at either end. These make the car look wider and more squat, while saving you the bother of fitting wider wheels. The panels are usually made from glass-fibre and are secured and finished in the same way as a front spoiler.

Fitting and finishing hints
If you decide to fit a front spoiler, rear spoiler, and side panels, it will pay you to do all three jobs at the same time. It will be far cheaper to have the bodywork resprayed in one session than to have it done in stages.

You should not be too disappointed if the finish of any glass-fibre body panel is a little less than perfect. Even the best-made panels can have slight ripples, which are not immediately noticeable but show through when the final coats of colour are applied. Nevertheless, before you buy panels, inspect them as closely as possible and ask for different ones if you are not satisfied with the finish.

Fortunately, it is easy – although time-consuming – to make the surface smooth. To do this, you apply coats of body filler, rubbing each one down, until the imperfections are gradually filled. Once again, this will save you money if you are preparing the job for a professional to finish.

Headlights and reflectors

Pop-up headlights of the kind fitted to expensive sports cars look extremely smart. Without going to this expense, you can create almost as good an effect by fitting headlamp shields. They are made from tinted perspex and are simple to screw into place. As well as improving appearance, they also protect your headlamp lenses from flying stones.

You can also fix reflector panels to the rear end of your car. Some carry the car name – most popular models are catered for – while others come in plain red. Both types provide an extra safety bonus, since they give additional reflection at night.

Getting the job done

Remember that you do not have to be a d-i-y enthusiast to customize your car. Almost every supplier of special body kits will carry out the fitting and re-finishing for you to your own specifications if you do not feel confident that you can tackle the job. If you decide to do this, ask to see a car the business concern has already customized to judge how high the standard or workmanship is.

Whatever modifications you plan, find out if they involve cutting into the bodywork first. If you plan to keep the car for a reasonable period, this may not matter. However, you must bear in mind that the car may be harder to sell with the new panels – not everybody has the same taste – and expensive to convert back to its original state.

Fitting auxiliary lights

You can fit any of the three basic types of auxiliary lamp – spotlamp, driving lamp and fog lamp – to your car, but, before deciding to do so, you should be aware of their different functions, advantages and limitations. A spotlamp, for instance, gives a long-range pencil beam, but is impractical for normal driving.

Like a spotlamp, a driving lamp produces a high-intensity beam, but this has less range and a much wider spread. A fog lamp gives an extremely wide spread of light, the beam being designed not to hit fog or mist head-on, so causing reflective dazzle.

You should either fit a pair of driving lamps, a pair of fog lamps or a pair of each. Do not mix the lamps.

Which lamp to choose

Before you decide whether or not a pair of driving lamps will help your driving, take a night-time drive along a road you use frequently, noting how effective your headlights are. All headlights are made as a compromise – they will either give you good long-range visibility, with a limited spread of light, or vice versa.

Having established this, you can be sure of buying a set of driving lamps to complement your headlights, rather than fight against them. There are many types available to meet

There are three types of auxiliary lights you can fit – spotlamps, driving lamps and fog lamps. All are available in round or rectangular shapes. Choose the shape to match the existing car lamps.

Accessories

individual needs. You can start, for instance, from a spread of about 30° degrees and choose a lamp that gives up to 450 metres penetration. Measure the overall depth and width of each lamp and check that there is enough space to fit them.

Fog lamps are similarly marked by their manufacturers with specifications of their depth of penetration and spread. Make the same dimensional checks.

Similarly, pick a set of fog lamps to match your headlights – either round or rectangular. Generally speaking, rectangular lamps are not as efficient as round ones, unless the set you choose is an expensive one. In this case, the difference is negligible.

Fitting auxiliary lights

The simplest way to fit auxiliary lamps is with brackets attached to the bumper bolts. If you do this, make sure that the brackets are steady, as otherwise the lamps will flutter, so distracting oncoming drivers.

You can also fit a special grille with a cut-out to accept other lamps. Such grilles are available to replace the conventional grilles on most popular models of car. Front spoilers incorporating cut-outs are available as well.

All such lights come with full wiring instructions. It is important to follow these carefully, especially when it comes to fitting a relay to avoid the risk of a circuit overload.

The legal requirements

Your auxiliary lights must comply with the law. The maximum permitted height from the ground to the top of the lens is 120cm (4ft) and the minimum

height from the ground to the bottom of the lens is 50cm (20in). The lamps must be fitted so that their external edges are no more than 40cm (16in) from the outermost parts of the car.

If you are forced to fit lamps at less than the legal height from the ground to the bottom of the lens, they can still be used, but only in what are legally defined as adverse driving conditions. This means that fog lamps can be mounted as low as you wish, but only used when necessary. Driving lamps must be wired to go out when your headlights are dipped.

High-intensity rear fog lamps are now compulsory fittings on all new cars. Such lamps must not be closer than 100mm (4in) to a stop light, and at least 250mm (10in) from the ground, but no higher than a metre (3ft 3½in).

A dash warning light – usually supplied with each kit – should be fitted to warn you that the lamp is switched on.

Sunshine roofs

Though you can fit a do-it-yourself sunshine roof kit to your car, it is usually preferable to have one fitted professionally. The job involves cutting metal accurately – sometimes through bracing sections needed for strength – and removing and

A sunshine roof will add value to your car and make driving more pleasurable. The cheapest is a tinted, see-through fixed panel, though, for a little extra, a roof that tilts to allow in fresh air can be fitted *(below)*. The most expensive types are the steel sliding roof and the retractable vinyl type *(above)*.

replacing trim. It is all too easy for an inexperienced do-it-yourself enthusiast to botch the job.

A see-through fixed sunroof is the cheapest buy. This provides extra light, but no additional ventilation. The tilting type, which lets in fresh air, costs more, but some models are also removable. Steel sliding sunroofs, or retractable vinyl units are the most expensive. Many steel roofs have the option of electric operation.

Fitting extra instruments

Fitting additional instruments and gauges to your dashboard means advance planning. Decide exactly how many of these you want and choose a place for them that gives you enough space to fit them, allows their wiring to be concealed and lets you see them clearly from the driving seat.

It is more practical and attractive to group such instruments together than to add them wholesale in random positions. Choose instruments that match each other and complement your existing equipment in finish – matt-black or chrome – and shape.

You can buy mounting pods and brackets to take such instruments. The pods can be fitted above or below the dashboard, using self-tapping screws, small nuts and bolts or self-adhesive strips.

All extra instruments come with full fitting instructions, which should be observed exactly, especially when it comes to wiring them in to an existing electrical circuit.

Oil pressure gauge

There are two types available – an electrically operated gauge or one fed by a capillary tube. The latter gives a more accurate reading.

Electrical gauges come fitted with two spade connectors. One wire is fed through the bulkhead to the engine bay – this may involve drilling a hole – and should be fitted with a rubber grommet to prevent chafing. It is then connected to the existing oil pressure switch on the side of the engine block. The other wire should run from the gauge to a convenient point near the dashboard.

The capillary type needs no extra wiring, apart from its light. The crucial item in the kit is the T-piece connector. Unscrew the existing oil pressure switch from the engine block, screw it into the T-piece and fit the whole assembly to the block. The original wire is reconnected to the switch and the capillary tube fitted to the remaining thread on the connector. The tube is passed through the bulkhead – drilling may be necessary – and the other end screwed to the gauge. Make sure that the tube does not touch or come near any hot engine components when

The instrumentation on many cars is basic. Even when such gauges as oil pressure and water temperature are fitted, they may show only a simple scale, marked in green and red. More sophisticated gauges to monitor most of the car's vital functions can be fitted as extras, or as replacements for standard instruments.

Accessories

routing it under the bonnet. If necessary, tape it out if the way.

Water temperature gauge

If your car is fitted only with a water temperature warning light, or if you want more accurate readings than the simple conventional gauge can supply, you can fit a water gauge that actually shows the temperature of the coolant. In both cases, the new gauge is relatively easy to install. One wire from the gauge is passed through the engine bay's bulkhead to replace the existing wire on the sender unit, normally located near the radiator's top hose and the thermostat housing. The other wire goes to earth.

The wire on some gauges is also temperature sensitive. It is passed through the bulkhead as before and connected either to the existing sender unit or to the one provided with the kit. It must not touch or pass near hot engine components – the readings will be false if it does. Coil it up if it is too long, making sure it does not become kinked.

Battery condition gauge

Battery condition gauges, or voltmeters, are becoming more popular than ammeters, as they tell you not only that the battery is being charged, but also the actual state of charge of the battery. To check this, you need not start the engine – all you do is switch on the ignition.

In common with a water temperature gauge, such gauges are easy to fit, one of the two wires being connected to the ignition switch and the other to earth. The gauge itself is divided into two sections, usually marked 'on charge' and

'off charge'. If the needle swings to 'off charge' when the engine is running at more than idling speed, check that the connections have not been reversed.

Tachometer

Tachometers – or revolution counters – work by electronically counting the low tension impulses from the coil. Most of them translate this information into a reading on a dial, similar to a speedometer, though some recent models give a digital read-out.

The majority of tachometers can be adjusted to suit four-, six- and eight-cylinder engines. Their size varies, which means you can choose a size of tachometer to match your speedometer, or your other extra instrumentation. Small tachometers have separate control modules that must be mounted independently, whereas the components of large tachometers are fully integrated within the unit.

To fit a tachometer, you must wire the instrument to the coil and to earth.

Wheels and trims

The range of alloy wheels is enormous – your choice is limited only by what you can afford and the dimensions of the wheels. It is vital to check the width before you make your purchase.

By law, neither wheels nor tyres should protrude outside the bodywork when viewed from above. If the rim you fit is excessively wide, this can cause the tyre to foul the bodywork, or a suspension or steering component. Remember, too, that wider rims require wider tyres.

Sports wheels always make a car look more attractive and there are many manufacturers producing varied designs to suit most cars. Some wheels are of the 'split rim' design *(above)* which means any one design can be adapted to whatever width tyre you possess. If you are fitting wider rims than standard, make sure the larger tyres do not foul the bodywork or any steering/suspension components. If the tyres protrude beyond the edge of the bodywork, you will have to fit wheel arch extensions.

As an alternative to a standard diameter rim, you can fit wheels with a larger diameter, but still keep the gearing the same by fitting low-profile tyres – that is, tyres with a lower height. If your car has 335mm (13in) wheels, for instance, you can fit 350mm (14in) diameter rims and 60-series tyres – that is, tyres whose height is 60% of their width. Whatever type of wheel you choose, however, it should be specifically designed to suit your car, because the wheels should match the wheel stud positions and wheel nut shape exactly.

For a fraction of the cost of alloy wheels, you can fit attractive aluminium or plastic trims. These are held in place with spring clips and can be removed with a tyre lever, just like a hub cap.

Fitting electric washers

Most cars can be fitted with electric washer kits. Basic kits consist of a small pump, extra plastic tubing, wiring and a switch. More complex models have their own fluid reservoirs and a built-in pump, but these are more expensive.

The most convenient place to mount the pump is usually the engine bulkhead. Use self-tapping screws. Connect one section of the plastic tubing to the inlet stub of the pump – this is marked with a directional arrow – and the washer reservoir. Fit the other section between the pump's outlet stub and the washer jets.

The pump must be wired up to the ignition switch as well as to its operating switch to provide power. This means passing its

Electric screen washer kits are much more effective than the standard hand-pumped system and can be fitted to most cars. Other kits on the market enable you to repair defective electric washers.

Accessories

connecting wires through the engine bulkhead into the car. This may involve drilling a small access hole. Fit a grommet to stop the wires from chafing. Locate the operating switch within easy reach of the driving seat.

When you wire up the pump, follow the maker's instructions carefully. If the connections are accidentally reversed, the pump will either run backwards or suffer internal damage.

Rear screen wash/wipe

Nothing is more infuriating than driving with a dirty rear window. If you own a hatchback or estate car, you can deal with the problem by fitting a rear screen wash/wipe system. Such systems are extremely useful safety aids. You can buy the two units separately, or as a combined kit.

When fitting a wiper, you must check that the kit you choose is suitable for your car. This is because each kit contains a special paper template, which you use to determine where the hole for the wiper spindle should be drilled. Once you have established the correct position, surround the area with masking tape and use a centre punch to make a small indentation to stop the drill from slipping.

The spindle itself comes with two sealing washers. These must be fitted in the correct order to stop water getting into the car. Wire up the wiper motor to a convenient ignition-fed power source.

You fit a washer in the same way. The jet will come with its own fluid reservoir and plastic tubing for the connections between jet, pump – this must be wired up carefully according

You can fit a rear screen wash/ wipe kit only to an estate car or hatchback as space is needed behind the panel to fit the motor for the wiper. The kit contains everything you will need to fit the unit, but you will have to cut holes in the bodywork for the motor spindle and the washer jet.

There are several different types of electronic ignition system available, most of which can be fitted in a couple of hours. The best type does away with the contact breaker assembly completely. The kit *(left)* has a rotor that fits over the distributor shaft. The segments on the rotor break a light beam, which triggers the high voltage current to the spark plugs.

to the manufacturer's instructions – and reservoir. Again, the system operates off the ignition.

Electronic ignition

By fitting electronic ignition to your car, you will increase starting efficiency and marginally improve fuel economy. Electronic ignition also needs less maintenance than a conventional ignition system.

There are two types of electronic ignition unit. The first consists of a module, which is mounted independently of the distributor but wired into its circuit. Such units are designed to boost the spark at the plugs, and, at the same time, to considerably increase the life of the contact breaker points in the distributor. Many of them are fitted with an over-ride switch, which allows you to revert to the normal system if the module fails.

The second type is the contactless system. This is more expensive than the module system and takes more effort to fit. However, it has one great advantage. As no components physically touch, they cannot wear out.

The job should take approximately two hours from start to finish. You begin by removing the existing distributor baseplate, the rotor arm and the contact breaker points. The next step is to fit a special baseplate, which emits an infra-red beam. The rotor arm is replaced by a slotted disc – known as a chopper – which breaks the beam at regular intervals. In other words, it does the same job as the contact breaker points, but, instead of breaking the circuit mechanically, it does it electronically.

Electric fans

A water-cooled engine needs a fan for a very small percentage of its working life – usually only when idling, or in slow-moving traffic. Thus, a conventional belt-driven fan often unnecessarily absorbs power from the engine, as well as creating unwanted noise. Electric fans, on the other hand, are controlled by a thermostat and operate only when required.

The fan will either come with brackets, which bolt to holes you drill in the bodywork, or with inserts that fit into the radiator. Depending on the layout of your engine, you should position the fan between radiator and engine to suck air inwards, or in front of the radiator to drive air outwards.

You can mount the thermostatically controlled switch on the radiator, or connect it to one of the coolant hoses. You wire up the fan to an ignition-fed power source. The best kits incorporate an over-ride switch, so that the fan on and off manually if the thermostat fails.

Index

Page numbers in **bold** type refer to the main entries; *italic* numbers refer to the illustrations.

A

AA, 9
acceleration, driving
   technique, 146
   over rapid, 144
accelerator, cable, 120; *120*
   checking, 51
   description, *120*
   maintenance, 120; *120, 121*
accelerator pump, faults, 87
accessories, **174-203**
   exterior, **174-5**, **194-99**, **200-2**
   interior, 175, **188-93**, **199-200**
accidents, insurance cover, 18
   motorway, 148-50
adjustable spanners, 168
advertisements, second-hand
   cars from, 16
aerials, 191-2
   electrically-operated, 175,
   191-2; *191*
   fitting, 192
aerosol paints, 184, 186, 187;
   186, 187
air cleaner, 49-50; *49*
   checking, 50-1
   description, *116*
air-cooled engines, 40
air dams, *see* spoilers
air filters, checking, 51
   cleaning, 117
   description, 49-50; *49*
   faults, 76, 78, 80,
   82, 84, 86
   maintenance, **116-7**; *116, 117*
   replacing, 116-7; *117*
   types, 116; *116*
air intake, 48, 49-50
air leaks, inlet manifold, 76, 79,
   85, 87
air pressure alarm systems, 23;
   23
alarm systems, **22-3**
alternators, checking, 47
   description, 44, 45; *44*
   maintenance, 107
   see also drive belts
ammeter, interpreting, 101
anti-corrosion, guarantees, 20,
   21;
   rust proofing, **28-9**
anti-freeze, 40, 42, 62, 112, **113**
anti-roll bars, 59
   faults, 102
anti-squeal shims, 102
aquaplaning, 147
auctions, second-hand cars, 17
automatic transmission,
   description, 31
   flat batteries in cars
   with, 68
   repairing, 163

towing by cars with, 157
towing cars with, 68, 189
axle stands, 169, 171
axles, noises from, 103

B

baby seats, 155; *155*
bank loans, 10
batteries, charging, 108; *108*
   checking, 38, 46, 108;
   108
   description, 36, 44-5;
   36, 44
   draining, 62
   electrolyte, 39, 44, 47, 98,
   108; *108*
   faults, 70, 71, 72, 94, 95,
   96, 98
   flat, 62, **68-9**
   maintenance, 106-7, 108-9;
   108-9
   terminals, 109; *109*
   testing, 108; *108*
   winter starting, 62
battery chargers, 68, 107, 108,
   169; *108*
   using, 108, 171; *108*
battery condition indicator,
   175, 200
   interpreting, 101
big ends, 34
   worn, 89, 99
block core plugs, leaks, 91
body kits, 174, 194; *194*
body work, checking garage's
   work on, 166
   checking second-hand cars,
   14
   choosing garages for, 163
   filling dents, 180-3; *180-3*
   filling holes, *178-9*
   personalised, 194-7
   protecting, 174-5
   repairing rust damage, 174,
   176-9
bonus-protected policies, 18,
   19
boot spoilers, *see* rear spoilers
boredom, while driving, 153,
   175
brakes, checking garage work
   on, 166
   description, 31, **52-4**;
   52-3
   disc, 53, 54; *52*
   drums, 53-4; *53*
   drying out, 148
   dual-circuit systems, 52
   faults, 102
   noisy, 102
   servo assisted, 53; *52*
braking, contol, 149
   skidding and, 148
breakdowns, 161
   dealing with, **64-9**
   diagnosing, 62-3, 164

isolating the cause, 63
   off the road, 65-7
   problem solving, **106-7**
   safety, 64
   temporary repairs, 69
   warning signs, 63, 65, 172; *64,
   172*
breather hoses, 51; *49*
brokers, insurance, 19-20
bulbs, checking, 139
   faulty, 94, 95
   flash units, 140
   headlamps, 139
   replacing, 69; *69*
   spare, 172
   types, *139*
bump starts, 68
bumpers, painting, 195
buying a car, **8-17**
   and cost of driving, 12
   budgeting for servicing, 12-
   13
   checking the car, 13
   depreciation calculation, 13
   insurance, 8, **18-20**
   new cars, 8, **12-13**
   pre-planning, 8, 12-13
   the purchase, 13
   second-hand cars, 9, **14-17**
   size of car, 12
   test driving, 13, 14-15
   warranties, 9, 20-1

C

cables, choke, 121; *121*
   clutch, 142, 143; *143*
   maintenance, 120-1
   throttle, 120; *120*
calipers, brake, 54, 55; *52*
camshaft, 34-5; *33*
caravans, manoeuvring, 157-8;
   158
   towing, 145, 156-8; *156, 157*
carburettors, *33*
   checking, 51
   description, 48-9; *48*
   faults, 74, 75, 77, 78, 79, 81,
   85, 86, 87
   fixed jet, 48; *48*
   twin choke, 48; *48*
   variable jet, 48, 49; *48*
carpets, cleaning, 26; *25*
carry-cot restraints, 155; *155*
cassette players, 188-9
   care, 193
   tape maintenance, 193
   see also sound systems
charging batteries, 108, 170;
   108
children, booster cushions,
   154-5; *154*
   as passengers, 154-5
   seat belts, 154-5; *154, 155*
chips, painting out, 184; *184*
chisels, 169, 171
chokes, automatic, 75, 77

cable maintenance, 121; *121*
   checking, 51
   description, 49
   faults, 74, 75, 77, 82
   operation, 63
   using, 146
chrome, polishers, 25; *25*
   restoring, 27
city driving, 146
claims, insurance, 20
cleaning cars, 9, **24-7**, 174
   compounding, 26, 184, 187;
   26-7
   drying, 24
   polishing, 24
   restoring the shine, **26-7**
   underside, 28
   upholstery, 36; *25*
   washing, 24
clutch assembly, 30-1
   adjusting the cable, 142, 143;
   143
   checking, 55, 142
   description, *142*
   faults, 103
   hydraulic, 54, 55;
   142-3
   replacing cables, 143
coil springs, 57, 58; *57*
   checking, 59
coils, checking, 38-9, 130-1;
   130, 131
   description, 36; *36*
combination units, 190
comfort, 145, 153, 175; *153*
compounding, 26, 184, 187; *26-7*
comprehensive insurance, 18
computers, buying cars by, 16-
   17;
   on-board, 145
   radio tuning, 190
condensation, 76
condensers, 37; *37*
   checking, *125*
contact breaker points, 37; *37*
   checking, 39, 125
   electronic ignition and, 203
   faults, 72, 73, 76, 80, 84
   fitting new, 127; *127*
   setting gap, 126; *126*
contaminated fuel, 79, 85
coolant, 40-1
   checking, 42
   draining, 112-13
   leaks, 35
cooling system, checking, 42-3,
   112; *112-13*
   description, **40-2**
   draining, 112-3
   faults, 100
   maintenance, 106, 112-5
   overheating problems, **90-4**
   topping up, 113
corrosion, guarantees against,
   20, 21
   repairing, 174, **176-9**
   rust proofing, **28-9**
cork gaskets, 136
costs, depreciation, 13
   of driving, 12
   insurance, 8

new cars, 8, 12
second-hand cars, 9
servicing, 12-13
see also finance
country driving, 146-7
crankcase emission valve,
faults, 75
crankshaft, 30, 34
worn bearings, 89
crankshaft pulley, *33*
crawler, 169
creeper, 169
cross ply tyres, 60
customised cars, **174-5**, 194
front spoilers, 195-6; *195*
rear spoilers, 196; *195, 196*
side panels, 196
simple styling, 194-6
wheel arches, 196
cylinder blocks, 32, 34
cracked, 92
cyclinder bores, worn, 87, 88
cylinder head, 34-5
faults, 91, 92
cylinders, 32-4
description, 30
hydraulic, 52, 53, 54

D

dampers, 31, 58
checking, 59
faults, 102
dampness, 172
dashboards, 63
extra instruments, 175, 199
interpretation of instruments,
98-101
dealers, finance schemes, 11
new cars, 8, 13
second-hand cars, 17
warranties, 21
demisting the car, 147
dents, filling, 182-3; *182-3*
keying the surface, 181
pulling out, 180; *180-1*
tapping out, 180
diagnosing problems, **62-3**
differential, 31
dipstick, 35
disc brakes, checking, 55
description, 53, 54; *52*
noise, 102
distributor, *33*
checking, 39, 124-5; *124*
description, 36-7
faults, 72, 73, 80, 83, 84, 88
maintenance, **124-9**
do-it-yourself maintenance,
161
doors, rust proofing, 29; *28*
double wishbone suspension,
56, 57; *56*
drag, reducing, 144
drills, electric, 170
drive belts, 41
checking, 42, 43, 47

faults, 88
maintenance, 107
drive shaft, *33*
driveplate, broken, 89
driving, **144-59**
in adverse conditions, 147-8
boredom during, 153, 175
child passengers, 154-5
comfort, 145, 153, 175; *153*
in the country, 146-7
defensive, 144
discipline, 146
economical, 144
fatigue during, 152
in fog, 148
fuel economy, 144-5
icy conditions, 148
on motorways, **148-52**
passing discipline, 147
potential hazards, 146
in rain, 147-8
rattles and vibrations,
152
safety, 144, 145, **146-55**
seat belts, 154
seating position, 153-4; *153*
skidding, 148
snowy conditions, 148
tension during, 152-3
in towns, 146
driving lamps, 197; *197*
wiring, 198
drum brakes, checking, 55
description, 53-4; *53*
noise, 102
dwell meters, 126-7, 170; *126,
170*
using, 171
dynamo, checking, 47
description, 44, 45; *44*
faults, 98
maintenance, 107
see also fan belt

E

earth connections, faulty, 94,
95, 96
economy, fuel, 144-5
economy warning light, 144
electric fans, 41, 43, 91, 100,
203; *41*
fitting, 203
electrical circuits, checking,
137; *137*
relays, 137
see also fuses
electrical system, checking **46-
7**;
description, **44-6**
faults, **94-7**
maintenance, 106-7
safety, 65-6
electrolyte, 39, 44, 47, 98, 107,
108, *108*
checking, 47
electronic ignition, 203; *203*

emergency telephones, 65, 152
engines, checking garage
work on, 166
checklist, **35**
cleaning, *25*
description, 30, **32-5**; *33*
failure to start, 62, **70-6**
flooding, 62-3, 75
four-stroke cycle, 32
lubrication, 31, 34, 35, **134-5**
noise, **88-9**
operation, 32
overhead cam, 34; *33*
overhead valve, 34; *33*
overheating, **90-4**
performance faults, **77-87**
seized, 70
starting faults, **70-6**
engine mounting, checks, 35
equipment, *see* tools
exhaust centres, 163
exhaust manifold, 34
checks, 35
exhaust system, faults, 76
stainless steel, 174-5
temporary supports, 172
exhaust valves, faults, 76
expansion tanks, 41; *40*
checking, 42

F

fan belts, 41; *33, 110*
adjusting, 110; *111*
checking, 42, 43, 47, 110; *110*
description, 41; *40, 41*
faults, 88, 91, 94, 95, 98, 100
maintenance, 107, **110-11**;
110-11
replacing, 111; *111*
spare, 172
temporary repairs, 69
fans, *33*
checking, 42, 43
electric, 41, 43, 91, 100, 203;
41
faults, 91, 100
fatigue, avoidance, 152
dangers of, 152
feeler gauges, 169; *170*
using, 171
filler cap, 41; *40*
checking, 42
fillers, 182
applying, 182; *182*
rubbing down, 183; *183*
filling holes, *178-9*
filters, *see*:
air filters
oil filters
finance, bank loans, 10
buying cars, **8-11**
credit sale, 11
dealer schemes, 11
finance brokers, 10
hire purchase, 11
interest, 10

mortgages, 11
finance brokers, 10
flasher units, checking, 140
faulty, 97
fitting new, 140
testing switches, 140
flat batteries, **68-9**
see also batteries
flooded roads, 147-8
flooding, engines, 62-3, 75
flywheels, 34
faults, 70, 71, 89, 103
fog, driving in, 148
fog lamps, 174, 197, 198; *197*
mounting, 198
rear, 198
security, 32
foot pumps, 172; *173*
four-stroke cycle, 32
front spoilers, 174, **195-60**; *195*
front suspension, description,
56-7; *56*
front-wheel drives, 32; *32*
fuel, contamination, 79, 85
economy, 144-5
grades, 84, 88
spare can, 172
fuel flow, checking, **118-9**; *118,
119*
faults, 72, 74, 75, 79, 83
fuel injection, description, 50
fuel pipe, 50; *49*
checking, 51
faults, 72, 74, 75, 79, 83
replacing, 172
fuel pumps, 50; *49*
checking, 51, 118
description, *118*
electric, 50; *49*
faults, 74, 75, 79, 83
filters, 118, *118*
fuel system, checking, **50-1**
description, **48-50**
fuel tank, 50; *49*
checking, 51
faults, 74, 75
fuse boxes, 46; *44, 138*
checking, 47
fuses, blown, 95, 96, 97
checking, 47, 138; *138*
description, 45-6; *44*
line fuses, 138
replacing, 69, 138
spare, 172
temporary repairs, 69

G

garages, body repairs, 163
briefing a mechanic, 163-4
checking the work of, 160-1,
165-6
choosing, 160, 162-3
estimates from, 160, 164
facilities, 160, 162
inspecting, 162
servicing and repairs by,

160-1, **162-7**
specialist, 162, 163
gaskets, 35
replacing, 136; *136*
sealing compounds, 136
temporary, 136; *136*
gauges, extra, 175, **199-200**
reading, **98-101**
gear levers, noisy, 103
gearbox, *33*
description, 31
faults, 103
generator, *33*
checking, 47
description, 45; *44*
faults, 94, 95, 98, 101
maintenance, 107
radio interference, 192
see also:
alternators
drive belts
dynamos
glass fibre, finish to panels of, 196
hole filling, *178-9*
glass-fibre cars, suppressing interference, 193
graphic equalizers, 189; *189*
guarantees, *see* warranties
gudgeon pin, 34
worn, 89

H

hammers, 169
handbrakes, 52, **53**
checking, 55
description, 53; *53*
locks, 22
handling ability, 31
headlamps, checking, 139
customizing, 197
sealed beams, 141
heat exchangers, 42
heaters, 42; *42*
hire purchase, 11
holes, filling, *178-9*
hose brushes, 24; *24*
hose clips, 114, 172; *114, 173*
hoses, breather, 51; *49*
checking, 43; *113*
cooling system, 41; *40*
faults, 106
hydraulics, 54
leaks, 90
replacing, 114; *114*
spare, 172
temporary repairs, 69, 106
hydraulic clutches, 54, 55; *142-3*
hydraulic suspension, 58
checking, 59
hydraulic system, checking, **54-5**
description, **52-4**
hydro-gas, 58
hydrometer, 108; *108*

I

icy conditions, 148
idle fuel mixture, 82
faults, 77, 81
idle speed, 81
faults, 77, 78, 103
ignition system, checklist, **38-9**
condensation, 76
dampness, 172
description, **36-7**; *36-7*
electronic, 203; *203*
faults, 70-2, 76, 84
radio interference, 192-3
ignition timing, 84
adjusting, 128-9; *128, 129*
faults, 76, 78, 80, 81, 87, 88, 92, 101
stroboscopic, 128-9, 170, 171; *129, 170*
ignition warning light, interpretation, 98
improvements, **174-5**
in-car entertainment, 177, **188-93**
indicators, checking, 140
faulty, 97
fitting new units, 140
testing switches, 140
inertia seat belts, 154
inertia starter motors, 36; *36*
checking, 38
description, *132*
inlet manifold, 34; *33, 49*
inlet valves, faults, 76
instruments, extra, 175, **199-201**
reading, **98-101**
insulation tape, for emergencies, 172
insurance, 12, **18-20**
bonus-protection, 18, 19
buying, 18
choosing cover, 18
choosing an insurer, 18-19
claims, 20
comprehensive, 18
consultants, 19
knock for knock agreements, 19
ratings, 8
third party, 18
third party, fire and theft, 18
insurance brokers, 19-20
Insurance Brokers Registration Act, 19
interference, radio, 193-4

J

jacks, buying, 169
safety, 54, 66
using, 67, 171
jump leads, 68, 172

K

knock-for-knock agreements, 19

L

lacquers, 187
lane discipline, motorways, 150
leaf springs, 57, 58; *57*
checking, 59
faults, 102
lever arm dampers, 58
lights, auxiliary, 174, **197-8**
faults, **94-7**
legal requirements, 198
towing, 156
see also bulbs
loans, bank, 10
finance brokers, 10
financial, 10-11
interest, 10
lubrication, engine, 31, 34, 35, **134-5**

M

McPherson struts, 56, 58; *56*
checking, 59
faults, 102
magnet test, on bodywork, 14
main bearing, faults, 89, 99
maintenance, importance of, 106, 144
routine, 9
see also servicing
manifolds, *see*:
exhaust manifold
inlet manifold
mole grips, 169, *169*
using, 171
Motor Agents' Association, 17, 163, 167
motorway driving, **148-52**
breakdowns, 64-5
emergency action, 150-2
joining motorway, 150; *151*
lane discipline, 150
leaving a motorway, 150; *151*
at night, 150
road signs, *151*
mud flaps, 29
multimeters, 170

N

new cars, buying, 8, 12-13
night driving, on motorways, 150
noise, 63
driving, 102-3
engine, **88-9**
telling a mechanic about, 164

O

octane rating, 84
oil, changing, 35, 134; *134*
checking, 134; *134*
engine, 30, 34, 35
refilling the sump, 135
topping up, 134; *134*
oil filters, 35; *33*
replacing, 135; *135*
oil pressure gauge, 175, 199-200; *199*
oil pressure warning light, interpretation, 99
oil pump, faults, 99
oil sump, 35, 99, 135; *33*
overhead cam engine, 34; *33*
overhead valve engine, 34; *33*
overheating, 40-3, 81, **90-4**
temporary repair, 69
owning a car, **8-29**
buying a new car, 8-9, **12-13**
buying second-hand, 9, **14-17**;
insurance, 8, **18-20**
routine care, 9
security, 8, **22-3**
warranties, 9, **20-1**

P

painting, aerosols, 184, 186, 187; *186, 187*
chipped painted work, 184; *184*
finishing off, 187
lacquers, 187
masking, 185; *185*
preparing, 186
primer, 186; *186*
restoring paintwork, 26-7
scratches, 184; *184*
spray, **185-7**
washing down, 186
panels, repairing rust damage, 176-7; *176-9*
see also:
cleaning
painting
Panhard rod, 59

passengers, children, 154-5
pendulum alarm systems, 23; *22*
personalizing cars, **174-5**, 194
  front spoilers, 195-6; *195*
  rear spoilers, 196; *195, 196*
  side panels, 196
  simple styling, 194-5
  wheel arches, 196
petrol, contaminated, 79, 87
  economy, 144-5
  grades, 84, 88
  spare can, 172
  see also fuel
petrol leaks, 50
  see also fuel pipe
petrol pump, *33*
petrol tank, *see* fuel tank
pinking, 84, 88
pipes, hydraulic, 54, 55
  see also:
  fuel pipes
  hoses
piston rings, worn, 89
piston slap, 89
pistons, 34
  hydraulic suspension, 58
pliers, 169; *169*
plug spanners, 168, 172,
  using, 171
plugs, *see* spark plugs
points, 37; *37*
  checking, 39, 125
  faults, 72, 73, 76, 80, 84
  electronic ignition and, 203
  fitting new, 127; *127*
  setting the gaps, 126; *126*
  polarity, 38
polishing, 24-5, 174
  compounding, 26, 184, 187; *26-7*
  polishes, 25; *24*
  restoring the shine, **26-7**
  scratches, 184
polyester sealants, 25
pre-engaged starters, 36; *36*
  checking, 38
  description, *132*
  testing, 133
primer paint, 186
problem solving, **106-7**
protection, cleaning and
  waxing, 24-7
  insurance, 9, **18-20**
  security, 9, **22-3**, 175
  warranties, 9, **20-1**
pumps, electric washers, 201
  see also:
  fuel pumps
  water pumps
punches, 169, 171
punctures, 60
  changing wheels, **66-8**; *66-7*
  emergency repairs, 172
pushrods, 34; *33*

Q

quadraphonic sound system, 190

R

RAC, 9
radial tyres, 60; *60*
radiators, checking, 42, 112; *112*
  description, 40-1; *40*
  draining, *113*
  faults, 90-1, 100
  temporary repairs, 69
  topping up, 113
radiator caps, 91, 100
  checking, *112*
  removing, 66, 113; *113*
radiator grilles, painting, 195
radios, **188-93**
  aerials, 191-2
  combination units, 188, 189
  fitting, 192
  FM reception, 188, 189
  improving performance, 189-90
  interference, 192-3
  speakers, 190-1
  wiring up, 192
  see also:
  cassette players
  sound systems
rain, driving in, 147-8
rattles, 150
rear-engined cars, 32
rear lights, checking, 139; *139*
rear screen washers and
  wipers, 202-3; *202*
rear spoilers, 174, 196; *195, 196*
rear suspension, description, 57-8; *57*
rear-wheel drives, 30, 32; *32*
reflector panels, 197
relays, checking, 137
remould tyres, 61
repairs, **110-43**
retread tyres, 61
rev counters, 175, 200
ring spanners, 168, 170, 172
road signs, on motorways, 151
rocker arms, 34; *33*
  faults, 88
rotor arm, 37; *37*
  checking, 39, 124; *124*
rubber cone springs, 58
rust, guarantees against, 20, 21
  proofing against, **28-9**
  repairing damage, 174, **176-9**
rust-converters, 29, 184
rust-proofing kits, 29

S

safety, breakdowns, 64
  driving, 144, 145, **146-55**
  electrical system, 65-6
  in the engine compartment, 43, 65-6
  motorway breakdowns, 64-5
  radiator cap removal, 66, 113; *113*
  repairs, 65
  tyres, 60
  using jacks, 54, 66
scratches, painting out, 184; *184*
screen washers, electric, **201-3**
  rear, 202-3; *202*
screwdrivers, 169
  circuit test, *170*
  emergency kit, 172
  using, 161, 170, 171
sealed beam headlamps,
  description, *141*
  removing, 141; *141*
  replacing, 141
  testing, 141
seat belts, 145, 154
  for children, 154-5; *154, 155*
  generation belts, 155
  for rear seats, 154-5; *155, 156*
seats, 175
  cleaning, 26; *25*
  covers, 175
second-hand cars,
  advertisements for, 16
  auctions, 17
  buying, 9, **14-17**
  buying by computer, 14-17
  checking, 14
  dealers, 17
  engine noises, 15
  road-tests, 14-15
  warranties, 20, 21
security, 9, **22-3**, 175
  for accessories, 23
  alarm systems, 22-3; *22, 23*
  handbrake locks, 22
  rules of, 23
  steering locks, 22; *22*
  wheel clamps, 22
  window etching kits, 22
servicing, budgeting for, 12-13
  checking garage's work, 165-6
  do-it-yourself, 161
  by garages, 160-1
  importance of, 63, 106, 144, 165
  warranties and, 20, 21
servo-assisted brakes, 53; *52*
  checking, 55
shock absorbers, 31, 58
skidding, 148; *149*
small end, 34
snowy conditions, 148
socket sets, 168; *169*
  using, 170
solenoids, 36; *36*

checking, 133
sound systems, 175, **188-93**
  aerials, 191-2
  cassette players, 188-9
  combination units, 189, 190
  fitting, 192
  graphic equalizer, 189; *189*
  improving performance, 189-90
  interference, 192-3
  mounting, 190; *190*
  power amplifier, 189
  quadraphonic, 190
  radios, 188
  speakers, 190-1
  stereo, 188, 190
  terminology, 193
  wiring up, 192
spanners, 168; *164, 169*
  adjustable, 168
  emergency kit, 172
  using, 161, 170
spare pares, for emergencies, 172; *173*
spare wheel, 172
spark plugs, 36, 37; *33*
  checking, 39
  description, 37; *37*
  faults, 71, 76, 80, 82, 84, 85, 88
  spanners, 168, 171
  spare, 172
speakers, 190-1
  fitting, 192; *191*
spoilers, fitting, 195
  front, 174, 195; *195*
  rear, 174, 196; *195, 196*
spotlamps, 197; *197*
spray painting, **185-7**
  masking, 185; *185*
  preparing, 186
  spraying, 187; *186, 187*
springs, 31
starter motor, *33*
  checking, 38, 132, 133
  description, 36; *36*
  faults, 70, 71
  inertia, 36, 38; *36, 132*
  jammed, 130-1
  maintenance, **132-3**
  pre-engaged, 36, 39, 133; *36, 132*
  removing, 133; *133*
  solenoids, 133
starting, with flat battery, 68
  see also ignition systems
steering, checking garage's
  work on, 166
  description, 31
steering locks, 22; *22*
stereo sound systems, 188, 190
stolen cars, insurance, 18
  security, 22-3
stroboscopic timing, 128-9
  using, 171
sumps, 35, 99; *33*
  refilling, 99
sunshine roofs, 175, 198-9; *198*
suppressors, radio
  interference, 192
suspension arms, 58-9

faults, 102
suspension system, checking, **59**
  checking garage's work on, 166
  description, **56-9**
  front, 56-7; *56*
  rear, 57-8; *57*
  towing and, 157
switches, faulty, 96, 97
  indicator, 140
  testing, 137
synchromesh, worn, 103

T

tachometer, 145, 175, 200
tanks, 50, 51; *49*
  faults, 75
tape, masking, 185
tape recorders, *see* cassette
  players
tar, on paintwork, 26-7
telephones, emergency, 65
telescopic dampers, 58
temperature gauges, faulty, 93
temperature sensor, faulty,
  93, 101
tension, while driving, 152-3
test drives, buying cars, 13,
  14-15
theft, insurance, 18
  security, 9, **22-3**
thermostats, 172
  checking, 43, 115; *115*
  description, 40, 41-2
  faults, 92, 93, 100, 101
  housing, *33*
  removing, 115; *115*
third party insurance, 18
throttle, cable maintenance,
  120; *120*
  faults, 86
  linkage, 51
  see also accelerator

tools, **168-71**; *168, 170*
  basic kit, 168-9; *168-9*
  choosing, 168
  electrical, 170, 171
  maintenance, 171
  survival kit, **172**; *173*
  using, 161, 170-1
torches, 172
torque wrench, 168, 169-70
  using, 171
torsion bars, 58
tow ropes, 158, 172; *159*
towbars, 145, 156; *157*
towing, 68, 145, 156-9
  caravans, 145, 156-8; *156, 157*
  cars, 158-9; *159*
  trailers, 145, 158
town driving, 146
trailers, towing, 145, 158
transmission, checking
  garage's work on, 166
  description, 30-1
  see also automatic
  transmission
tread patterns, 60-1
triangles, warning, 65, 172; *64,
  173*
tubeless tyres, 60
tyres, causes of wear, 105,
  104-5
  changing wheels, **66-8**; *66-7*
  cleaning, 27; *25*
  cross ply, 60
  description, 31; **60-1**
  and driving style, 104
  faults, **104-5**
  inspecting, 104-5
  legal requirements, 61
  low-profile, 200
  maintenance, 104, 106
  markings, 61; *61*
  noise from, 102
  pressure, 104, 144
  radial, 60; *60-1*
  remoulds, 61
  retreads, 61
  sizes, 61
  tread patterns, 60-1

tubed, 60
tubeless, 60
  in wet weather, 147

U

ultrasonic alarm systems, 23;
  22, 23
underbody sealants, 29; *28*
underside, cleaning, 28
  rust proofing, 29
upholstery cleaning, 26; *25*
used cars, *see* second-hand
  cars

V

vacuum advance-retard
  mechanism, checking, 125
  faults, 101
valves, clearance, 81
  faults, 81, 85, 87, 88
variable jet carburettor, 48, 49;
  48
vibrations, 152
vinyl roofs, cleaning, 27; *25*
voltmeters, 170
  interpreting, 102
  using, 171

W

warning lights, interpretation,
  98-101
warning triangles, 65, 172; *64, 173*
warranties, anti-corrosion, 20-1

arranging independently, 21
  new cars, 8-9
  second-hand cars, 9, 20, 21
washers, electric, **201-3**
washing cars, 9, 24, 174
water dispersant, 172
water hoses *see* hoses
water pump, *33*
  checking, 43
  description, 41; *40*
  faults, 88, 91
water temperature gauge, 175,
  200; *199*
  interpreting, 100-1
wax polish, 25; *24*
wheel alignment, faulty, 102
wheel arches, personalised,
  196; *196*
  rust proofing, 29; *28*
wheel brace, 172; *173*
wheel clamps, 22
wheel ramps, 169, 171
wheels, alloy, 174, 200; *200*
  changing, **67-8**; *66-7*
  cleaning, 24, 25, 27; *25*
  security devices, 23; *23*
  spare, 172
  trim, 200
windows, cleaning, 26; *25*
  driving vision, 145
  electric, 175
  electric washers, 201-3
  etching, kits, 22
  rear screen wash/wipe, 202-3
windscreen wipers, faulty, 97
  using, 147
  see also washers
windscreens, emergency, 172
  insurance, 18
winter conditions, 62, 93
wipers, faults, 97
  rear screen, 202-3
  using, 147
  see also washers
wiring, checking, 38
  description, 46
  polarity, 38
wrenches, self locking, 169, 171

Acknowledgements

The Paul Press Ltd thanks the following companies and individuals for their help and assistance:

Britax Ltd
Car Mechanics Magazine
Champion Sparking Plug Co Ltd
Ford Motor Company
Holt Lloyd Ltd
Chris Keys

Nothwood Spares and Accessories
Street Machine Magazine
Trico-Folberth Ltd
Uniroyal Ltd
C.P. Witter